Congratulations to

Carmen Maria Machado

Winner of the

2018 Bard Fiction Prize

Carmen Maria Machado, author of *Her Body and Other Parties*, joins previous winners Nathan Englander, Emily Barton, Monique Truong, Paul La Farge, Edie Meidav, Peter Orner, Salvador Plascencia, Fiona Maazel, Samantha Hunt, Karen Russell, Benjamin Hale, Brian Conn, Bennett Sims, Laura van den Berg, Alexandra Kleeman, and Karan Mahajan.

The Bard Fiction Prize is awarded annually to a promising emerging writer who is an American citizen aged thirty-nine years or younger at the time of application. In addition to a monetary award of $30,000, the winner receives an appointment as writer in residence at Bard College for one semester without the expectation that he or she will teach traditional courses. The recipient will give at least one public lecture and meet informally with students.

For more information, please contact:

Bard Fiction Prize
Bard College
PO Box 5000
Annandale-on-Hudson, NY 12504-5000

COMING UP IN THE SPRING

Conjunctions:70

SANCTUARY:
THE PRESERVATION ISSUE

Edited by Bradford Morrow

What seems most permanent is only permanently fragile. Cultures, societies, ecologies, the arts and sciences, histories, governments, the very Earth itself can be eroded or erased in far less time than it took for them to come into being. Once compromised, can they be salvaged, renewed? Even language, that essential human tool, isn't immune. A study at the turn of the millennium estimated that nine of ten indigenous languages worldwide will be extinct by the end of the century. Although the estimate has been revised down by about half, this is scant cause for celebration. Things fall apart, to be sure, but they sometimes can be saved.

Conjunctions:70, Sanctuary: The Preservation Issue, explores the myriad ways in which we go about preserving what might otherwise be forfeited. Whether trained specialists or laypeople who *care* about something, preservationists come from every stratum of life. The archivist who discovers lost manuscripts, the local historian who keeps a daily record of her community for posterity. The paleontologist who unearths fossil records, the seed-collecting gardener who saves a rare strain of heirloom tomatoes. The Monuments Men who recovered Nazi-looted artifacts at the end of the Second World War and those who repatriated them to rightful owners. Old two-by-two Noah and taxonomist Linnaeus. The archaeologist who uncovers centuries-old artworks and the suburban girl who collects enough cheap books at yard sales and Salvation Army stores to build up a library and thereby a store of the most fragile thing of all—knowledge. All can be preservationists.

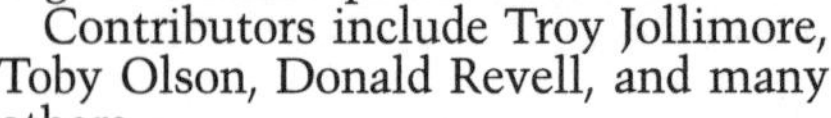

Contributors include Troy Jollimore, Toby Olson, Donald Revell, and many others.

One-year individual US subscriptions to *Conjunctions* are only $18 (two years for $32) for today's most innovative fiction, poetry, and narrative nonfiction. To read dangerously, subscribe or renew at conjunctions.com, or mail your check to *Conjunctions*, Bard College, Annandale-on-Hudson, NY 12504. For e-book editions of current and selected past issues, visit openroadmedia.com/ conjunctions. If you have questions or wish to request an invoice, e-mail conjunctions@bard.edu or call (845) 758-7054.

CONJUNCTIONS

Bi-Annual Volumes of New Writing

Published by Bard College

CONJUNCTIONS is published in the Spring and Fall of each year by Bard College, Annandale-on-Hudson, NY 12504.

SUBSCRIPTIONS: Use our secure online ordering system at conjunctions.com, or send subscription orders to CONJUNCTIONS, Bard College, Annandale-on-Hudson, NY 12504. Single year (two volumes): $18.00 for individuals; $40.00 for institutions and non-US. Two years (four volumes): $32.00 for individuals; $80.00 for institutions and non-US. For information about subscriptions, back issues, and advertising, contact us at (845) 758-7054 or conjunctions@bard.edu. *Conjunctions* is listed and indexed in JSTOR and Humanities International Complete and included in EBSCO*host*.

Editorial communications should be sent to Bradford Morrow, *Conjunctions*, 21 East 10th Street, 3E, New York, NY 10003. Unsolicited manuscripts cannot be returned unless accompanied by a stamped, self-addressed envelope. Electronic and simultaneous submissions will not be considered. Do not send work via any method requiring a signature for delivery. If you are submitting from outside the United States, contact conjunctions@bard.edu for instructions.

Cover design by Jerry Kelly, New York. Cover art by Christy Lee Rogers (christylee rogers.com), archival photographic pigment prints from the *Reckless Unbound* collection, 2012. Front cover: *The Unending Journey*. Back cover: *Reckless Unbound*. © Christy Lee Rogers 2017; all rights reserved by the artist.

Conjunctions e-books of current and selected past issues are distributed by Open Road Integrated Media (openroadmedia.com/conjunctions) and available for purchase in all e-reader formats from Amazon, Apple, B&N, Google, Indiebound, Kobo, Overdrive, and elsewhere.

Retailers can order print issues directly from *Conjunctions*.

Printers: Edwards Brothers Malloy, GHP

Typesetter: Bill White, Typeworks

ISSN 0278-2324

ISBN 978-0-941964-85-2

Manufactured in the United States of America.

TABLE OF CONTENTS

BEING BODIES

Edited by Bradford Morrow

IN MEMORIAM

John Ashbery

July 28, 1927–September 3, 2017

Longtime contributing editor and dear friend

To have been loved once by someone—surely
There is a permanent good in that

—from "When the Sun Went Down"
Conjunctions:4, 1983

EDITOR'S NOTE

IF THE BODY IS a temple, it is one very complex, heterogeneous, mutable temple. We are conceived by bodies neither ours nor of our own choosing. We then are born, grow up, live our lives, and perish—all within the ever-changing context of our bodies' encounters with the world. The writers and artists in *Being Bodies* address a wide range of what can happen to a body. A memoir of distance running counterpoints a meditation on resurrection. The story of an injury is juxtaposed by an uncommonly candid confession of a young man who struggles with gender identity and sexual preference. Virgins and those experienced in the ways of the flesh are here, as is a moving poem about a dying mother whose son must see to her final times. Venus is invoked; so are dead girls and the corpse of a venerated writer. In every contribution come fresh insights into what it means to inhabit, for a brief moment in time, our bodies. As readers turn each page, perhaps a self-awareness of hands and eyes and individual memories of what their bodies have experienced may become more vivid than before, because reading and thinking are not only cerebral activities but physical as well.

I would like to take this opportunity to welcome the excellent Nicole Nyhan, who has been a valued editor at *Conjunctions* for many years, as our new managing editor.

—Bradford Morrow
November 2017
New York City

The Extraordinary Life and Historic Adventures of a Servant Called LITTLE, Written and Drawn by Herself

Edward Carey

This being a likeness of her pencil.

IN WHICH I AM BORN AND IN WHICH I DESCRIBE MY MOTHER AND FATHER

IN THE SAME YEAR that the five-year-old Wolfgang Amadeus Mozart wrote his Minuet for Harpsichord, in the precise year when the British captured Pondicherry in India from the French, in the exact same year in which the melody for "Twinkle, Twinkle, Little Star" was first published, in that very year, which is to say 1761, whilst in the city of Paris, people at their salons told tales of beasts in castles and men with blue beards and beauties who would not wake and cats in boots and slippers made of glass and youngest children with tufts in their hair and daughters wrapped in donkey skin, and whilst in London, people at their clubs discussed the coronation of King George III and Queen Charlotte, many miles away from all this activity, in a small village in Alsace, in the presence of a ruddy mid-wife, two village maids, and the terrified mother, was born a certain undersized baby. Anne Marie Grosholtz was the name given to that hurriedly christened child, though I would be referred to simply as

Marie. I was not expected to live long. I was not much bigger at first than the size of my mother's hands put together. After I had survived my first night, I went on, despite contrary predictions, to breathe through my first week. After that my heart still kept time, without interruption, throughout my first month. The pocket-sized thing was pigheaded.

My lonely mother was eighteen years old at my birth, a small woman a little under five foot, marked by being the daughter of a priest. This priest, my grandfather, made a widower by smallpox, had been a strict man, a fury in black cloth, who never let his daughter out of his sight. After Grandfather died, my mother's life changed. Mother began to meet people, the villagers called upon her. Among the people she met was a soldier. This soldier, remaining a bachelor somewhat beyond the average age, possessing a somber temperament brought on by witnessing so many appalling things and losing so many soldier friends, took a fancy to Mother because he thought they could be happy, so to speak, being sad together. Her name was Anna-Maria Waltner. His name was Joseph Georg Grosholtz. They were married. My mother and my father. Here was loving and here was joy. My mother had a large nose, in the Roman style. My father, so I would come to believe, had a strong chin that pointed upwards. That chin, so I would understand it, and that nose seemed absolutely to fit together. After a short while Father's furlough was over and he returned to war. Mother's nose and Father's chin had known each other for three weeks.

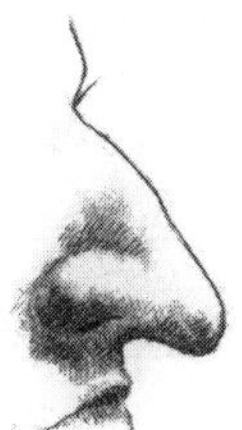

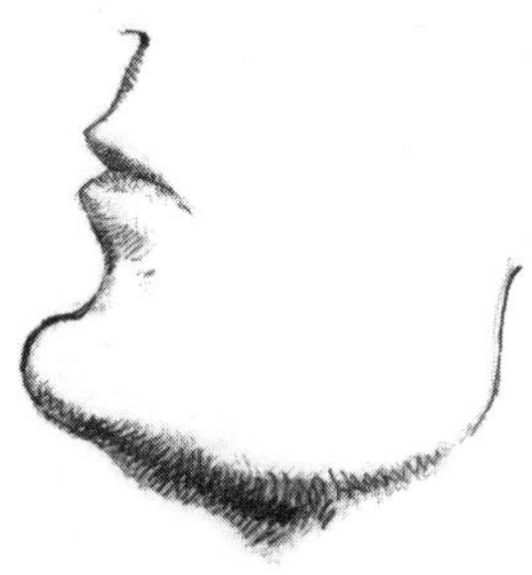

I was born of love. The love my father and mother had for each other was forever present on my face. I was born with both the Waltner nose and the Grosholtz chin. Each attribute was a noteworthy thing on its own, and nicely gave character to the faces of those two families. Combined, the result was a little ungainly, as if I were showing more flesh than was my personal due. Children will grow how they will, some proclaim themselves prodigies of hair growth, or cut teeth at a wonderfully young age, some are freckled all over, others arrive so pale that their white nakedness is a shock to all that witness it. I nosed and chinned my way into life.

CONCERNING MY EARLY YEARS

I remember the village a little. Small houses, people who seemed bred to fit inside them. I recall sharp hedges, I see snow, berries, crab-apples, dogs, rabbit meat, rosemary, holding hands with another village girl whose name I no longer know.

Since girls of my stamp were not schooled, it was Mother who gave me education through God. The Bible was my primer. Elsewise, I fetched in logs, looked for kindling in the woods, washed plates and clothes, and cut vegetables, fetched meat. I swept. I cleaned. I carried. I was always busy. Mother taught me industry.

"Discover," she would say, "what else you can do, you will always find something. One day your father will return," she said, "and he will see what a good and useful child you are."

"Thank you, Mother. I shall be most useful, I wish it."

"What a creature you are!"

"Am I? A creature?"

"Yes, my own little creature."

Mother brushed my hair with extraordinary vigor, sometimes she touched my cheek and patted my bonnet. She was probably not beautiful, but I thought her so. She had a small mole just beneath one of her eyelids. I wish I could remember her smile, I know she smiled.

At the age of five I had grown to the level of the old dog in the house next to ours. Later I would be the height of doorknobs, which I liked to rub. Later still, and here I would stop, I would be the height of many people's hearts. Women observing me in the village were sometimes heard to mutter as they kissed me, "Finding a husband will not be easy."

On my fifth birthday, my dear mother gave me a doll. This was Marta. I named her myself. I knew her body (about a sixth the size of my own) so entirely as I moved it about, sometimes roughly, sometimes with great tenderness. She came to me naked and without a face. She was a collection of wooden pegs, which could be inserted together in a certain order to roughly resemble the human figure. There were seven pieces that made up Marta. Marta, save my mother, was my first intimate connection with the world; I was never without her. We were happy together, Mother, Marta, and me.

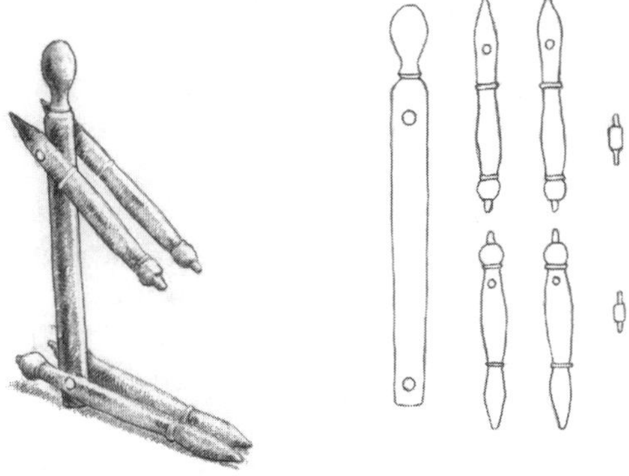

THE FAMILY GROSHOLTZ

Father was absent during those beginning years, his army finding ever more excuses to postpone his next furlough. And what could Father do about it, the poor dandelion seed was sent wherever they blew him; he was absent but he was not forgotten. Mother would sometimes sit me on the joint stool by the fire and instruct me about Father. I took much enjoyment in saying the word "Father," and would sometimes when Mother was not about, in my private way, address the stove as "Father" or a chair or chest, or various trees, and bow to them or hug them, in rehearsal for my father's return. Father was everywhere about the village, Father was in the church, by the cowsheds. Father was an upright man, said Mother. And he would surely have remained so in our minds had he never come home. But then he did return.

Actual Father had been forced into retirement. He was not even forced into retirement by a battle, because there were no battles in Europe that year; rather, in fact, he was forced into retirement as a result of a malfunctioning cannon during a parade. The cannon had been damaged at the Battle of Freiberg in 1762 and its repairs must have been shoddy, for the single appearance of the faulty instrument caused irrevocable change in my life. One Sunday parade, the cannon's last, it was lit to mark a salute but it was somehow tremendously blocked, and it sprayed, backwards, sulfur, charcoal, saltpeter, and scorching pieces of metal in a wide arc. Father was within that wide arc, and because of that he was finally allowed home.

Mother was beside herself with worry and with joy.

"Your father, your father is coming home to us! And soon he will be quite recovered. I feel certain of it. Your father, Marie!"

The man who entered the house could not enter it without assistance. The man was pushed. The father who arrived was a father in a wheelchair. Father's yellow eyes were moist, they did not seem to recognize anything in the wife who stood before him, nor even did they show any change when the wife began to tremble and moan. There was no hair on top of Father; that erupting cannon had scalped him. Most of all, though, what was lacking about this poor bundle contained in a wheelchair was the inferior maxillary bone, largest bone in the human face, most frequently called the lower jaw.

Here and now I must make a confession. It was I who pronounced my chin as Father's. Otherwise why else would I have such a proud, rude thing about me? I had never seen Father, but not seeing him I desired to have his presence upon my person, so that it was daily understood that I was his and he was mine. I cannot now say for certain, these early years being so far away and the other actors in them being no longer upon the stage, whether it was in a spasm of longing that I declared my chin to be his only after his arrival, or whether I had always believed in it. But it not being there was the thing and I longed to understand and to make a fuller picture of the man who was my father in distress. I wished to see him complete and fancied my face could complete the portrait, because the portrait before me was such an unhappy, ruined one.

The man in the wheelchair may have been lacking his lower jaw, but in its place had been fitted a silver plate. This silver plate was molded into the shape of the lowermost portion of a very average human face. This silver plate was taken from a mold, and so it could be estimated that several tens of unfortunate people had exactly this same silver chin that Father had now. The silver plate could be detached. Father came in two pieces, which could be fitted together with a little pain.

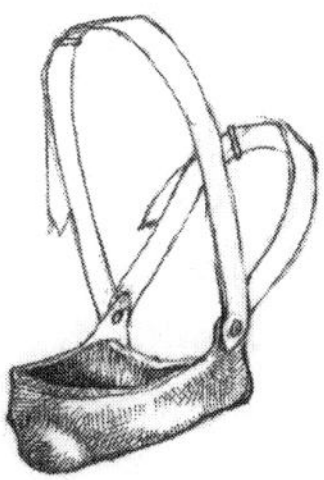

Poor Father had no idea where he was, he was incapable of recognizing his wife, nor could he tell that the little girl silently watching him was his own daughter.

The midwife was hired again, a fond, breathless lady with very thick arms, who adapted herself to any paying occasion, and there was the doctor from the nearby village, Doctor Sander. Father was put in the small room beside the kitchen, he never left that room, he just lay in it all day, sometimes looking out of the window, sometimes at the ceiling, but never, I think, exactly focusing on anything. I sat with Father long hours, and when he did not talk to me I gave him some words, and imagined all the things he would want to tell me.

After Father's arrival, Mother climbed the stairs to her bedroom and closed the door. She spent more and more time in bed. Doctor Sander said that my mother was in a state of pronounced shock and must be slowly encouraged back to calm. Her whole body changed after Father's arrival, her skin grew shiny and yellow, like that of an onion. She gave off new smells. One morning I found her outside barely clothed lying on the ground, in winter, crying.

I went from one parent to the other. From Mother upstairs to Father downstairs. I read to them both from the Bible. I had the joint stool, my extension, which I positioned at various stations around the perimeter of Father's bed, depending on his needs. I was present when Father was cleaned and washed. The midwife was affectionate to me, she sometimes held me fast to her and in those moments I was surprised at how big bodies could be and held her back with all possible force. We ate many meals together; I think she must have given me some of her food. When she spoke to me of my father she frowned in concern; when she spoke of my mother she shook her head.

One morning as I sat beside him, Father died. He shook a little and rattled, only a tiny bit, and then was dead. It was a very small death. I watched carefully. It was even gentle. Father quietly, barely noticeably, left us. The last small noise was the sound of the last Grosholtz thought in his Grosholtz head making its way out. I still sat beside him holding his hand when the midwife came in. She knew immediately that Father was no longer to be numbered among the living. She gently put Father's hand back on his chest and moved the other one beside it. She took me to the house of her daughter; I must have slept there the night.

Father was buried. The matter in the box, which we were invited to throw earth on top of, was not complete. Doctor Sander had given me Father's silver plate, which, he said, was worth money. It had a certain weight to it, about that of a tin mug filled with water. I could not help wondering if Father would miss it, and that it really would have been better remaining with him. I wanted to dig up the earth of his grave and slip the jawplate in. How on earth otherwise was he going to talk in heaven? But then, when I thought it through, it was not Father's chin, not really, it was modeled from someone else. I was sure that I alone had Father's chin, keeping it always about me a little beneath Mother's nose.

Father had left behind him a military uniform, a silver plate, a widow, a half orphan, and penury. Father's army pension would not suffice. For Mother and me to survive, Mother needed to find work. Doctor Sander, active on our behalf, discovered through his medical connections that a Doctor Curtius of Berne Hospital was in need of domestic help. Employment, usefulness, and business, said Doctor Sander, would save my mother's health. Mother, with unhappiness displayed throughout her shining body, sat down to write to Doctor Curtius. Doctor Curtius wrote back.

Shortly afterwards, sometime in 1767, Mother and I found ourselves on a cart being driven towards the city of Berne. I sat next to Mother in the cart holding on to Mother's dress with one hand and on to Father's jawplate with the other, Marta lay in my lap pocket; the Family Grosholtz was on the move. We rattled away from the village of my birth, away from the pigsties, and the church, and Father's grave.

We would not be coming back.

IN WHICH MY MOTHER AND I ARE INTRODUCED TO MANY WONDERFUL THINGS, SOME OF THEM IN ROSEWOOD DISPLAY CASES, AND I COME TO WITNESS MY SECOND DEATH

A Berne night consists of gloomy rising buildings, narrow and unlit medieval streets, shadow people moving about them. Berne Hospital appears helpfully enough, looming above its preceding streets. We were set down in front of the hospital, our single trunk, which had once belonged to our priestly antecedent, placed beside us.

There is a great black gate in the center of Berne Hospital's front, wide enough for two carriages to pass at once, a great titan's mouth that swallows patients into its vast and mysterious insides. It was towards this black gate that Mother and I approached. There was a bell. Mother rang it. The noise echoed all around the empty hospital square. Somewhere nearby someone was coughing and spitting. A tiny square of wood in the gate opened, a head appeared, we could barely see it.

"No thank you," said the head.

"If you please—," said Mother.

"Come back in the morning."

"If you please, I've come for Doctor Curtius. He's expecting me."

"Who?"

"Doctor Curtius. We're to live with him, my daughter and me."

"Curtius? Curtius is dead. Five years since."

"I had this letter from him," Mother strained to insist, "a week ago."

A hand stretched out, taking the letter, the hatch was closed again, we could barely hear people talking behind it before it opened once more, the head reappeared. "*That* Curtius, the *other* Curtius. No one has ever come asking for *that* Curtius before. He doesn't live on grounds, he's off on Welserstrasse. You don't know where that is? Country people, is it? Ernst could guide you, I suppose." There was another voice behind the gate. "You will, Ernst. Yes, you will if I say. Ernst will show you. Go round the corner, you'll find a side door, in the side door will be a lantern, waving. Beneath that waving lantern will be Ernst."

The hatch closed again and we shuffled on towards Ernst, who came out to greet us. Ernst had a nose that twisted in the opposite direction of his face; his nose set forth one way, his face quite another; he had clearly been in many fights during his young life. Ernst was dressed in the black porter's uniform of the hospital. "Curtius?" asked Ernst. "Doctor Curtius," Mother said. "Curtius," Ernst said once more and off we went.

Only five minutes from the hospital was a small, mean street. This was Welserstrasse. Walking down Welserstrasse that night I thought the houses seemed to be murmuring to us, *"Don't stop here." "Keep moving along." "Out of our sight."* Ernst finally halted at a house thinner and smaller than all the rest, squeezed in between two bullying neighboring residences, poor and neglected.

"House of Curtius," said Ernst.

"Here?" Mother asked.

"Even here," confirmed Ernst. "I came here once myself. Shan't ever again. What's inside, I won't say, but I will say I never liked it. No, I don't do Curtius. So you'll forgive me if I go back now before you knock."

And off he went, with his contrary nose, at a much quicker pace, taking light with him. We put down our trunk. Mother sat on the trunk and looked at the door, seeming perfectly content for such a door to be closed. So it was I who stepped forwards at last and knocked three times. Four. And finally the door opened. But nobody came out into the night. It remained open, and nobody came to meet us. I waited for a while with Mother, until I tugged on Mother's hand and she at last gathered herself up and we, with our trunk, stepped inside. Mother quietly closed the door behind us, I took a good handful of Mother's dress. We looked about in the shadows. Mother suddenly gasped: she had seen someone. Over there! Someone was lurking in the corner. It was a very thin, long man. So thin he seemed in the last terrible stages of starvation. So long his head nearly touched the ceiling. A pale, ghostly face, the meager candlelight in the room trembled about it, showing hollows where cheeks usually are, showing moist eyes, showing small wisps of dark, greasy hair. We stood by our trunk, as if for protection.

"I came for Doctor Curtius," Mother explained.

A long silence, and in that silence the head nodded, barely.

"I wish to see him."

There was a slight noise from the head that may have been "Yes."

"*Could* I see him?"

The head quietly, slowly volunteered, as if it were a coincidence, "*My* name is Curtius."

"I am Anna-Maria Grosholtz," said Mother, trying to hold on to herself.

"Yes," said the man in the corner.

The introductions exhausted, there was another silence. At last the man in the corner spoke again, very slowly, "I. You see, I, I'm not so used to people. I haven't had much practice lately. I'm very out of . . . practice. And you need to have people around you, you need to have people to talk to . . . or you might forget, you see . . . how they are exactly. And, in truth, what to do with them. But that'll change now. With you here. Won't it?"

There was a longer silence.

"Shall I, perhaps, shall I, if you're ready, show you the house now?"

Mother, a great unhappy look on her face, nodded.

"Yes, perhaps you'd like to see it. I'm so glad you're here. Welcome. I meant to say that before. Welcome. I meant to say that when you first arrived. I had the word ready, I was thinking of it all day. But then, ah, I forgot. I'm not used . . . you see . . . not used," said the doctor and slowly unraveled himself from his corner. He seemed made of rods, of broom handles, of great lengths, tall and thin, to move with many stretched limbs as if he were a spider, unfolding the great length of himself. We followed, keeping our distance, I held on firmly to Mother's dress.

"There's a room at the top, up these stairs, just for you," said Curtius, pointing the candle up the stairs, "for you alone. I'll never go up there. I do so hope you'll be happy," and then, with more confidence, "Please, please to come this way."

Doctor Curtius opened a door off the hall and we stepped into a small passageway. At the end of it there was another door; a little light came from underneath it. This was surely where the doctor had been when I had knocked. "This room," said Curtius, "is where I work." Curtius stopped in front of it, the great length of his narrow back towards us, he paused now, straightened himself as much as he could, spoke slowly and precisely, "Please to come in."

Ten or more shielded candles were burning inside the room, illuminating it wonderfully, showing us a place so cluttered it was impossible to understand instantly. Long shelves filled with corked bottles, inside them colors in powder. Other shorter shelves contained different, thicker bottles; these had more persuasive glass stoppers, which hinted at the possibly fatal personality of the viscous liquids they contained, black or brown or transparent. There were boxes filled with hair, it looked like, wasn't it, human hair. Positioned across the length of a trestle table were various copper vats and several hundred small modeling tools, some with sharp tips, others curved, some were minute, no larger than a pin, others were the size of a butcher's cleaver. In the center of the table upon a wooden board was a pale, drying-out object.

It was difficult to name this object precisely at first. A piece of meat? The breast of a chicken perhaps? But that wasn't it, and yet there was something certainly so familiar about it, something everyday about it . . . something . . . it was a something . . . the name of that something, the missing word, was on the tip of my tongue. And that, how the realization caused a jolt, was it! It *was* a tongue! It looked like a human one, upon a trestle table! And I wondered: if it was indeed a tongue, how did it get here and where was the person who had lost it?

There were other things besides tongues in this room. The most impressive part of the atelier, I saw now, was to be found in rosewood display cases, each clearly labeled, in shelves up and down, left and right, covering up most of one wall. Among the labels, all written in a fine calligraphic hand in sepia ink, were the following words: *ossa, neurocranium, columnae vertebralis, articulatio sternoclavicularis, musculus temporalis, bulbus oculi, nervus vagus, organa genitalia*. There was another sign just by the tongue on that table; this read *lingua*.

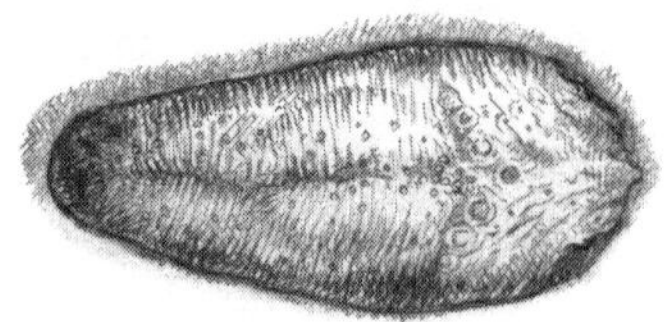

I was beginning to understand. Body parts. A room filled with body parts. There I was, a little girl looking at all of the parts of the body. We were being introduced to one another. Bits and pieces of the human body, this is a little girl called Marie. Little girl called Marie, these are bits and pieces of the human body. I took another handful of Mother's dress and stood directly behind her, but looking out.

Curtius spoke now, "Urogenital tract. With dangling bladder. Bones. From the femur, the strongest and largest, to the lachrymal, the tiniest and most fragile of the face." He was introducing us to the contents of his room. "Many muscles too, all labeled. Ten groupings of the head, from occipitofrontalis to the pterygoideus internus. Many of the ribbons of arteries from the superior thyroid to the common carotid. Veins too, the cerebellar, the anterior saphenous, the splenic and the gastric, the cardiac and the pulmonary. I have organs! Either individually resting on a bed of red velvet or situated with their neighbors displayed on the wooden boards. The impressive intricacy of the ear's osseous labyrinth. Or the long, thick clouds of intestines—both the small and the large, such long and winding ways."

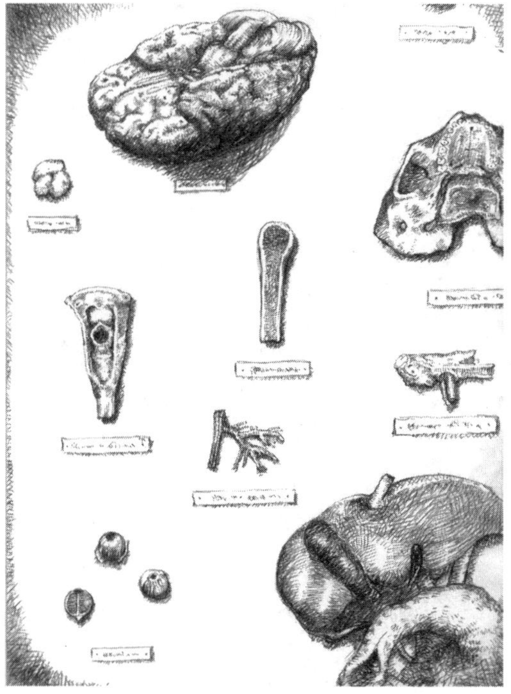

Mother regarded the room, looking increasingly unwell. Curtius must have begun to understand Mother's horror, for he hurriedly continued now: "*I* made them. My osseous labyrinth, and my gall-bladder and my ventricles. They look real. Don't they look real? You know you must say yes, but they're not. No. Though they do look it. Yes. Because, in fact, you see, I made them."

We turned to look at him. We had been so surprised at the objects all about this room that we had failed at first to see the most significant object inside it. Doctor Curtius, in the light. Doctor Curtius was a young man, younger than Mother. When I had seen his long, shadowy form move the length of itself about in the darkness I had assumed him to be old, but now I saw him both long and thin, both shy and passionate, and young, breathing excitedly. Six feet of leanness, rising far above us in the corner of his atelier, his thin nostrils flaring slightly now, he was clearly so proud of his room, watching us looking at his work. His cheeks went inwards not outwards. The thinness of his nose seemed to carefully tightrope walk down his long face. Veins palpably stretched themselves across the sides of his forehead. And now the enormous and thin hands of this strange man

came inwards, and met each other before his narrow chest, I thought he might be about to pray but instead he began to clap. It was not a loud noise but an excited beating, as of a small pleased child at the promise of something sweet to eat, a happy noise that sounded so out of place here in this room. His upper body stooped over his clapping hands as if perhaps there were a pale bird trapped there, flapping before his heart, and he was anxious that it should not escape.

"I made them all. Every one. Out of wax. And many more besides, this being but a fraction. The great majority housed in the hospital. Visited frequently!"

When Doctor Curtius had finished introducing us to his atelier that first night in Berne, I turned around to see Mother again. Her face was pale and sweaty. She did not say anything. We all three stood in silence, I still behind Mother, until Curtius, disappointed, I suppose, at Mother's apparent lack of appreciation, wondered if perhaps we were tired from our journey and needed to sleep.

"Most tired indeed, sir," she said.

"Good night then."

"Oh, excuse me, sir," Mother said. "Our papers, I suppose you should take them."

"No, no, I don't think so. Please to keep them yourselves."

She took the trunk upstairs, I followed. She closed the door to our small room. Curtius could be heard wandering about downstairs. Mother sat by the window for a long time. In the end, I helped steer her towards our bed. We did not sleep that first night in this new place. Mother held on to me. I, in my turn, held on to Marta. In the morning we were still, all three of us, holding each other. Three small women, very anxious.

Before we went downstairs, Mother said to me, "We are bound now, you and I. Do you understand? Our every action must be to please him. If he abandons us we are lost. So long as we remain in Doctor Curtius's employ, so long do we persist. Be of good service, dear daughter."

When I took a handful of Mother's dress, she said, quietly, sadly, "No."

Mother took the keys. We scrubbed floors. Mother cooked. We went shopping; the market was frightening to her. The objects on sale, all that meat hung up, cut open, all those divided fractions of animals, or whole animals but strung up by their feet, or whole birds with lazy necks and bloody beaks, hanging like felons—all these, and the eyes of fish, and the flies, and the meat of living people's hands, spotted with gore, all this recalled to Mother, again and again, what she had seen in Doctor Curtius's atelier.

Doctor Curtius spent the day in his atelier, and rarely came out. When he did appear he seemed surprised to see us there, and whispering, "Not used . . . not used," would retreat back to his room. When it was time for his lunch, Mother, the Waltner nose flared in desperate disapproval, loaded the food on a tray. She held the tray above the kitchen table, but, shuddering, causing the soup to spill, had to lower it again. I led her to a chair and sat her down. I carried the food in to Doctor Curtius. He was bent over his table, a portrait of three tongues: the actual separated human tongue, his perfect wax duplicate, and his own tongue in concentration sticking out between his lips.

"Soup, sir," I said.

He did not say anything in response. I left the soup with him and closed the door. It was the same later that day when I entered the atelier saying, "Stew, sir." It was the same in fact throughout the first week. Twice Curtius came into the kitchen for the shortest of times to say to Mother, "I'm so pleased you're here, so pleased, so glad, so . . . happy," after which Mother's hands sought her crucifix.

During the second week, when we had, I thought, grown more used to one another and kept to our own silences throughout the house, there was a visitor. This visitor was from the hospital. He was dressed in a similar black uniform to Ernst's, but was called Heinrich. Heinrich had an unimpressive nose and other unremarkable features, I cannot now recall any of them, or indeed anything of him beyond his unexceptional name. Mother and I were shocked by the sudden noise of Heinrich's knocking. Mother nervously answered the door. Heinrich held up a lidded metal box. He said with a great grin upon his youthful face, "Delivery for Curtius. I'm Heinrich, I do the bringing, we'll be seeing a lot of each other. What have we got today?" And lifting the lid and poking at a muslin-covered object within, ruminated thus, "Bit of a diseased gut, I reckon."

Mother closed her eyes and crossed herself. I stepped forwards, aiming to be useful, and held out my hands.

Heinrich looked uncertain.

When he reluctantly passed the box to me, Mother hurriedly closed the door. She looked at me for an instant as if I were no longer recognizable, then retreated to the kitchen. I followed to ask her if I should take the object in, she nodded fiercely, waving me and the box from the room. I went to the atelier.

"Bit of a gut, sir," I said, leaving the box on the same portion of the table where I always left him his meals. This time Doctor Curtius did look up.

Mother found it increasingly difficult to work, she often sat in the kitchen with her hands on her small crucifix. Flies in Curtius's house, and there were always flies, caused her to panic utterly, for flies could travel throughout the house, could get into the atelier, and from there spread the news of the atelier everywhere about. Now Mother often sat still, her eyes closed, but perfectly awake, whilst I moved about to her instructions.

Two days after I had delivered the parcel to Doctor Curtius, I was sitting on one of the chairs in the kitchen by the fire, whilst Mother on the other side was reading to me from the Bible, when Doctor Curtius faintly knocked and came in.

"Widow Grosholtz," he said. My mother closed her eyes. "I would like, if it isn't too much trouble, Widow Grosholtz, and I'm delighted, at all this . . . company. I should like help in my atelier. Tomorrow first thing would be best, I think. I should like to teach you how to handle my work, so that you don't harm it. I should like you to get properly acquainted with it. I'm sure you shall come to love your new duties."

Doctor Curtius saw Mother give a slight nod. But I was not taken in by it. I had clearly observed that Mother's nod was in fact a shudder misinterpreted as a nod.

"Good night then," he said. "Thank you."

Back in our attic room, Mother put me to bed, she kissed me on the forehead and said, "Be useful, Marie. You are a good child. Be useful. I'm sorry, I cannot. I have tried, but I cannot."

"You cannot what, Mother?"

"Do be good now, quieten down. Good night, Marie."

"Good night."

She told me to close my eyes and go to sleep instantly. She told me not to look; whatever else, I must keep my eyes shut and my face turned away. I heard her busy arranging things, pulling one of the sheets from the bed, a chair being moved. I went to sleep.

When I woke up, the candle was out. It was the early hours of the morning. Mother was not in the bed beside me. A faint blue light was coming into the room. I could just make out something dark suspended from the rafters. I did not recall ever seeing that object before. More light slowly arrived and I began to understand what this object was. Mother had hanged herself.

Fretting, I held one of Mother's feet but that naked foot gave me no comfort; it was a cold foot after all and in that coldness was the awful confirmation of Mother's passing. A woman's death is a simple enough thing, perhaps; women will always be dying, no doubt several women have died as I have been writing this sentence, only this one woman who concerns me now, this one woman tied up to the rafters, unlike all the others in the world, this woman was my mother. Whose dress should I cling to now? There would never be any dress clinging for me ever again. Before I had always had Mother to hide behind; now I was exposed. Mother's death was not a quiet, thinking death like Father's had been. Mother's death was about business, it was all hurried action; mother had jolted herself out of life. Her cold nose had swung away from me, the signal post of her rejection.

"Mother," I said, *"Mother!"* But Mother, or that hanging thing that was only partly Mother, kept herself very quiet. In my panic I flailed around for something, I searched for some solace, some protection, and found only Marta. I think Doctor Curtius must have heard me crying, for he called to me from the bottom of the stairs.

"Where's your mother?" he asked. "It's time. It was agreed."

"She won't come, sir."

"She must, it was agreed after all."

"Please, Doctor."

"Yes?"

"I think that she is dead."

I have cast a wood pigeon to play the role of my mother.

And so Curtius climbed the attic stairs. He opened the door, I followed behind him. Curtius knew dead bodies. He was an expert in dead bodies and their slumped faces. And here, he immediately recognized on opening our bedroom door, hanging up like a coat, was yet another example.

"Stopped," he said, "stopped."

He closed the door. I stood beside him at the top of the attic stairs.

"Stopped," he said again, bending down close to me, in a whisper, as if it was a secret. He walked down the stairs. At the bottom he turned round to me, nodded once more, and whispered, with tears in his eyes, as I saw now, his face collapsing into a grimace of terrible sorrow, "Stopped," and walked out of the building, closing and locking the door behind him.

After a long time, I sat halfway down the stairs with Marta. We sat very still and waited. Mother is upstairs, I thought. Oh Mother is upstairs and Mother is dead.

At last men came from the hospital. Doctor Curtius was with them. "I can't make people work," he said. "I can unwork them, I can take them apart, yes, I'm actually good at that, considerably accomplished at that, in fact, but they'll never work with me. They won't. They refuse. They shut up. They stop." The men from the hospital walked up the attic stairs, stepping around me and Marta, barely regarding us at all. The oldest of the hospital men led this hurried procession; he was the one who opened the door. All the men went inside, except Curtius; he was kept outside, they closed the door on him. And so we both remained outside and both, I think, began to consider that we had done something terribly wrong, otherwise why wouldn't they let us come in too? Doctor Curtius, shy now, did not look at me, even though we were very close to one another. Young Doctor Curtius, and he seemed now extremely young, a child almost, looked at the door all the time. When the door opened, the oldest of the men said, quietly and slowly, "Take the girl downstairs. Keep her there." Curtius shook his head, he spoke in a very small, very hurt voice, "If you make me touch her, Surgeon Hoffmann, I think that she'll die too."

"Nonsense. Come now, Philip. Philip Curtius, you can do this."

"I'm not sure, I'm really not sure."

"Take the child downstairs. Let us attend to matters here."

"But what do I do with her?"

"It doesn't matter," snapped the surgeon, "just get her away from here."

The door was closed on us again. After a moment, Curtius tapped me on my shoulder. "Come," he said, and walked down the stairs towards his atelier. He left the door open.

I put Marta in my pocket so she would be safe. I stood up and slowly followed. Not sure exactly how a person should go about comforting a child, childlike though he seemed himself, Curtius looked about him, and seemed to find the answer in a box of bones upon one of his shelves. He handed me, with great kindness, I remember, a human scapula, the right, I think.

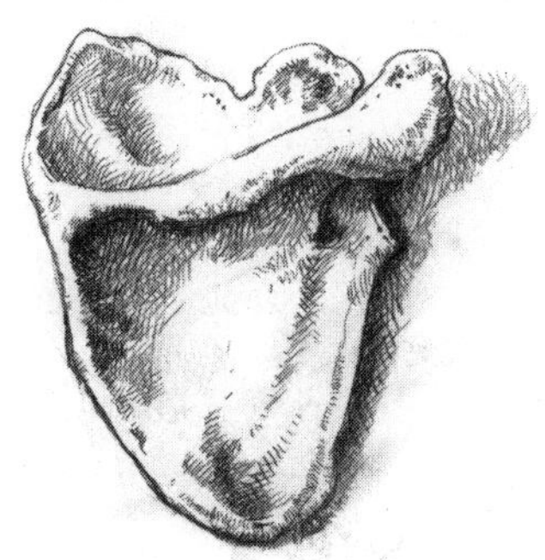

"It's a good bone," he whispered to me, "a great comforting bone. This part of the shoulder girdle is large and flat and triangular, and is excellent for stroking. Yes, a wonderful, soothing bone."

After a time Surgeon Hoffmann came down to find us sitting together in the atelier, I on a stool, Curtius on the floor beside me, rummaging through a box of bones.

"And this, you see, is the temporal bone . . . and this the left parietal . . . and this the sacrum—wonderful, aren't they? All my old friends!"

"It is done," said the surgeon.

I kept very still.

"Now," continued the surgeon, "what is to become of the child? Some place must be found for her."

"Can I keep her?" asked Doctor Curtius quickly. "The child. Can I keep her?"

I was the subject of a discussion. I didn't move.

"Out of the question," said the surgeon.

"Oh, I'd like to keep her."

"Why on earth?"

"She isn't frightened."

"Why should she be?"
"She holds bones."
"And what does that signify?"
"She's ugly and short."
"Those are not qualifications."
"She is quiet."
"And then?"
"She may be stupid, I do not know. But for now, if you don't mind, if I may, I'll keep her."
"Is she useful to you?"
"I shall train her."
"Well," said the surgeon, "keep her for now for all I care. Until something better can be thought of."

Pedalo

Dina Nayeri

BY MIDMORNING THEY HAD settled on Lac de Sainte-Croix, but Roya lagged. She took a nap, spent a long time with her head in the sink, letting cold water run down the back of her neck, then insisted on making lunch. She packed her bag slowly. Searching her purse, she found three one-euro coins, five British pounds, and a quarter. By the time she shuffled out behind Max, the iron latch on the crumbling gate groaning into place, shedding its rusted skin onto their hands and sealing the staircase in musty darkness, it was nearly four thirty.

Max started up the Peugeot, an old stick shift guaranteed to bring on Roya's morning sickness. He typed *St. Croix* into the GPS unit that was duct-taped to the dashboard.

At least the sun isn't so brutal now, said Max.

Then what's the point of the lake? said Roya.

Roya had wanted to go to the other lake, the shockingly blue one farther away. She had seen photos of it online—from distant hillside roads, it looked like a sapphire puddle caught in the hollow of the forest's cupped hand. Lac de Sainte-Croix was such a consolation prize; maybe they could try again tomorrow, she suggested, wake up at a decent hour and get an earlier start. She imagined cool water and the smell of mint; she imagined watermelon and pressed lime, a refuge from the endless nausea.

Max wondered what would happen if *he* played so fast and loose with the complaints. The Roya of last winter would have rolled with the changes; she would have scratched his head the way he liked and asked excellent questions to pass the time. He struggled not to remind the Roya of this summer that she was the one who couldn't drive stick and had chronic passenger-side illness. She was the reason for the sleeping in and the driving slow. If he were alone, he'd be at the nicer lake right now, which, by the way, was called Esparron. Instead he reminded himself that he wasn't alone anymore, and that he didn't want to be (hadn't for a long while now).

Limes, doctor's bill, bug repellent, Roya murmured, fingers fluttering again, keeping their own silent count. Max was unsure if she knew she was speaking aloud. She turned to him and mumbled, where did I put that bag of oranges?

Do you want an orange? She didn't answer—of course she didn't.

Max never asked about the counting because Roya was pregnant and uncomfortable and because they were unmoored in Barjols, a decaying village of his youth, not hers—she had come only for his sake. Besides, she had been his for only five months, two weeks longer than the pregnancy, and new couples are supposed to stumble around blind with euphoria, their flaws blurred for each other. They're supposed to be kind. Roya and Max had been euphoric and kind until Barjols, then, quick as a pinched nerve, something had changed.

She knows now that it's not glamorous, thought Max, actually living in Provence—not so much carafes of rosé in lavender fields as moldy cheeses befouling your fingers and your car seats, old women in fading cotton dresses, teeth blackened, yelling at each other from windows, their husbands like gray smudges marring photos of the fountain, the market, the church. These things, they learned, plus an unusually high incidence of toxoplasmosis: these are Provence. *The Tox*, Roya called the invisible sickness, that baby killer, each time she waved away the gooey *Banon* or the stinky *Epoisses*. Max found the word charming.

They were renting a five-hundred-year-old pension that once housed the town hall—a short-run plan, a reflex. On their second day, Roya had stepped out of the bathroom (not so much out of it as beyond the curtain separating it from Max's work space), and said, I need a doctor, nothing urgent. Minutes later, standing before a graying man in a graying lab coat and a furor of stiff eyebrows, Max shuffled as Roya tried to communicate with hand signals. She made a horrifying gesture like dough stretching, then gave up and turned to Max: What's the word for discharge?

You mean like, Max muttered, and the doctor said, *Pertes*.

Right, said Roya and forced out a weak chuckle. Her fingers danced.

Describe, said the doctor. He had a heavy accent and fleshy face, and every word sounded as if it were spoken through a mouthful of crusted bread.

I'll wait outside, said Max in French, then to Roya in English, we'll go for a glass of wine after, OK? Or a cappuccino. He wanted to remind her that here in France, she could have a glass of wine or a cappuccino right up until she gave birth.

Now, ten minutes into the drive, Roya was breathing funny. Can we stop for something cool? she asked, wiping her glistening brow.

Don't you want to just hurry and get there? Before it gets cold?

Max looked at his watch. It was four forty. How late did lakes stay open?

If it's cold, what's the point? She didn't snap. They hadn't yet snapped at each other, not ever. Maybe it was coming next. He tried to change the subject.

So Becks is getting married, he said. She wrote last night. You were asleep.

Oh yeah? Roya sat up. She didn't tell him that she never slept anymore, that she had felt him beside her, idling on his computer. Is that . . . are you OK?

He squeezed Roya's clammy hand. I'm fine. It's good news.

A minute or two passed in silence. Did she say who the guy is?

Max nodded. Some knob who advised her on her mortgage. They're going to buy up cheap properties in Walthamstow and retire as landlords.

Ick, she said. She swallowed hard as he took a sharp turn. Her mouth tasted like pennies. I guess you can never tell with people. Maybe Becks met her match.

With that, Roya retreated to her private space again, a place implied by trilling fingers and faraway eyes, that corner of her mind where everything was orderly. Then, remembering, she said, Oh, we have to stop for cash.

Right, he said, but the banks close at four thirty. Can we make do with the card today? And I have a few euros somewhere.

They had a joint bank account now; they had opened it timidly, out of sheer necessity, when they had arrived in France. No more of that awful who-pays-this-time pause in checkout lines, after meals and at gas stations, which, for Roya, had almost ended things. Not that she expected Max to pay—before the pregnancy and France, they were poor adjuncts floating around New York—but she expected him to offer each and every time, and to mean it; to convince her that he meant it, so that she could refuse precisely half the time. That seemed a graceful way to be fair.

I think we should stop for money, she said.

No, he said, grinning, trying much too hard to be lighthearted for her. These days, Roya had begun to notice, Max spent hours trying to be himself, the himself he had been so naturally just a few months before, when she had found him enough to fall in love with, to have a baby with, to *keep* a baby with. We're going to the lake. I'm taking you two to the lake.

Roya rested her head on the window, the flimsy safety glass rattling a little and splattered with a neat line of dead mosquitoes. The upholstery smelled like an airplane cabin after a long flight, musty and hot, a kind of deep-down grime that doesn't wash out of fabric.

I need something cool, Roya panted, but Max didn't respond.

What Roya wanted to say, and had wanted to say since they arrived in Barjols, was that their bed was too small. That was the source of everything: the reason she was sick, that their day didn't begin till noon and why she couldn't manage a modicum of kindness toward this man she had declared the love of her life before all her friends and family, not in a lush garden wedding, as she had with the first one, but on Facebook, with a pregnancy announcement and a quiet, almost apologetic, change in her Relationship Status. In their tiny village bed, the long limbs she had loved, his equine legs, his swaddling arms, now prodded her awake. She sat up noticing things: the thin, itchy sheets; the family of mosquitoes idling overhead, waiting to continue their attack on her engorged calves and ankles. But how could she suggest, after just five months, after they had shared sorrowful stories of divorces—of the years they had each spent falling out of love, losing their grip on sex until it slipped like a panicked fish from their fingers, then retreating to beds in opposite rooms—how could she, after all that, suggest that already she wanted to sleep apart? Men are fragile, Roya knew, wounded most by the things that matter the least. You want to paint the wall gray? Maybe you're unhappy. You want more closet space? Maybe I'm not enough for you.

Five o'clock was closing in. Max gripped the steering wheel and peeked at his watch, hoping Roya hadn't noticed. He was still thinking about Becks.

Once I saw a couple take their baby into a sex shop, said Max. Maybe that was their thing before.

Probably, said Roya. Remember my friend Christopher? His second wife used lame corporate jargon for everything. *Honey, let's just 80/20 this wedding. I don't have bandwidth to take the kids today.* Chris loved it; said she made him feel safe.

There's something tragic about *bandwidth* in that context, said Max.

There's something tragic about falling in love with a cliché generator.

I fell in love with Becks after she threw a Malteser at a bike messenger.

Hah, said Roya, but didn't laugh. Watch the turns, OK? I'm trying not to throw up. Actually, we need to deposit that check too, Roya said, fingers tapping her cheek. She was trying to hide the counting, to tone it down. Max saw and he loved her more.

Sweet, you're so crazy, he said. He dug in his pocket for his toothpick as he spoke. I could tell you didn't want an orange, he said, his voice teasing. I'm getting the hang of you now. It doesn't actually matter what the thing is. Sometimes you'll say, Max, where are those five balls of lint from before?

This time she let escape a real laugh, a good and hearty one.

Roya wished she could just let it go. She whimpered, trying for a sweet tone. Can you please stop at the bank on the way? It'll bug me, and it's not even five.

The lake is an hour away, he said, if we stop we'll miss it.

The lake doesn't have a closing time, Max. And if you'd just done it instead of arguing—

Irritated by her own voice, she returned to silent fuming. This is why men always win; we have shrillness and they don't. I'm so tired, she said. I barely slept.

I know, love. They drove in silence up the main highway, through two desperate-looking towns that appeared after the vineyards and apple orchards gave way to auto shops and cheap pizzerias with crumbling brick facades. Then they hit a smaller dirt road and the orchards returned, the last of the wild lavender in patches here and there, like missed spots after a hasty mow.

The Peugeot wasn't easy to handle. Now and then it jolted and Roya gasped, quietly at first, then self-indulgently, with hard sighs and grunts and a hand on the belly. Max glanced over but said nothing—for weeks she had barely acknowledged all he had done. The cooking, the daily cleanup. Did she notice? Did she know that he had washed the sheets after she complained that they itched? Hung the laundry out of the window and bought extra clothespins? He had divided her vitamins into daily doses, making sure she took the prenatal one in the morning, the calcium at night, that the DHA stayed in the fridge. He watched her food, distracting her from her incessant cravings for ice cream and soy sauce and ketchup, not just because he didn't want to poison his daughter, his precious first child, but for Roya too, for her own sake. She grunted again, her cheeks swelling for a second, as if she were holding in a mouthful of spoiled milk. Theatrical Roya. She was like a cartoon sometimes.

I'm sorry, it's an old car.

I didn't say anything.

Roya glanced at Max; he had taken out one of the wretched floss picks. He had a family-sized bag of them, tiny minty-green axes that he used to hack at his gums several hundred times a day. It was a sickness, she thought, and he left the used ones everywhere. She found them under chair cushions and in folded sheets, in the hamper and behind the oven, scattered inside the Peugeot and once even in her purse. If she could sleep, they would litter the ghostly halls of her nightmares; they would crunch underfoot as she lifted rusty door latches to Tox babies and bankruptcy.

More silence. Five o'clock announced itself, wedging its way between them. Max dug deep—he scraped past today's misfires and irritations to what he actually felt: grateful, for Roya, for his daughter. He would try harder, he vowed. Roya had been disappointed so often before, married for years, divorced for years, and now here she was suddenly tossed into a foreign country, no family except a man with whom she should be having her thirteenth or fourteenth date, maybe the theater this time, or a dinner party, or an overnight trip to the Berkshires.

In the next town, Max had an idea. He pulled a hard left, stopping in front of a village bar and café. Wait here, he said.

But you said we didn't have time, she shouted to the closing door.

He emerged from the café, dropping change into his pocket, two ice-cream cones leaning together in the other hand. Though they had the good, homemade stuff he loved, he chose Cornettos, mass-produced garbage that tasted like melted-down plastic bottles. But Roya's palate was crazy right now. And Cornettos were her favorite, so . . . One time didn't matter to her health. Or the baby's. He smiled as he presented his offering, expecting delight, like a child holding a picture he had made. But Roya was clutching her belly and moaning loudly, jerking on the door handle until it opened. She slid out and slammed the door shut.

You said we didn't have time for the bank. She heaved and spat onto the grass. She started to say something else, but didn't have time. She stumbled away from the car and vomited into the bushes, splashing the front tire.

Fuck, said Roya, spitting and wiping. Her hands trembled in a new way, alarming Max. He wanted to help, but found himself afraid to touch her.

Here, eat this, he said, tearing open her cone and holding it over her. A drop of cream fell onto her bare shoulder. She flinched. He had an urge to cross the street and wait; now he had made her sticky, on top of everything.

You said we didn't have time for the bank.

You said you wanted something cool.

Can we please just go? She took the ice cream and got in the passenger's seat. I have no fucking clue what she wants, Max thought. It was five fifteen.

It isn't easy to drive a stick shift and eat when you're not on a highway, but Max was too proud to ask for help. He held the wilting cone in his mouth, bits of chocolate melting on his tongue or falling down his cheek, as he changed gears and negotiated turns and tuned out Roya's grunts. Once she relaxed, though, it was satisfying to listen to her eat. She was like the thirsty children you see around the docks after a long day on the lake, sitting in wet puddles on rented pedal boats, sighing and humming and gulping, unaware of the nakedness of it, their closeness to something feral suddenly palpable.

I hope the pedalo rentals are still open, he said.

What's a pedalo? She was calmer now, sated. He breathed out. Five twenty, time still to salvage the day.

Pedal boat. So we don't have to lie on rocks or swim in the sludge by the beach. We'll pedal it out to the center of the lake. It's great. You'll love it.

A piece of the cone fell from the corner of his mouth and Roya retrieved it. Carelessly she brought it to her own lips. Max loved these newer, more intimate gestures between them. He loved that the sharp, scummy smell of her waking mouth was now familiar, that he knew when the pains in her legs would come and how to speed through the arc of her anger—sugar and cream, always. Or if he was in a worrying mood, watermelon, eaten with their arms hanging out of the window, over the stone ledge and the clothesline holding their underwear and T-shirts, spitting seeds in the empty square where once people had gathered to bring their important matters to the town hall. Maybe because he was thirty-nine, or because they were in Provence, or because his divorce was five years in the past, its memory dulling, new rituals didn't frighten him. These small repetitions slowly coming to light, they made him feel settled and domestic, part of a solid couple, real, with the beginning of a history and a baby soon to come. She smiled sleepily in his direction, leaned back, and said, That sounds like just the thing.

Roya practiced her deep breathing through the next twenty minutes of twists and jerks and sudden stops, Max riding the clutch and giving away how long it had been since he'd spent real time in these vineyards, picking these sunflowers and rosemary, driving to this lake. *All my summers,* he'd said in her studio in New York, *let's just throw everything into storage and go. Fuck this place. We'll wither here.*

The main parking area was full, cars stacked two or three deep with no hope of getting out. They found a cul-de-sac near a quieter part of the lake, but they had to walk through brambles, change into their swim clothes between the car and the bushes. Max took the opportunity to empty his bladder. Roya recoiled.

Her ex-husband prepared for things. He never peed in bushes.

Max hadn't cut his hair in six months.

Her ex-husband purchased maps and guidebooks and stopped for cash.

Max had a spot of chocolate still on his chin. Sometimes, even in public, even in London or New York, he crunched cartilage off the ends of chicken bones.

Yesterday she had found an old guidebook, twenty years out of date, in the dusty glove compartment of the Peugeot. It was stained at the edges and some pages were stuck together, others warped by rain, coffee, red wine. About Barjols it said:

> For all its springs, streams, and fountains, BARJOLS, 16km west of Cotignac, is a depressing place. The town has still not recovered from the closure of its tanneries, and many of the people at the Saturday market on Place Émile Zola seem as glum as characters from a Zola novel.

In the parking area, they lathered on sunscreen. They stowed their backpacks and most of their clothes in the trunk, taking only their sunglasses (his a flimsy drugstore pair, hers the last expensive relic of a previous life), one bank card, and their landlord's old bath towels, frayed and stained in unseemly spots, in unseemly shades. They hiked in flip-flops through the brambles and rocks down to the lake, where a café made out of a shed and three umbrellas was waiting to ease their passage with espressos and cigarettes and sodas and ice cream. A row of pedal boats bobbed in the water—it was five forty now and the sun was waning. Max asked in French for a pedalo and an Orangina for Roya. The woman behind the makeshift bar, a ragged chain-smoker in a bikini who might have been thirty-two or forty-eight, lifted the clear lid of a travel cooler, slammed the bulbous bottle onto the counter, and said in English, Two euro. How long you take pedalo? A handwritten sign by her elbow read *pedal-eau,* not *pedalo,* which is how Roya had imagined it and almost certainly how Max had meant it.

Max said, in more precise French, We'll start with an hour and see how the sun holds up. We'll take the more stable one, the four-seat one there, since she gets sick. He turned to Roya, who had some college French, and smiled, squeezing her shoulders as if to say, The fun's about to start. He placed his bank card on the counter beside the sweaty orange bottle.

No machine, said the woman in English. Cash only. I charge eighteen euro for one hour and we finish the day at six hours and half, so you may have fifty minutes.

Roya groaned and scratched the bites on her ankles. One was bleeding. Max glanced at his watch, then back at Roya. Love, you don't have a twenty, by any chance?

She glared, clutching her belly, already bursting out of the two-piece aquamarine suit that the salesgirl had promised would last through nine months.

It's fine, sweet. It's totally fine. Just stay here and count the minutes while I go get the change in my pants or find an ATM or sell my body or something.

But you only had a few euros before, Roya whispered, ignoring the ill-timed joke. And then you bought the ice creams, so there's probably nothing left.

Can you please hold that pedalo for us? Max said in English this time. The four-seat one. I'll be right back. And if we do forty-five minutes . . . ?

The woman rolled her eyes, yes, yes, thirteen euro fifty.

But all Roya could see was the smear of chocolate on Max's chin. Rage boiled up her neck. A teenage boy, probably the woman's son, was unhooking the first pedalo in the line and stepping into the shallow water, checking its pedals.

As Max disappeared back up the little hill, Roya thought of a trip she had taken years before, when she was thin, graceful, married. Or, actually, she had thought herself graceful, but her husband had never agreed, not on her best day. During a holiday, years into their marriage, they had driven into Belgium, to Bruges, for his friend's wedding—acres of manicured lawns, morning coats, women in feathered hats and fascinators—and Roya had worn the wrong underwear. They had changed into their formal clothes in the bathroom of a pizzeria in the outskirts of the medieval city. She had stepped out in the harsh light in her silk dress, a dusty-rose garment thin enough to fit in her purse, though it cost many hundreds of dollars. I can see the line of your underwear, he had said. When she removed them, he said, Now I can see *everything,* Roya, holy shit, and we're so late already.

They had hurried to the ceremony, and Roya had kept a huge shawl wrapped around her body like a bath sheet. When she looked down into her lap, she could see small hairs easily escaping the fabric, catching the dress where it draped over the curve of her thigh and fell into the dark hollow between her legs. How ugly such a delicate thing can seem. She remembered an ancient test Iranian mothers concocted for potential daughters-in-law—a thin piece of silk casually dropped to the floor near the girl's bare feet. She would then walk across it, feigning ignorance of the test. If her heel lifted the fabric, her skin was too rough. What would those women think of Roya, losing such greater stores of dignity to the fabric? They skipped the cocktails prior to the reception and rushed into Bruges city center, a centuries-old tourist town, a Saturday afternoon—hopeless. They had visited Bruges several times but had never noticed any businesses other than beer makers and chocolatiers, waffle shops and mussel vendors. In the car, he had yelled at her, eyeing her dress with open disdain. All that OCD and you can't come prepared? Why can't you be elegant? He mumbled about her carelessness until it stopped stinging her, until the shame gave way to a tinge of pride, a kind of survival-grade calm—no one else would have made *this* mistake; believing that much made Roya unique, alone in her strangeness. *There's no one like you, Roya joon,* her mother had said long ago. *No one has happy fingers like these.* If Roya's baby inherited this itchy corner of her brain, she would say exactly those words, in exactly that way.

That day in Bruges, on a touristy street among postcard and shoe stores, the miracle of a lingerie shop. A tiny fiftyish woman with an ash-blonde bob took one look at her and knew the problem. Oh, darling, she said, is this how things have gone in New York? We aren't progressive enough for all *that* here in the country. Roya laughed, relieved that she wasn't the most hopeless case this saleswoman had seen—because you don't joke with the hopeless cases.

The shop had only one piece that might work, a body-shaping slip with thick shoulders, too thick for the spaghetti straps of Roya's dress. The saleswoman helped Roya into it, then eyed her for a moment and dashed off to the shop next door for a roll of tape, which she used to fasten the bust and the rolled straps of the slip to the skin below Roya's breasts. There we are, she said and charged two hundred euros.

Max returned at five fifty-six. A new patch of dirt was encrusted on his cheek.

Let's just go home, said Roya.

No, said Max. We came to swim. I'm going to swim.

It's cold, said Roya, her anger rising. She reached for his chin, wiping roughly. Geez, can you wipe your mouth?

There, it's done, thought Max, the first time she snapped at me. It's a new thing at least. A thing that real couples do. A thing we should expect after the baby comes. Our first time shouldn't be in the black and foggy early days of parenthood.

He turned to the woman behind the makeshift counter. He was already exhausted. He wiped his brow, exhaled, muttered, Well, now that it's half an hour . . .

Yes, nine euro. She sighed, shook her head at him. Orangina is on the house.

Max poured a rustle of small coins into her hand. Some of them were caked in dirt and Roya thought she saw a ball of lint, like blue wool from a winter sweater. He must have turned over every seat and emptied every slot in the damn Peugeot. Maybe he had approached a swimmer, or shaken out trousers discarded on the beach. With Max, these things were possible.

Still inside the memory of Bruges, an uneasy smile came over

Roya. She loved Max, nearly-forty boyish Max. He wouldn't know how to react any other way than to laugh at the sight of a silly woman in a pricey dress, muff exposed, even if that silly woman was the one on his arm. He might even be proud—what a story!

She reached over, willing kindness back into her fingers, and wiped the rest of the caked dirt from his chin. This time he pulled away. Stop, he whispered.

Roya and her husband agreed to be friends; now they never speak or write.

Max and his wife didn't agree to be friends, but sometimes they check on each other, after natural disasters or when one has been sick.

Max and Roya sat in the front of the boat, bare feet on the slimy pedals, silently waiting for the boy to release them. Behind them, the two empty seats felt farcical, insinuating the children they might have had if they were a normal couple in their late thirties, having met in youth, dated for a span of months, spent the right number of dollars and Sundays and tears on each other before committing for life, if they were renting a pedalo with the right amount of cash ready in canvas totes or straw shoulder bags stuffed with beach towels and this year's travel guides, and if neither of them was indulging in a runaway teenage pregnancy twenty years too late, no chocolate smeared on either of their faces. When the boy nodded and let go of the rope, they pedaled in unison, finding their rhythm quickly. A few yards out, Max peeled off his shirt, a tattered thing with scattershot holes all along the shoulder seams and collar.

I'm getting in.

Should I wait? said Roya. The pedalo squeaked and rocked under them.

Get in, have a swim, said Max. Wait, no, actually someone has to stay with the boat. We have to swim one at a time.

That sounds like the least fun thing ever.

OK, but please just try.

They were still close to the shore and as their voices rose, a sunbathing woman lifted her head and squinted at them. They stopped speaking and pedaled harder. Once or twice, they veered left as Roya's toes slipped off the pedal into something cold and sludgy that had grown in the damp, dark space underfoot. They struggled to pedal in unison, a strenuous task requiring more coordination and harmony than they had expected. Roya panted. The squeaking assaulted the nerves, and, after another ten or so yards, they slowed.

All right, I've had enough, said Max and stopped pedaling. Roya stopped too. They sat on the still lake, the only pedalo on the water this late—a pair of teenage boys were returning theirs. The lake gulped and rested again. Max checked his watch. They had spent ten precious minutes. Look, we only have twenty minutes left. If we jump in, have a swim, and pedal a bit farther out, it'll have been worth it.

Roya wanted to argue, but she too hated waste. She loved Max for his penniless habits. This shared sensibility bonded them: that they wanted to live simply, to avoid lavish things, to make a modest, artistic home, to save leftovers in washed ice-cream tubs and do their own cleaning, and if they showed up to a party with a grotesque wardrobe malfunction, to easily accept their role as the evening's conversation piece, not run away and drop two hundred euros on an itchy, rashy fix.

Max got up and stretched his long, wayward limbs. As he prepared to dive, he shook the pedalo and her sunglasses plopped into the lake. He stared bewildered into the dark water, the glossy brown frames vanishing. He scratched at a pimple on his hip and flashed Roya a miserable wide-eyed look. Now the trouble spot in her temple was throbbing, her eyelids were swelling, and her thigh muscles numbing, as if the sun were pulling her last stores of energy down past the horizon.

Roya and her husband had agreed to sleep in separate beds when she became nocturnal for a project, then, when she saw that he didn't care, the next project and the one after that. Now she wanted to ask Max if there was a way to sleep separately for a time, then come together again. Or did it always end up slipping into forever? But before she could arrange her words, she said, I thought you had it more together than this.

Max steadied himself and the squeaking slowed. More together than what?

Her voice was low and tired, worse than if she had raged. All the puttering, she said, the digging around for money, the twenty minutes of pedalo for nine euro. Can I ask you something? Did you ever read the guidebook description of Barjols? I mean, I get it. It's your childhood. But there are a dozen villages close by and you could have just . . . I'd just really like for you to read it. Roya exhaled and flung up a hand as if she thought she might as well say this one last thing too: You're the only person I know that this would happen to.

That's the shittiest thing you've said to me. Max moved to dive but hesitated. You know what? Fuck your bullshit yuppie regrets. It's not even really you.

The sunbathing woman on shore sat up, gawking at the pair, the fortyish pregnant idiots who had rented a boat just to pedal out twenty yards and sit in the middle of an empty lake, bobbing and fighting and drinking orangeade.

You don't know what's not me, muttered Roya. That's the thing, right? We don't know any of that stuff. There are things I know about the baby from the way she moves. There are things I know about you. And neither is very much.

Why are you being so mean today? said Max.

What he wanted to ask was, what do you want? She had chosen him, not one of the buttoned-up corporate men of her past. Why did she boil and rage when he didn't behave like one? I do so much for you, he said. Didn't I run out for vitamins the day we found out? Haven't I cooked you every kind of fish and made a thousand sour crunchy salads and done all the washing up?

Hey, I wash up, she said, avoiding his glare. She retied her ponytail and tucked her hands under her haunches, then changed her mind and started inspecting her cuticles. She touched the water. He bent back a torn flip-flop with his other foot. They sat in silence for a beat or two.

No one I know would've said a thing like that, said Max.

A thing like what?

A thing like: *This would never have happened to anyone else I know.*

Max checked his watch. Ten minutes left on the rental. Feeling the warmth draining from his limbs, he said, you know, you're kind of a special case yourself.

Roya's cheeks were numb but she knew she was crying from the look on his face. Did he have to say it? Wasn't it obvious that they weren't normal? That nothing was respectable or planned or good? That she counted with her fingers at almost forty . . . forty and pregnant by a stranger with cracks at the balls of all his sandals, juvenile hair unwashed but dropping floss picks like a bread-crumb trail? Why did she always think men would fix it? When you're alone, you have long pockets of time to store your strangeness, your ticks. You can take an hour and be ugly and safe.

But Max remembered everything, the joyful, the foul, all of Roya's offhand chatter, even when she didn't mean any of it. He gave her no practice runs. He forced on her a constant nakedness, skinlessness, but his vigilance also lessened her need to count. When he packed, nothing got left behind. He never went to bed without tidying up. He poured the last three almonds into the new bag and wrapped the last sliver of butter alongside the new stick and wiped behind the faucet and draped the bath mat over the window ledge. If she mentioned a poem, he read it. Once she mentioned that her belly was outgrowing her underwear; two days later he pulled over at a shitty clothing chain. Should we get underwear? he said.

The day Roya found out she was pregnant, Max ran out and bought four kinds of smoked fish. Google says you need DHA. He made her an omelet with green herbs and avocado sliced so evenly she didn't want to eat it and ruin the effect. She thought, This is the nicest meal of my life. The realization made her cry with old grief and new joy but when he asked what's wrong, she only said that she was afraid of the birth. How will I push out a whole baby? I'll be nothing but a gaping hole.

Max stroked her hair and started to tell a joke. So a guy walks into a doctor's office and his asshole is all bloody and just wrecked . . . Roya nodded, giggling at the way Max spoke, slowly, with lots of dramatic pauses, but wildly too, with his hands, with his long fingers. The guy says, Doctor, doctor, I was on safari and I was violated by an elephant. But this doctor, he happens to know a little something about elephant anatomy, right? He says to the guy, You poor man, you've been through so much but . . . elephant penises . . . they're not this substantial. And the guy sighs and hangs his head and he says, I know doctor, but . . . the thing is . . . he fisted me first.

Roya spat out her coffee, head over arms. She thought, I've met my match. She wiped her mouth. Max laughed too, kissed her hand, looked at her for a long time. Then he jolted out of the moment. Oh shit, should you be drinking coffee?

Now the old pedal boat creaked and sputtered water under them.

Maybe we're doing it wrong, said Max. He let out a slow sigh. I don't know.

Maybe she had let this go too far, thought Roya, her eyes closing. The sleeplessness was making her cruel. She struggled every night, but each time she fell under, she was jerked awake by one of Max's long legs or wiry arms or his wild curls in her face. She recalled that, with men, the way to end fights you cause with your hormones or your motion sickness or your painful, swollen limbs isn't to blame those trite, true things. It's to confess something new, something that, while less true, is heavier. And it should be costly and messy too, a chunk of your heart.

It doesn't feel like you love me anymore, she said. You loved me so much before, and now . . . I'm this burden. Maybe you expected someone different.

The words didn't give her relief. Instead she felt false, like she was pawning a handy half-truth, a catchall, just to end the fight. Though how had the words arrived on her tongue so quickly? Why did the tears that accompanied them flow so easily, as if she had punctured a watery sac to get to them? Max looked at her, his blue eyes sympathetic, his sun-bleached hair hiding the gray.

We have to go back now.

The sun was dropping low and he shaded his eyes with one hand. The café owner and her son were fumbling with the slack ropes of their pedalo, waiting. Before they returned, Max dove in once, traveled four strokes out, then returned to the boat. He wrapped himself in a bath towel and shivered himself dry like a hound.

OK, he said, now we did something.

She laughed, arranging her feet on the slimy pedals, familiar now, not so bad.

I love you, Roya, he said, just as much as I did.

Then he was silent and the squeaking of the boat made his words absurd. It saddened Roya, watching the sun bleed out over the water, its blues deepening, the old boat struggling, its dried-out gears gasping for a drop of oil as Max waited and watched her, shoulders dropping as if they'd soaked up all the afternoon's tension.

We didn't have much time, he said, but I know you.

Roya wiped her eyes and smiled. I know, she said, sniffing. That's not it.

The shoreline drew close. Halfway in, they could hear the boy telling a joke, his mother chuckling softly, her face transforming for her son.

What is it then? Max said.

You think I'm a special case?

He shrugged. She sipped on her Orangina. It was still cool and the small citrus bubbles hissed on her tongue. Now the beach too had emptied out. The woman and her son had dropped the ropes and begun to dismantle the tables, to pull the metal shade over the counter. Roya imagined the darkening lake from far above, one boat on the quiet water. She thought of their small bed, the months of growing still left to do, and all the ugly and the strange that you just can't hold in.

The café owner was waving, but neither Max nor Roya rushed to pedal. They bobbed on the water, ten yards out, ten minutes over their time.

Four Body Poems
Bin Ramke

WHAT WAS THOUGHT THEN

A body boils with life after
the mind goes to vapor. Microbial.

A wisp arose from her body abandoned
there on the table for looking with one's
own eyes: a bit of steam in a cold
room. Molecular. One rose
by her bed back home.

An incompleteness theorem means
she could never formulate correct and complete
descriptions of the set of natural numbers

her life did add up: Mom. When I see
the photograph of Kurt Gödel by Arnold Newman
I think of her death. She had been breathing long
noisy breaths then a quiet crept
behind my sister and me,
murmured beyond us as we sat.

A blackboard that
had been used is now erased.
Gray dusted now
wisped with a vaporous powder of chalk.

I suspect that mourn is related to murmur
but others say otherwise. Silently we still
watch the body lie.

Bin Ramke

BROTHER AND SISTER SILENCE

Body felt only body but not
only other body but the outer in
interior. Or a skin removed and tossed

a snake skin found in the forest electric
translucent. ((*Who did* you *see die* said my sister
in the dark after the funeral, both of us thinking

necessary thoughts in the night not dreams) (dreams
explain the world as (long as) you remain asleep)
Who did *she* see die so young

as that? Only one.) No one ever we
said to each other each to the other.

BODY PARTS

There are three body parts: top,
bottom, and middle.
There are seven types of fusion: cold,
warm, hot, north, south, young, and old.

These are the ages of anxiety: the sixties,
twelve as a new birthday approaches,
and old, all numbers greater than mine.

The numbers of the angels are engraved
thusly: first, and first, and first, and . . .
However freely we translate, the French
for seventy is rendered only one way.
The number of the stripes of the lily
is seventy. The number of a small,
livable country is twelve. Or so.

To number is not to name. The past
is unnameable, and is one. The parts

of the body are beyond reckoning.
The first of the parts of the body is head.
The second is foot. Between is chaos,
which is another word for innumerable.

THE SONG OF THE THREE HOLY CHILDREN

*—Which followeth in the third Chapter
of Daniel after this place.*

What the child knows is enough
of the body the mother was always was
what the child knew never

sufficient for salvation Consider
the days of milk and breast
the nipple as sun her planetary

textures, felt on lips the edge
of the known universe
child's toy, her joy, their song

of milk and comfort
of the doubled breast
the pairings of pleasure

every suck and song
internal holy
and humorous sung

from the mouth of the children
the words
present re-presented

O ye heauens,
O all ye waters that be aboue the heauen,
O all yee powers of the mother, O yee Sunne and Moone,

praise and exalt aboue all for euer.
O ye starres of heauen, O euery showre and dew,
O all ye windes, O yee fire and heate,

anyone's bible will do but the danger
of awareness growing within
the child at the breast

shattering song shattering
his mother's night
arising to feed furious

O ye nights and dayes,
O ye light and darkenesse, O yee yce and colde,
O ye frost and snow, O ye lightnings and clouds,

yet mothers might move in mind
from time to time
place to place

O let the earth blesse, praise and exalt aboue all for euer
. . . O all ye beasts and cattell,
O ye children of men, praise is another

word and not-word, world
out of fire again you would walk
then rest wrested to be

saved from a self to be salvaged like ships to
know knowledge and sing it like milk;
Who died and left you?

Body Politic: A Tenso

Rachel Blau DuPlessis

X. You're talking
of destabilized distortions,
distension, disgust,
—these words aren't good enough?

Y. I plod amid the murk of lexicons.
        Shift. Grift. Spit. Spot.
                Swamp. Sump. Begrudge. Begrunt.

X. Listen—is Zero beginning, negative beginning
better or worse than not beginning?

Y. Fart. Shark.
        Gas. Tum.
                Heartlost, gorge tossed
tongue-tied, lame-ass
        migraine—
                brain m'udded . . .

you think this anatomy
becomes too much, too crude?

X. A lesson on an abject Object?
Embarrassing. Maybe. I'm muddled.
Not sure.

Y. Such physicality—does it lessen art?
Which is, anyway, define it—what?

X. It's falling into any muck
that I despise. The body's only part of that.
Battered. Flattened.
Suddenly front loaders

begin crushing monuments that
we flattered ourselves had been preserved.
Crash of rafter, insulation batting,
shards, veneers, and scrips
of what we hold in common
ripped. Off.

And then to see what was revealed—
Splintered surfaces
formerly concealed.

Y. Anxiety so narrows me
the room shrinks in.
I can't un-stink my skin.
You say the room itself is crushed
outside to in.
Are you still whole? Am I?

Now and here, each beating minute
socks another social rip, shock
and trumpery
an Ubu Roi–dum drum
of suppurating
treachery.

X. Watching the newspaper
with dead eyes, its
pixels sutured over mutilation,
the lurk, the sullen, flaunting shapes
have dragged and drugged me down
And so I fight to stand and not give way.

Y. Super-real, sur-real, un-real—unsortable.
Really cannot follow it.
My lump in the throat—
a clump of undigested cannot-swallow-it.
That's why I mutter.
There's something rogue and rotten
in the Tupperware tub.
And we compelled to eat this spoil up.

X. A tragic tryst
twists words and will,
unutterable, puffed with bloat.

Y. So then why clarify?
Why smooth words out?
What good is it?

X. The old dilemma.

Y. Your flaunting "old" here doesn't help at all.
The feelings more acute than that defense—
the ennui of it all (you know),
like this is old news that's already
been retold, worked over
and worked through.

This may be true.
I care and do not care.
Why would I deny "history"?
But now and here
raked over, scored on,
floored in the hold of consequential fakery—
my body's being played—
it hurts its hurts
without your smart analogies.

X. I didn't mean
to put you down or mock.
But so distressed
and so disconsolate I am—it's easy
grasping for the snide-y joy of
snark, the ready
coblas of insult and shrugs,
even the seductions of
minor narcissisms.

Poised within a shattered realm—
I guess I know you know this whole
"dilemma" has been "seen before."
As if saying "this is old,

from theory or historical debate"
would take the rot and hurt away.
Well, stupid me.
        So yes, awry.
        It's dissolute eroding and reckless
        malignity. A motivated plundering.
        And yes, it wrings the will. I'm not exempt.

Y. It wrings my body.
Every organ hurts.
I belch as if my gut propels
its urgent sour forth,
expelling out a high-turned meat,
but never spit enough
to exorcise
these bilious bursts
of acidic solidity.

My voice is smashed and small.
Unstable. Stuttered. Rough.
And finally—to ". . . feel that, no matter
how much you call out,
it is not enough."

X. I am urgently fluent.
The social is tragic.
Convergences of events
have shredded language and left it
hung with frayed and knotted
remnants so distressed, it's
best (I say) quickly
to re-weave it, even
into its own shadow.

Y. Which covers up and makes things
quasi-nice, and tidied up.
Me—barely fluent.
The social now a crime in progress.

X. And yet I cannot even find
my flooded feelings, they are so confused:

is this "elegiac rage"
"despairing anger"
"paralyzing call"?
How to scream
to stop the crime
while you are being gagged and tied.

Y. Hog-tied.
Tongue-tied. This
being either theme
or the first variation.
Trying to "say something"
even (duh)—if we "see something"—
it's like some bad joke.
Layers of trick play
undercut and undermine . . .

it's boring, it's pain, it's not worth talking about again.
There aren't enough milligrams of
proton-pump inhibitors
to clean my wringing stomach-hands
all clear and sweet and without spot.
Why not just stop?
Is formulated talk such great relief?

X. Please don't stop.

Y. This is awkward and inadequate.
It's ugly stuff.

X. So what?

Y. I cannot listen to my voice.

I cannot even hear my voice
within the cradle of my rocking
once sure-footed ear.
My parts are mal-fired ooze
bruising from a bloody fall,
exile grappling for directions,
sans signposts.

Is my body still my own?
Symptoms have become the only signs.
I'm sick with rage.
I'm sick with rage I fear is impotent.
The heart, the lung, the gut
besmirched, be smut.

X. Always the time is before the war or
after the war, which overlaps with wars
before this war, hints of
texting war, geopolitical plotting,
automatic genuflection.
No reflection. Headline:
"MAN HAPPY WITH HIS NEW PROSTHETIC LEG."
For him I'm glad, but better he should have both legs.

Y. The body politic—
No cell has been untouched.

X. Suppose
that there are people who'll come after
who will approve and benefit
from what we felt and what-we-did or
will-we-can—
our calling out. Resistant acts.
What do you think?
What are our chances?

Y. Even
thinking "no," or barely whispering "perhaps,"
has forced me further from my life.
This exile so extreme,
so full of loathing both for now
and then for then,
then after that for whatsoever-ever-comes . . .

X. . . . that tensing, tense songs and this
mixed tenso-talk
have thrust time culpably
into a raging
futurial obscurity,

intensities wailing—
no-word words,
awaiting waiting.

Y. Then thinking "no," one starts
to register
the wager that you choose to make:
whole body thrown into the "game"—

when you become the die.

X. To throw oneself into this time
throws oneself away?
This is my space. And here is the time.
Poetic realism lets the mark be seen.
The smudge of the letter on the page,
my single body marching with its poster

has bearing. Has status.
Is part of argument, may be the brief itself
no matter how inchoate, how unstrung.

Y. But this is a grit-filled room, my eye
is sanded from a hijacked sleep—
jostled dreams colonize my insomnia
with bullying intimacy.

X. The time we suffer must now be endured.
And named. And braved.
It may seem negligible. Or provoke further pain.
"It is not negligible" is what I will affirm.
But I don't know.

Y. I know you know all this is all
obstinately liminal.
Stepping into the terrain with others—
on gnarled unstable feet—
Is this a vow to "gray literature"? Reportage?
Documentary? Diagrams?

X. It's a vow to know.
To try to act and say.

Y. Can I, May I, Might I
find the space between
before and after—now?

X. Though it's true—with utmost wishes
where we walk, and with hope
that stuttering subjunctives
will become adept
at all the will-we-want,
the might and may—

I know I also must accept
the fate of trace, the fate of compost.

February–April 2017

Traditional Chinese Massage Number 1

Sallie Tisdale

TRADITIONAL CHINESE MASSAGE Number 1 is a set of odd-shaped little rooms on different levels, connected by narrow, short stairways so steep they are almost ladders. The air has the faint scent of flowers. Elaborate reflexology charts are pinned up on the walls and a fountain burbles by the door. A young Chinese man in a white uniform greets me with a quick bow and hands me a laminated menu, as though I were ordering pizza. Through a picture window I can see the busy corner of Raadhuisstraat, one of Amsterdam's main streets, where crowds walk by with brisk purpose. The other way, through a low archway, I see a couple of towel-covered armchairs and a giant banana palm.

While I'm reading the menu, a man carefully steps down from a tiny WC on a platform beside the palm, his face dazed. He stops to stare at the huge aquarium across the back wall, swaying gently in time with the large tropical fish.

I am staying over in Amsterdam after several weeks in Uganda. My feet hurt from walking on cobblestones after the weeks on red clay. I have made this trip before. The little airport in Entebbe is the last cocoon of Africa's familiar chaotic warmth, a hint of humidity even in the locked concourse lounge. But the moment I walk down the gangway onto the plane, I'm in Holland again, the KLM attendant all blond Dutch firmness and "Yes, please" and "No, madam." The shift between countries is like the gap between waking and a dream, though I'm never sure which is which. It is always a red-eye flight; the descent seems to last forever, sliding past glittering platforms of light on the water into a scarlet sunrise, over dikes frosted with snow, down the flat canal-striped fields and blocks of square houses. The airport is bright and clean, with lots of clogs and tulips for sale. Instead of the damp, curious maze of Kampala, its mob of cars with blaring horns, Amsterdam is angular and packaged. The supermarkets sell shrink-wrapped pancakes. The streets have one lane for cars, one lane for bikes, a smooth-rolling tram, and wide sidewalks for polite pedestrians. In Uganda, I clutch the waist of my boda boda driver on careening rides over bumpy side streets, down alleys and up blind hills. In Amsterdam, my taxi driver wears a suit and tie.

I tell the young man that I want a head and neck massage for thirty minutes; I'd love more, but I'm guarding my euros. A middle-aged woman appears a few minutes later. She is about five feet tall with a square face, false eyelashes, dark eye shadow, and big fake-diamond earrings. She leads me up past the aquarium and then again up to a loft space, where two massage tables are separated by curtains. I glimpse a slender naked woman lying facedown on the far table, her long blonde hair covering her face.

"Take off all your clothes," the woman tells me in accented English. "Leave panties." She waits for me to comply. This is more than I had bargained for with a neck massage, but I begin to undress. Finally, she steps forward with a hint of impatience and unfastens my bra, folds it up, and sets it aside, and watches me until I'm down to my underpants. Then she points to the table. I lie down on my stomach. She covers me with rough, warm towels and rubs strenuously for a few minutes, all over, in big, sweeping circles.

Then she sits at the end of the table and starts rubbing my right foot with vigor.

This is pleasant, but—I am worried about money, about translation, about the bargain I've made. I raise my head and say, "Excuse me, but I wanted a head and neck massage."

She simply shoves me back down.

"It goes from here"—she whacks the sole of my foot—"to here"—pointing at my head. "*Not* from here"—pointing at my head—"to *here*!" She whacks my foot again, and continues to massage. And suddenly waves and shivers run through my scalp, down my neck, my shoulders, down my back. My entire body begins to tremble. She switches from foot to foot, left to right to left, and she is doing things to my feet that I have always wanted someone to do, things I didn't even know I wanted.

Then she drops my foot and walks up to the head of the table, squats down, and peers into my face.

"Do you want the whole hour?" she asks.

I can only nod.

Downstairs I hear a man's voice: "Uh! Oh! Yeah!" A rhythmic squeaking starts, mingled with loud groans and long sighs. Squeak, squeak. "Uhhh! Ohhhh." Squeak.

*

I had been working at the clinic in Ddegeya, a farming village near the Tanzanian border. The hours there—divided into perfect halves of light and dark—are spent very close to other people. I pass the day dressing wounds, examining feet, drawing blood, listening to rattling chests, peering down throats. I take tepid bucket showers in a dim concrete room with high windows open to the courtyard, listening to children shout and play. I sleep on a narrow bunk bed in a room with five other women. Every car ride, every meal, every walk is close to other people; I am never alone. I squat to defecate in one of the stifling box-shaped wooden rooms in a row on the hill; others squat near me, our sounds mingling with our smells.

This outrageous life, this sensual, uncomfortable, crowded life, confounds and binds me. I love it there; I don't belong there. My Ugandan friends, more modest and reserved about almost everything than I am, are more at ease with their own skin, with their lack of almost everything, their hard work, their pain. They laugh harder and more often than I do. Bodies are the center of a world filled with crested cranes as tall as men stepping carefully through cornfields, mobs of sticky, giggling children, curvaceous dances that make me weak with desire. I grew up in a small town in California, the child of a lapsed Methodist and an apostate Catholic who had compromised on the Lutheran Church of America. A Calvinist is buried not that deeply in me. I wear sensible underwear and never take naps. But Uganda has stolen a little of that away. I eat meals smoky from the fire while the rain thunders down, drink milk tasting of the cow's grassy supper, wake to the rooster crowing in the sooty dark, walk in mud so thick I must pull my foot up with each step. And I feel deeply content. Yet I relax in the reserve of Amsterdam, its stacked boxes, the polite queues, the careful breakfasts of toast triangles and cheese slices and chocolate sprinkles. There the parts of me that have been tightly bound as long as I can remember are allowed to be tight, expected to be tight. Where I am not surrounded by beautiful smooth-skinned women rubbing themselves with lotion and braiding each other's hair while they laugh. I love to be touched too; I have never had the courage to join the circle of braiding.

At home, I occasionally visit a petite middle-aged woman named Liz. A part of me would like a critical matron with a Prussian accent, but I have to settle for the soothing, pastel-colored spa aesthetic, with its trance music and scented candles. Liz seems to be a solid citizen, although there is a crystal under the table and she ends each session by walking around me, playing a set of musical chimes for reasons I have not been able to discern. Like many massage therapists, she's tougher than she looks and can talk external rotators and occipital insertion points with the rest of them. Liz leaves the room when I undress, holds the blanket up as a curtain when I roll over, and tucks it carefully around me to avoid unexpected exposure. Does she know I'm afraid to be seen by the woman who is touching me everywhere? One appointment with Liz at a time, I begin to relax. Sometimes she stands beside the table where I lie prone under warm blankets and just rocks me; rock, rock, one hand on a thigh and one on my side, like winding a watch. She knuckles up my neck to dig her fingers into my scalp and I turn into her hands with a purr. Later, I am embarrassed that I purred.

At Traditional Chinese Massage Number 1, the woman goes back to my feet and gets serious: punching, pinching, drumming on my feet, my legs. Then she climbs on top of the table and sits on my bottom and starts pulling my hair, pinching, drumming on my scalp.

"Tell me if there is pain, OK?" she murmurs. And when I finally say *ouch* in a small voice, she nods sagely and says, "That is why you here!" and continues.

Ouch, I say, in a tentative voice, as she pummels my arm. *Ouch!* as she punches on my leg.

"This has spirit inside"—she punches my thigh—"You know, spirit?"

She whips off the sheet, pulls down my underwear, and gets to work on my gluteus maximus. I want to flee; I almost roll off the table. She is using both thumbs, the heels of her hands, and the points of her elbows on muscles I am not used to having rubbed at all. "This is good, yes?" she asks, not expecting an answer. She pounds, scratches, digs in. It is quite painful.

"Roll over." I roll over, and she starts to massage my belly. My soft, round belly. My fear of censure is so strong, I am wound so tight around the fear of being judged for my body and found wanting. I don't think I can allow this; I start to reach up and push her hands away. "Good for your body" is all she says. Her breath is sweet and I tell myself that she will never see me again—or, more to the point, *I* will never see *her*. This is a city of dreams, after all, where cafés fill with smoke and beautiful women wait in rose-tinged windows. I am too shy to visit them, but this is not so far away.

*

In New Orleans, a city so full of the perfume of humanity that one sometimes must stop to clear the sinuses, I went to Happy Feet and sat in a white chair by a white ottoman draped in white towels and drank fragrant tea from a white china cup while a small woman bathed my legs. In another city, I visited a salt spa and laid in a small room with walls of indigo lit only by low copper light from incandescent salt blocks while a skinny young man with long brown dreadlocks kneaded my back. In Manhattan, a friend and I climbed a steep, narrow stairway until a burglar alarm began clanging and a young Asian woman appeared and beckoned us up. No one spoke that day; we gestured, she nodded, and led us past a room of silent women doing piecework on industrial sewing machines to two chairs behind curtains where teenage girls waited.

In India, it was Ayurvedic. I was traveling with my friend Thomas, who is a sybarite and wants to get massages all the time; I watch his cheerful greed with a little envy and only a trace of Lutheran disapproval. An elderly physician and his wife met us in our boardinghouse lobby and led us silently into a nearby windowless room empty of everything but a large bed. We were traveling as brother and sister because a friendship between a man and a woman is difficult to explain in India. Being family meant we could do everything together, including this. The couple indicated that we should undress completely, so we giggled and took off all our clothes and laid facedown, side by side under rough, stale sheets.

The doctor and his wife shut the door and turned off the lights. The room was very dark. The doctor pulled the sheet down and straddled Thomas and his wife straddled me. She worked a long time on my scalp, my breasts, my belly and buttocks. Between my buttocks. I could feel the four of us rolling on the bed, our shifting weight; I heard the gentle slap of skin on skin, Thomas's occasional groan, voices in the lobby outside the door. When all was done, the couple stood primly outside the door while we dressed. Even Thomas was a little rattled.

I returned to the same boardinghouse in Varanasi not long ago. This time I was met by a middle-aged man with a dapper mustache and a five-o'clock shadow, a round cannonball belly, glasses, and very hairy forearms. He introduced himself as Ashish—"Not *hash*ish!" he laughed, a necessary clarification for Americans staying along the river in the old city. The ghats were littered with ageing longhairs looking for ganja and another month's rent. Earlier that day I'd seen a fat, half-naked Frenchman with lots of tattoos and a big topknot, wearing a sari made of faux leopard fur.

I asked Ashish for a head and feet massage. "For this you do not need to take off your clothes," he acknowledged, his head bobbing back and forth in the Indian way of the negative. "But there is oil." I didn't want oil on my shirt, so I took it off and sat on the edge of the bed with a towel draped over my shoulders. We hardly spoke. He sat behind me, kneeling upright. Massage is part of medicine in Ayurveda, meant to cleanse and balance the body. It is a bit improvisational, searching, the practitioner thinking it through—demanding, unpredictable. You can't roll with the solid kneading of muscles one gets in a deep-tissue massage, which has a logical unfolding. He pulled and twisted my hair up hard and hit with a fist on the top of my head. He scratched, tickled, shook, and prodded. The towel fell off, then my bra straps slid down until I was topless. His cell phone rang more than once; I could feel him glance at the screen and put it away. My neck, it gradually became obvious, started at the tailbone and extended to my elbows. My feet appeared to begin at my upper thigh. At times his fingertips were as light and deliberate as a spider's feet; at other times, hard knuckles pressing into pressure points. I was sprawled on a hard bed in a dim room off the lobby of a crowded little hotel, listening to the staff argue and laugh and pray. I could hear music and doors slamming and children calling and motorcycles racing by. He knelt behind me, pulled my head back into his hard belly, and kneaded, rubbed, and soothed the skin of my face and throat, stretching my head back, back into his belly until he leaned his chin on my forehead and I could feel his grizzled beard tickling my skin. Then he told me to lie down and gently rubbed my face with every inch of his fingers, lightly sliding his hands across my eyelids, my lips, everywhere.

"Better?" she asks in the white room off Raadhuisstraat, moving to the top of the table. A rhythmic slapping begins on the other side of the curtain. She slides her hands down my chest, onto my breasts, rubbing them in circles. Suddenly the room fills with a strong herbal scent and I can feel warm oil. Her hands slide up and down my legs, my arms, my neck, and into my hair, oily and perfumed.

It's here, right here, that I fall apart, that my fraught relationship to skin seizes up. Here where it feels best of all. This was medicine, this was cleansing; this is what doctors and nurses, like whores, are given permission to do. This is all *about* permission, that's the point—to go inside, to go where others don't, or won't, to do what is needed and wanted and feared in equal measure, to get past the gluey reserve. Past the stacked boxes. This intimacy with a stranger is beyond what I might do with anyone else. There are things, all kinds of things, we can only do with strangers.

After a long time, she tells me to get dressed, which I manage to do without falling, and I carefully edge my way down the stairs. A large British man sits backward in a massage chair, moaning, while a tiny old Chinese man works him over. The masseur wraps his arms around the Brit's chest and bends him almost backward in the chair, and the man's face is manic and beatific all at once.

The woman sits me in a recliner facing the aquarium. She soaks my feet in a tub of soapy hot water, scrubs and dries them off, then works on my feet, every toe, every joint and bone. The nearby reflexology chart is in Dutch and I can grasp only a few of the words for the points she is pressing, but shivers run up and down my limbs.

"Is this too strong?" she asks.

"No, not now," I tell her. "But the massage hurt a little." She shakes her head. "This"—she mimics pressing with her thumb—"this is OK. But I use this"—she points to her elbow. She clearly thinks I am not fully committed to the program. But this feels lovely. She has a dreamy and distant look on her face. I watch the fish.

A young German woman comes up the steps and climbs onto the other massage chair. A Chinese man with one earbud running not very discreetly down his shirt begins to massage her shoulders. Three customers, three masseurs, four countries, all of us silent. All of us investigating bodies, learning the secrets of how we slide around and over each other in this dark and busy world.

Finally, the Brit stands up, shakes his head like a prizefighter who's taken a hard right hook, pulls his coat straight, and stumbles past me out the door without a word.

I drift off, watching the fish. One is cut off from the rest by a long sheet of plexiglass; the fish gather in a school on one side, watching their isolated peer, then swim away.

Little Rooms
Stephen O'Connor

GINA WONDERED IF Vincent could hear her eyes opening. She conducted experiments. She would keep her eyes closed when she woke in the morning and listen to the way silence filled her house. Outside, birds would make their pointillist racket, and there was the sound of what she always wanted to be a distant waterfall, but was actually the traffic on the interstate at the bottom of the valley. Inside, except for the hum of the refrigerator motor (which didn't count as real sound to Gina), there was only silence. Gina thought of the silence as the element that kept her house upright and squared, just as air kept the sides of a balloon apart. She knew that idea made no sense, but that was just the way the silence felt when she was lying in bed with her eyes closed, listening.

Sometimes she would only listen for a few seconds, other times for a few minutes (three? five?—no way to know, since she couldn't see her clock), and every time it was exactly the same: the instant she opened her eyes, she'd hear the scrabbling of Vincent's toenails against the floorboards wherever in the house he happened to be—downstairs in the living room, where he slept on his hairy pillow, or on the rag rug right beside her bed, or on the windowed-in front porch where he liked to watch squirrels—and then the clickety-clickety as he dashed through the house to the kitchen, where he would slam himself against the back door and scrabble his nails some more against the frayed spot under the doorknob.

This particular morning started out like every other of the last nine years: Gina walked into the kitchen barefoot in her nightgown and unlocked the back door to let Vincent out. She turned on the coffeemaker and went to pee in the tiny bathroom under the stairs. Then she fetched her folded newspaper off the damp front stoop. When she came back into the kitchen she noticed Vincent out near the garage doing a twitchy dance with the front half of his body, as if he were a marionette being jerked by the strings attached to his head and shoulders. While the coffeemaker puffed and wheezed, she unfolded her newspaper and read about a suicide bombing in Turkey and a pole vaulter who had been paralyzed from the neck down. When she looked out the window again, Vincent was dead.

She knew he was dead from the way his front legs lay stick straight in the weeds, and because his tail tip didn't even twitch as she stepped out the back door and crossed the cold, wet lawn. But once she was standing with her grass-speckled toes less than an inch from his arched spine, she pretended that his mouth being open and his tongue lying motionless on a toppled mullein stalk meant that he was still breathing. She went back into the house, put on her raincoat and a pair of rubber boots, grabbed a red woolen blanket off her couch and her car keys out of an Italian salad bowl.

Gina happened to catch the vet just as she was getting out of her own car in the parking lot of the former dry cleaner's that was now her office. The two women stood side by side in front of the open hatch of Gina's Outback, where Vincent lay wrapped in the red blanket. The vet could do nothing but look stricken. She suspected chocolate poisoning. "Do you want me to do an autopsy?" Gina didn't see the point.

Gina was a designer at BettaType, a company that produced brochures, posters, fliers, and cards for local businesses—though, in fact, there were only four people in the office, and everyone was a designer, just as everyone was a receptionist, photographer, writer, researcher, and sales rep—except for Angie, who had founded the company with her ex-husband, Chuck (now a sports bookie in Florida), twenty-eight years ago, although she did all the other jobs too. Angie had been Gina's best friend in design school. "Oh God!" she said, when Gina told her the news. "Oh God! Oh God! Oh God!" Gina thought this was an overreaction, but when Angie said, "Stay home! Take care of yourself! Stay out all week if you want. Go someplace beautiful," Gina said, "OK."

Gina thought that dogs were happier than human beings. Of course, they too inhabited their little rooms of pain, or fear, or rage, just like all living things. But only for a minute. Maybe less. And as soon as they were out of that little room, it was all a tongue-flapping romp in a field full of rabbits, or the circling and settling down of tired bones on a hairy pillow beside the radiator, or it was a swift snatch of a chicken leg off the tabletop. Dogs didn't dwell on those little rooms once they had escaped them, and they didn't have a clue that many more little rooms were on their way. So they lived lives of constant joy, except for a minute every now and then. Maybe less.

Gina had mourned three dogs in the twenty-eight years she had lived in her house. Along the edge of the woods on the far end of her back lawn there were three stones in a row, each about the size of a soccer ball, which was the largest stone that Gina could manage to lift into a wheelbarrow.

And now there was a fourth.

In front of that stone Gina hacked through grass and roots and rocks and wet black earth, then brown, then orange, until she had made a hole large and deep enough that she could sit in it with her knees bent and not see anything but sky. The inside of her Outback was already beginning to smell like something between wet fur and old hamburger. Using the red couch blanket as a sling, she carried Vincent to the hole she had dug and slowly lowered him to its orange bottom. Then she let go of the blanket. By the time she had refilled the hole with earth, patted it flat, and covered as much of it as she could with a mosaic of sod chunks, the sun had made a right turn and was journeying toward the horizon. Her nightgown was plastered to her back with sweat.

She sobbed in the shower. She crawled between the covers of her bed. The strange noises of midday (lawn mowers, cicadas, cardinals, and crows) made sleep seem impossible. When she woke, her head was aching and hot, and the light outside the window had gone old gold. "I've lost a whole day," she thought.

She forced herself to put on the clothes she would have worn to work: pistachio pants, a sky-blue tunic she had bought the year before in Mumbai, matching jogging shoes. Gina had a larger than normal head, and a body that consisted mostly of straight lines. From a distance she looked like a gangly twelve-year-old—which meant the puffy crinkling at the corners of her mouth could be disconcerting, and her incipient jowls, and the unruly gray wires that drifted around her otherwise lank brown hair.

The pot in her coffeemaker was full and cold. She poured herself a glass and sat on her back steps.

She was trying not to dwell on emptiness.

Just by the pitch of the interstate noise, Gina could tell that it was 5:30 p.m., the time she normally got home from work. On almost any other day during most of the last nine years, this would have been the moment she and Vincent would have headed up the slope of Mount Quiddagunk, he constantly disappearing into the woods, then looping back to give her one of his open-mouth grins before disappearing again. Eventually they would settle side by side on the granite shoulder Gina called Lookout Rock. She would light a joint and gaze at a landscape of forested hills that receded through layer upon layer of mist until it was indistinguishable from sky. Vincent would lie next to her, panting happily, his hot back against her hip.

Time would pass. Her five fingers would circle amidst oily fur. The petty hatreds of her day would dissipate.

The whole idea of climbing the mountain without Vincent seemed a betrayal.

"What's the point?" she thought.

Gina brought two joints to Lookout Rock, finished them both, and watched the sun squash against the horizon's edge, turning from brilliant globe to golden oval to orange fringe to tremulous spark. Then it was gone.

When she stood up, she became aware that there was absolutely nothing but air between her eyes and the amber horizon. There were also the forested hills, of course, but all she could think about was the mass of air encircling the globe and rising to the edge of space, where, perhaps, it was slowly being absorbed into nothingness. Air on every side of her, except beneath the soles of her sneakers. For a moment she felt very, very small. Then she heard the voices. Men's voices. Grunts. Groans. Curses—though she couldn't make out a single word.

There were a lot of men. Five at least. Maybe ten. They were moving along the path that passed just beneath Lookout Rock and then wound uphill through the woods beside it. In a minute they would be spilling out onto the rock itself, and she would be alone in front of them, nothing behind her but that huge emptiness filled with air, and no way to escape but to edge between their shoulders and bellies.

Before she even knew what she was doing she had fallen flat to the still warm surface of the rock, hoping that she would not be seen—a stupid move, she realized instantly, because how would they not see her the very second they stepped out onto the rock? She would only be more vulnerable lying flat and facedown, and they would know exactly how terrified she was, and that would only make them feel more powerful.

She told herself to get back to her feet, but all she could do was hug the warm stone, sweat dripping into her eyes, and hope that the men stuck to the path and did not detour onto the rock to look at the purpling sky.

This was just that moment of the gloaming when the color had drained from the world, but the leaves, stone, and dried-out grass possessed a metallic luminosity. The men's voices grew louder, and then Gina could sense a dark stirring among the shadows beneath the trees where the trail mounted the rise and turned toward the rock. The stirring coalesced into a hulking silhouette that was soon joined by another and then another and then another. The men's voices were louder, but their words remained unintelligible, and Gina began to suspect they were speaking a foreign language. Then all at once, as the first of the men reached the very edge of the rock, a single sentence became clear: "Where the fuck we gonna bury him?" (Though later she would wonder if the man had actually said, "Why the fuck're we hurrying?")

The men did not come out onto the rock. They continued along the path up toward the peak of Mount Quiddagunk—eight of them, at least; maybe twelve. Gina was too terrified to count. But she did make out that two of the hulking shadows, walking one behind the other, were carrying a long pole stretched between their shoulders, and that dangling from the pole by a rope tied at either end was something long and heavy that looked like a human body wrapped in a blanket. Gina had only seconds to examine this object as it passed behind a scrim of dimly luminescent scrub trees, but the more she looked, the more the long object below the poles took on the shape and the heft of a human body.

Vincent died on a Thursday morning. On Friday Gina went to BettaType.

"Did you call the police?" Angie asked.

"I don't see how that's possible," said Gwen.

"What?" said Gina.

"That they could carry a human body all the way up that mountain."

"It wasn't that far."

"But still," said Gwen. "A human body is heavy. Especially a dead human body."

"They were big," said Gina. "Really big. And maybe they took turns."

"But why would they want to bury a body on a mountaintop?"

"Did you call the police?" Angie repeated.

Gina's smoke-blue eyes went doll still. "No," she said.

"Why not?"

"Well," she said. "You know." She was sitting at her drafting table. She picked up a colored pencil (green), balanced it on its point, and let it fall. "Murder is such a big . . . uh . . . thing. And I wasn't . . . I mean, it was so dark that all I could see—I couldn't see anything. . . . So I wasn't—you know—completely sure."

Gwen cast Angie a glance. Angie looked out the window.

At 5:30 p.m., Gina decided she would forgo her after-work walk, and have her joint in her living room, listening to the Brandenburg Concertos played on period instruments. That night a wind-stirred venetian blind knocked a bottle of hand lotion off the bathroom window ledge. Gina lurched up at the flat wham of the bottle striking the tile floor, her heart pounding, her throat so constricted she couldn't swallow, her head swirling with dire certainties: the men on the mountain had followed her as she made her way by phone light down the dark path. Now they were surrounding her house. She could hear them whispering. Trying the doorknobs. Jimmying her downstairs windows with slot-tip screwdrivers.

By Saturday morning these certainties seemed only a weird form of nightmare. She looked at herself in the bathroom mirror, shook her head. "What is the fucking matter with you?" But still, she stayed inside all day (it was raining hard—so hard that gray spikes leapt off her car roof and the gleaming driveway) and put all of Vincent's grimy chew toys into a black garbage bag, along with his hairy pillow, his tennis balls, his leash, and the rag rug beside her bed. She couldn't throw these things away, but didn't think it would be fair to subject her new dog to them—that is, when she could finally bear to buy a new dog. She vacuumed, sponged, and mopped the whole house, had her evening joint listening to Adele on Spotify, read *Cold Comfort Farm* until bedtime and masturbated before she went to sleep. She had a good night.

*

There was a man whom Gina thought of as her husband. He was not her actual husband, although he was the love of her life—a thought that could make her terribly sad, because she was only with him for eight months. He was married. He loved his wife, though he also loved Gina. She knew this because of the way he sometimes looked at her: a faint smile on his lips and his eyebeams slightly askew, as if he were about to swoon from sheer contentment. She knew because once he lunged across the dinner table, took her face into his two hands, and proclaimed, "You are so beautiful!" She knew because one time, after they had made love, she heard him singing softly, *"Because my love for you . . . will break my heart in two,"* in the bathroom while he was peeing. They almost never went out together because he was so afraid of being seen with her, but one time, after one of their breakups (they were, in fact, broken up more than they were together during those eight months), they met at a bar and got very drunk. She was careful not to kiss him or even to take hold of his hand as they sat at the table together, but at one point she did lean her face very close to his ear and whisper, "You know, I think of you as my secret husband."

"But I am *not* your husband," he said, almost angrily. "That's the whole problem."

"I know, I know," she said. "But that's how I feel."

"I'm not your husband," he said.

After that, he stopped calling her. And when she called him at his office, he never answered (he had Caller ID), and he never responded to any of her letters. A month passed. Then one day, as she was walking into a Staples in the Shopton Village Mall, she spotted him coming out of a CVS. He saw her too, turned his shoulder, and strode off into the parking lot. She caught up with him just as he opened his car door.

"Leave me alone!" he said. "Don't you understand? This is ruining my life!"

"I feel terrible too," she said.

"No!" he shouted. "I can't take this anymore. Leave me alone, you fucking bitch!"

She was twenty-six, and he was only the second man she had ever slept with. Not long after he slammed his car door and careened out of the parking lot, she slept with an orthodontist who drove her home from a party. She thought he would distract her from her misery, but he only made everything worse. After that, it was as if she had sworn a vow of celibacy, and it had now been close to a quarter of a century since she had even had dinner alone with a man her age. But that was OK. She was happy with her house, her garden, her dogs. Maybe it was better that she was on her own. Every now and then, however, the man she loved would come back into her mind, and she would think or even say aloud, "You will always be my husband," and then her entire body would be suffused with a quivery warmth that could last for hours.

In the morning, rain was still rattling in the gutter pipes, puddling her flagstone walk, and warping the pages of her newspaper. Just before 2:00 p.m., she glanced out the window and saw that the sky had gone sapphire blue and that a white sun was making rainbow glints in all the dangling droplets. Within minutes she was striding up the trail to Lookout Rock, water bottle in hand, joint and lighter in her hip pocket. What was there to be afraid of? Those men had probably just been campers carrying their equipment in a sling, or hunters who had shot a deer. The air was cool, sweet, and clean. Every breath was a breeze blowing dust from her brain.

It wasn't even three when she got to Lookout Rock, way too early for a joint, so she continued along the path the men had been walking, partly with the idea that she would keep her eyes peeled for evidence of trailside graves, but mainly because she had conceived the ambition of hiking all the way to the top of Mount Quiddagunk, where she would be able to see mountains in five different states, and where she hadn't been in years. How had her life gotten so routine?

After some hundred yards, she came across a path she had never noticed before. It was smaller than the one she was on, but scuffed grassless at its mouth, and worn into a shallow rut among the trees—so not a new path. It went downhill. Gina didn't want to go downhill. But if the men had actually intended to bury a body, wouldn't it make sense for them to go down into some hollow where the earth was softer and deeper? And wouldn't they also want to take a smaller and less-traveled path? A moment of indecision was ended by a curse at her own timidity.

As she walked along the smaller path, she lectured herself: "There is virtually zero chance that those guys were carrying a body. That was just weed paranoia. And even if they were carrying a body, they can't still be here. Why hang around the scene of the crime? Don't be such an idiot! It's a perfect day. Sunbeams everywhere. Birds singing. The world is filled with beauty!"

With minor variations, this lecture cycled through her brain for a half hour or more, and sometimes she really did experience something like pleasure at a veery's double-voiced, minor-key cry, or at that heady musk of drenched forest-floor mulch. But all it took was the faintest rustle or snap among the trees on either side of the trail and she would jump, her heart pounding so loudly it was all she could hear. And every now and then, amid the forest smells, she would detect the stench of rotting hamburger.

After a while the hillside fell away to the left of the path, and she could see a wide stretch of gray between the trees, perhaps a lake. But then she couldn't see anything, because the trail descended through a sort of ravine—a place where the mountain had ruptured, forming mirror-image cliffs on either side of a narrow, cedar-shaded gap. Only as she neared the very end of the ravine did she hear the voices: Grunts. Groans. Curses. Male rumblings that never quite consolidated into articulate speech.

A flash of heat from the center of her body emerged as a chilling sweat on every exposed portion of her skin. For a long moment she couldn't move, torn between the desire to run back up the path and another impulse that seemed half sinister and half a commendable determination to resist her fear and become the mistress of her own actions.

She continued along the path until she came to a gap in the trees through which she could see a group of burly men standing along the stone shore of what was indeed a lake—or perhaps it was a flooded quarry: the lake was rectangular, with sheer cliffs on three sides. The men were silhouetted against the sun-lit stone and water, so she couldn't make out their features or even the color of their clothing, though she thought they were wearing hunters' camouflage. Their heads were bent. They shifted from side to side, gesturing toward something at their feet. After a moment the group parted and—very briefly—Gina could see that there were two this time: two bodies, wrapped in some sort of dark cloth, motionless and distinctly human. She could see the shapes of their feet. The bent knee of one of them pushed up against the surface of whatever it was wrapped in, like the knee of someone reading in bed.

She took one step backward, then another and another, not turning to run until she was out of sight of the men and she was sure they could not hear her.

*

One form of emptiness is the zone of possibility that exists between truth and falsehood. It was possible that there were no wrapped bodies lying amidst the men on the lake's rocky shore. What looked like a knee may have been an oblong boulder or blunt branch stump on a log. Or possibly two of the men had been injured and were waiting to be medevaced. Or they were goofing around. Or they were participating in some sort of baptism ritual.

Which was more possible: that a group of men had brought one body up a mountain on a Thursday and two more on a Sunday, or that Gina had misunderstood the evidence of her own eyes and ears?

But, of course, people do get murdered. And gangsters, cults, and crazy people do go on killing sprees. And so it was possible that if Gina didn't tell the police what she suspected, more people would be killed and carried up the mountain.

But there were still other possibilities: Gina had, in fact, noticed the glance traded between Gwen and Angie, and she had interpreted it as yet another example of a problem she had struggled with her whole life: people didn't believe her. There was something in her voice and manner that made people think even she did not believe what she was saying. And it was true that, deep inside, she saw every juncture at which she had to choose what to say or do as an occasion for doubt. But doubt was not the same as lying. Or as being wrong.

Gina believed that, even if she was wrong, she should still tell the police what she had seen, just in case. But she also believed that the police would not believe her, that they might think she was crazy, and that possibly they would be correct.

The only way she could have enough faith in her story to induce people to actually listen would be if she could anchor it on at least one particle of fact: a spot of dried blood, a shovel, a patch of loose earth—anything beyond her mere perceptions and memory.

The night following Gina's discovery of the men and the two bodies was a sleepless melee of self-disparagement, fearful listening, and fantasies that verged on hallucination. Then all at once the darkness above her bed was charcoal gray, and she was possessed by the conviction that an act of courage was required of her.

She was standing beside the flooded quarry as the sun lifted above the cliff on the far shore. Six inches of yellowish fog veiled the mirror surface of the water, here and there coiling some two or three yards into the air, where it would fray into chaotic strands, then vanish.

She got down on her hands and knees at the spot where she thought the bodies had been lying. She found a single burned match and three crushed cigarettes. A half-full beer can balanced on a spherical rock at the water's edge. She investigated every little trail running from the shore into the woods, and every place where the grass or shrubbery seemed to have been disturbed, and came upon small collections of rain-flattened Kleenex, the ash and charcoal fragments of long-extinguished campfires, and, in two separate places, slick, withered condoms.

It was Monday, 7:45 a.m., and Gina had to be at work by nine. Only after she had been walking home for fifteen minutes did she realize she had taken the wrong trail. But when she doubled back, she walked for more than half an hour without returning to the lake. She doubled back a second time, looking for one of the two places where she had made a wrong turn, but went for an hour without spotting a single fork or intersection in the path. Gina did not understand how this could be possible.

She took out her phone to call Angie, apologize for being late, and say that she would get there as soon as she could. But her phone was dead. Had she forgotten to charge it? Or had the phone drained its batteries searching for a connection? No way she could know.

A dog barked. The barking grew louder as a cluster of shuddering stalks crossed a field of waist-high reddish grass. Now a dog stood on the path in front of her: rusty brindle, part boxer, but with a pit bull head and ragged yellow teeth that lacerated the air with every bark. "Good dog!" said Gina. "Good dog! There's a good boy!" The dog circled her in the high grass, lunging toward her calves with every new round of barking. "Hey there, boy!" said Gina. "What's the matter, boy? Good dog! Good dog!"

As a rule, Gina was not afraid of dogs, but this dog's ears were flat against its skull. Its lips curled entirely off its ragged teeth. As fear dampened her armpits, the dog went into a paroxysm of fury. It leapt into the air as it lunged. Its teeth touched her pants leg, once and then again. "Hey!" she shouted, taking an involuntary double skip backward. "Hey!"

On the far side of the reddish field, behind two wild and enormous boxwood bushes, Gina spotted a vinyl-sided trailer. In front of the trailer's open door, on a weathered plywood porch, stood a barrel-shaped woman with long gray hair and a red face.

"Could you call off your dog?" Gina shouted.

"Not my dog," said the woman.

"Whose is it?"

The woman jerked her thumb at the door behind her, but said nothing.

The dog lunged again, silently this time, and Gina felt a tug at her pants leg. "Please!" she shouted.

The woman put her fingers into her mouth and whistled, then shouted in a low, harsh voice, "Lu-*rae*! Get over here!"

The dog flipped head over tail as if it had been hit, then shambled back and forth across the path in a pair of figure eights. When the woman called again, the dog darted toward the trailer as rapidly as it had come, clambered onto the porch, and curled up at the woman's feet.

"Thanks!" said Gina.

"She wasn't gonna hurt you!"

"Well, thanks anyway!"

Gina was about to continue walking, but then remembered that she was lost. "Excuse me?" she called out.

"What?"

"I'm wondering if you could help me."

The woman didn't say anything, just looked at Gina with her hands in her pockets.

"I'm lost," said Gina.

"What?" said the woman.

"Could you tell me how I could get back to the lake?"

"I can't hear you!" shouted the woman.

Gina took a couple of steps into the reddish grass. "The lake! Which way is the lake?"

"I'm not going to shout. You want to talk to me, you got to come closer."

The dog was lying with its head on the plywood, so Gina ventured across the field. She stopped about ten yards from the woman.

"Which way is the lake?" she said.

"Which lake?"

"I don't know its name. The flooded quarry."

"Quarry!" The woman laughed. "Ain't no quarry around here."

"Well, it looks like a quarry. There are cliffs around it and the shore is flat stone."

"Ain't no quarry around here."

Gina came still closer to the porch and tried to describe the lake, but the woman clearly had no idea what she was talking about. So then she asked for the path toward Mount Quiddagunk.

The woman looked at her with that smile people have just before stepping on an ant.

"Kiddy-what?"

"*Quidda*-gunk," said Gina.

"What kind of a name is that?!" The woman laughed again and shook her head. "I don't know anything about that!" She pointed in the direction Gina had been walking. "The road's just down there, though."

Gina had been rocking back and forth the whole time she had been talking to the woman, and now she became aware of something that she had almost been aware of for a good twenty minutes: she needed to pee. As she had waded through the reddish grass toward the trailer, the need to pee had grown increasingly insistent, and now that she was contemplating walking away from the trailer she realized she was on the verge of embarrassing herself.

"Excuse me," she said.

The woman only stared at her.

"Could I possibly use your bathroom?"

The woman stared a little longer, then snorted. "Suit yourself." She backed away so that Gina could climb onto the porch.

The dog didn't even lift her head as Gina passed.

The room where Gina was standing seemed too long to fit inside the trailer. It was wood paneled, dark, and smelled like dentures. At its far end there was an arch, through which she could see the foot of a bed, and beyond the bed: an open door. Gina walked the length of the room as rapidly as she could while clutching her thighs together, but stopped halfway when she noticed a gaunt, yellow-skinned, white-haired woman lying on a couch in the corner, staring at her.

"Oh!" Gina said. "Sorry!"

The old woman did not acknowledge Gina's apology in any way and, as Gina resumed her journey, the old woman's eyes never shifted from the place where they had been staring.

When Gina came back into the room, wiping her hands on the seat of her pants, the barrel-shaped woman was standing just inside the door, twisting a rubber band around her long gray hair to make a ponytail. The old woman was not looking at her. She seemed still to be staring at that place at the center of the room that Gina had once occupied.

"That's my ma," the barrel-shaped woman said.

"Oh," said Gina.

"She's dying. Cancer."

"Oh," said Gina.

"I'm just waiting for it to be over."

Gina didn't say anything. Then she said, "Shouldn't she be in a hospital?"

"She don't want to go to no hospital." The woman looked over at her mother and smiled. "Ain't that right, Ma?! She hates the hospital. She hates doctors. In fact, she hates just about everybody. That's how come she lives all the way out here all by herself."

As far as Gina could tell, the old woman did not respond to anything her daughter said. She wasn't even looking at her daughter. It was possible, in fact, that her gaze hadn't shifted since Gina first walked into the room. Maybe she hadn't even blinked.

"You're a nasty old bitch, ain't you, Ma?" said the woman. "Nobody likes you and you don't like nobody neither."

Gina had been thinking that she would ask the woman if she had seen the hulking men in camouflage, but she changed her mind.

Another kind of emptiness is the gap between desire and object. Gina saw this emptiness as proof that we have no place on this earth. Desire assumes that its object is on the other side of the gap, whereas there is no other side. The object itself may exist, but the journey to the object does not, because the journey is endless, because nothing ever changes, because emptiness is where we start and where we end.

The road was not just down the path. Gina walked for hours and hours. Often she stopped and wondered if she shouldn't turn around and go back, but every time she decided it was best to keep going. When at last she got to the road, she didn't recognize it. But she had an instinct, and she followed her instinct. She walked and walked. The light failed. The darkness under the trees rose until it had encompassed the trees and then the whole sky, and she only knew the trees were there because she could hear the quiet clatter of leaf against leaf.

Eventually she came to a streetlight. Not long afterward she came to another, and then she had hardly left the pink dusk beneath one streetlight before she was walking through the pink dusk under the next. Finally she was walking down her own road, and off to the right was the constellation of shadows that she recognized as home. It was late and the sound of the interstate had diminished to the intermittent Dopplerizing drones of rocketing semis.

At first there was a light in her dining room—wavering, orange. Candlelight. But when she walked up the driveway, the dining room was dark. She entered the house through the kitchen door, and stood in the darkness listening. She heard the tick of cooling floorboards. Then the refrigerator motor kicked on. She walked into the dining room. Silence. No smell of wick smoke or melted wax.

After a while she went back to the kitchen and, still not turning on the light, filled a glass with water. She went into her living room, sat on the floor, leaned against the couch, and lit a joint. Sometime later, she awoke, her face pressed into the gritty nap of the rug.

She sat up. The room had changed. A vertical darkness in the corner behind the television had connected to a horizontal darkness created by the pink radiance of streetlight above the curtains. As she watched, the darknesses grew darker and then solidified. Gina looked away. When she looked back, she saw that the darknesses had coalesced into the shape of a man, whose head reached nearly to the ceiling and whose shoulders were as broad as a small couch. She looked away again, but she could not stop herself from looking back.

At first she did not know who the man was, and then she did: he was her husband. He had been waiting for her—for hours or days; for years, maybe. And when he swept her into his arms, she could barely breathe.

"I'm sorry," she murmured against his chest. "I'm sorry. I am so sorry. I can't believe you are finally here."

Beauty

Carole Maso

I'M IN MY GREEN VELVET DRESS again with the streamers at the shoulders in the ballroom turned crimson at the Machado House where we have come to honor the great writer and statesman M. Dignitaries have gathered—among them the Countess Cristina Leonor and her teenage son. . . .

There is a profundity to the body, and a madness.

Oh, someone sighs, *there's Carlos, making his usual entrance.*

Who is that wild child?

Oh no one important Ava Klein.

And half your age by the way. . . .

He appears to be bleeding—having somehow cut his hand on the punch bowl, rather dramatic don't you think?

And now coming this way.

Green how much I want you green, he says. He turns to me and my dress with streamers. A wind moves through my body as if through olive trees.

He limps to the periphery, *God knows why he's limping,* holding his bloody paw and I follow, drawn irresistibly to this bleeding Spanish saint reciting Lorca.

I secure a linen napkin as a bandage. There is a profundity to the body. And a madness. It harbors darkness, sadness, bells, a strange joy, deep song. The punch bowl shatters, something is lit on fire, the distinguished writer speaks, confetti and birds fall, champagne floats by in flutes. I'm alive for a nanosecond on this beautiful, burning earth.

in the Cloud Forest

the Abyss of Tears

the Gardens of Lamentations and Ecstasy.

His blood blooming through the linen and ice (scooped from the silver bucket). And already I am burning under his bleeding hand on this spinning earth. His body makes the room, drenched in red, spin.

From the body emerge: larks, nightingales. From the body: longing, deep song. Emanating from the body, the scent of jasmine and wolves.

Green how much I want you. . . .

The body grows wings, sings in new languages, creates philosophies. The body retains what the mind lets go. As one wakes heavy, leaden, having forgotten the tragic news in the night. The body recalls, harbors ruins, sorrow, keeps what the mind cannot.

I'm alive for a nanosecond. I am alive and burning under his bleeding hand.

But he's barely half your age—

Obviously a teenager Ava Klein.

Is that what he is?

For I have not dared look at him. The hairs on my arm stand on end. And there is a low call from the small of my back. And already I feel him brushing up against me—but so gently as to be imperceptible, as if a kind of torture.

Look, it's the countess now coming in for the kill. . . .

Not even you Ava. . . .

Whispers in the room, and a scarlet scrim descending.

The countess comments on my gray-green dress—*that particular shade, quite interesting*. Pulling her son away.

His turns to me, his blood gaze blazing, and wordlessly we leave the room. Knowing things as only the body can know them.

I dreamt we were alive. How many times after would our blood bloom as on that first night? I dreamt of the passage of the moon. I dreamt of the passage of the moon across the sun. The violet shadows. And the birds quiet and the darkness. And the weeping body and the body that each night voyages beyond the boundaries of the body. It is not infinity but it is something like it—that expansiveness, that awe, impossible to fathom. The words blur, and the feelings grow more and more imprecise. Yet more intensely felt. Those fugitive nights. All the molecules of the body opening onto wonder.

Viewed now as if from the afar:

The mortal blood rising in a red mist, ascending like the ruby-hearted Christ on the third day. And now staining the wild green where they find themselves.

As he fastens her to a tree. Her body, birds.

He tells her of the seven-hearted boy, the seven petals, the insomnia of the horse, the prayers in unison, the mute one, the body with wings, the transfigured night, the asphyxiation—that sublime descent. All is measure and recklessness. And her safe word, *choose a safe word,* her safe word is *green*. When the objective all along was that he take her to the speechless place, the mute island where no word, safe or otherwise, could be uttered.

Carlos adjusts the ropes
the gag
the garrote
the stirrups
the blindfold
the leash
the mask
the pale blue scarf
the tether
Leaving no room for doubt, or margin for error—

My safe word was green. A word to be uttered to indicate too much or too far, a word for stop, before wordlessness.

Just a little bit more burn now—at the place the body ignites. Floating lanterns illumine the night. And her body at last sails into the darkness and the stillness. . . . How to describe the feeling?

Have no fear
I'll be going far off
like an echo
I'll be going far off
In a boat
With no sails
& no oars.

And what is this taste for oblivion? For nothing more and always with him? Carlos singing at the place of horses and skulls, takes the scissors. This theater of the utterly absurd we were all too happy to perform. The body in plaster of paris drying. A kind of cast. Few points of entry. *It's like a comedy sometimes is it not?*

And what is the thing, unknown, indecipherable in her, that he brings up so urgently, this longing for both being, for living, and for nothingness, for erasure, for oblivion? She thought of what one body might do to another, instill in another—a taste develops, a predilection, and they marvel at the body's intelligence, the body's instincts for both survival and annihilation, and how he opened *whole worlds,* this most unlikely boy, and more than anything I wanted to be opened. The jet of blood, the mysteries of pulse, vertigo, the dark philologies of the body as Dalí has said, the central fire, the funnels of night.

The body when pressed, when pushed, when adored, when deprived, floods with beauty, nostalgia—memories, and the small child she was, her fingers on the piano keys. A whole octave. In green light. The tree leaves pressed up against the music-room window.

Blindfolded she ponders the gift of sight. The voracious, insatiable eye. In the soundproof room, she hears things—*the goddess Melancholy is black. Her light is all inside.* The body wails and keens. *Green how much I want you green.* The body dwells in darkness, profundity. Deep shadows, an eerie silence, the wind all of a sudden come up—all this, long after it passes, the body shall retain. Not an animal moved, and the birds went quiet.

A solar eclipse—during which the Countess Cristina Leonor assuming herself exempt, looked directly into the black sun, and soon went blind, her retinas singed. And though she could no longer see, it was revealed shortly thereafter that she had in the process somehow acquired the gift of second sight.

To announce this to the world she held a formal dinner at the Rochambeau House: *I can see the future.* She declared. *And the first thing I have seen is this: that woman is soon to die. It is evident in her face.* This uttered about Ava Klein, not yet thirty, and in the peak of vibrancy and health. *Look!* she declares as if it were proof: *The black dog that never leaves her side, and the stillborn child. Slit your throat now Juan Carlos,* the countess instructs, *because your bride is doomed and she will cause you only heartache I see it clearly now as if it has already transpired. You are following the bier. In your blacks. So dapper my son.*

Bereft, wrestling with ghosts, he weeps. Against the door now he's placed an alarm clock, a grandfather clock with a crown that chimes, an egg timer, a pocket watch. When the hour strikes he begins his rituals to the chiming of blood and bells. The tolling of bells and the blood toll. The body's desire to transcend its verdicts, its dark archive. *Alive.* The fury and rapture that lift us up into the air—the seething creature we make. The clocks unwind. Suture me back together now. Resurrect me. Retrieve me from the dead.

Black iris, black hollyhock, black horses. A procession. Birds fall now and hail, the real and the unreal mingle in a shatter of falling stars. The body is placed in a wooden box. The bones go to earth. The body, underground under the impossibly garish weight of the gladiolas, sighs. There's a skull, an apple, a horse. A still life. And a clock. The darkened drapery. The mossy wings. The cat is blue and trussed. She's seeing things.

For the body as much as you try to negate it returns. The body—and how it resisted their foolish games. The death charade they were lucky enough to stage for a time. And yet . . . Was it not a rehearsal in some way? The body is a boat, a dirt road, a begging bowl. The body houses the bells, and the death knell.

We stand before the Black Paintings. *Do you know what Miró said on his deathbed? He said I want to see The Dog of Goya.*

We stand before the Dog. There is not a single Spaniard who does not pray before it. Who does not lie prostrate.

His wounded hand. Poor paw she had said to the creature. *There is something monstrous about him don't you think? In the way children can be.*

That beautiful bleeding boy.

We'll make the light shine through.

With brilliant and sudden splendor now he has returned. From out of the obscurity and the distance and the years, he lifts us into the air, levitates us into the air once more. The body's late hallucinations. The body's resourcefulness. The body's profound attachment to aliveness. Carrying ruin and feeling, beauty, the blood vessels. To my hospital room. The hummingbird heart. The wing beat.

And who now cannot think of the countess when I am diagnosed with a rare blood disease, and then some time after that, when it becomes evident that an intricate and risky procedure would be necessary.

The nurses swoop and dive.

This should not hurt too much.

The vulnerable body

The porous body

The body of uncertainty and roses—our pure perishing.

The disembodied, bloodied paw floating in the room.

I'm in my velvet green dress again with the streamers at the shoulders. *The dead wear mossy wings* the Countess Leonor said absently that day staring at the black sun.

Now that the body betrays, now that the body poised at the edge of the abyss or so it seems, appears to be failing—that once unflappable body, the one thing that could always be relied on—the way it lit up in the dark, the way it went far, and then too far.

Swoop and dive, they take the vital signs.

And it is true. The more the body was canceled or erased, the more she wanted to live and her resolve grew despite her death foretold. She remembered it from here—a world of pure vibrancy and form. She cries out *green*!

He genuflects now before her. Small deaths all around them and confetti barely perceived and the distant sound of cheers as if from a faraway bull ring. The matador so small. A small red speck. From the blur, confined, the body rises. And there is no rising like it. And there is peace a while.

A wistful dark angel, bodiless, now presides. But it is not your time Ava Klein.

There's no hurry.
It's all right.
The angel
will wait
as long as it takes
to escort you
back
to vapor.

The longing of the angel around the bed. The desire to have a body. It would do anything for one. For it would be a privilege simply to feel—the way the flesh presses against earth, the way the blood from a gash flows warm and red, the way breath like wind inhabits the chest—for our instants on earth.

Your safe word is (inaudible) *I can't hear you anymore.*

Inside the body birds fall now, a black dog, a stillborn, perfectly formed, and hail, a girl playing a piano at her first recital, a big bow in her hair. The white ox passes through and the moon. And the dead wear mossy wings. The cat is blue and trussed. She's seeing things.

There is a profundity to the body. And a madness. It holds, it harbors darkness, sorrow, beauty, joy, melancholy, wonder.

He's back. His red gaze blazing. I am alive for a nanosecond. And without a word exchanged we leave this stark, white room together. Knowing things as only the body can know them. Imagining the wings I will soon leave on the sheet. . . .

Skeleton, Rock, Shell

Sejal Shah

> *Shells are chiefly protective and skeletons are mainly for support. Skeletons are, therefore, chiefly internal structures, whereas shells are external. In some animals the same structure may serve both as a shell and a skeleton. . . . Every animal with a shell must, at least in theory, decide whether a light but mobile shell is better than a heavy but immovable one. A shell may provide some protection, but it requires energy to construct and move; animals without shells save energy but are vulnerable to their enemies.*
>
> —William Lee Stokes in *Essentials of Earth History: An Introduction to Historical Geology*

I ONCE KNEW A MAN who told us to listen to the spirits inside stones. He held a rock in his hand. Think, he said, of what this rock has been through. How it has traveled.

I imagined the pressures of his hand.

I ignored the rest of the lecture, the importance of fossil fuels, and thought instead of my once-long hair.

Here is the whorl of a fingerprint, the loneliness of a shell.

Stones speak, he said, if you close your eyes and your mouth, if you listen. I crossed and uncrossed my legs. I leaned, tossed my hair, and enacted the look of the slightly bored: allowing the look of possible future intelligence to sprawl across me. After the lecture, when the others had collected their satchels and book bags, their long, red scarves, after they had filed out toward the glass-front dining halls and the miniature town, I stayed behind. I stole that rock he had left on the wooden lectern. I went home to my dorm room, the weight of the rock in my jacket pocket like a secret leaning, a weight pulling me in one direction, and I walked perhaps over-straight to compensate.

Sejal Shah

I want to say that I got to my room and closed the door.

That I silently pried the clothes off my body. I lit candles and incense (the only law I broke repeatedly, besides speeding) and that I balanced the stone on my stomach. That my hip became a sand dune. That the rock, feeling smoother as it passed over each bone, as it sloughed off cells—that this stone enraptured me. That it cleansed me. I lay in the bath, the water beginning to cool. I want to say that the weight of this rock succored me. I felt the boy parts of me: my hips, the buttons of my spine, percussing each notch of the sternum, as though my body were something I could unhook and step out of, and sometimes I did dream of this. Unhooking. The O'Keeffe of me. The body a dress I had grown tired of. I wanted to see my bones. I wanted to loosen my skin until I could see underneath. I wanted to return to bone.

Words conjure. Why not simply say it? The only oracle is in the bones, is in the pattern of what is left. Of what remains.

I once drank too much. I was not in a ceremonial way. I danced and danced. I wanted to erase you. Ease you into the sack of memory; any kind of regret, rising. This is the oracle of the bones. I drank so much I could not remember. I drank so much I could not push him away. I could say now: I didn't mean to. I could say: I tried to get warm, to dislodge you, a slow suddenness now sealed in my skin. A rock is a planet fallen to earth. I drank coffee after coffee, refastening my head, shaking my head from side to side, gingerly, like something that had once been whole.

I wanted to sleep and I wanted to not remember: aren't these the most elemental of human wishes? I am no different. He stopped my mouth with his finger. It is an unheated attic and it is nearly December. I will have to remember this night until I can forget this night. I want to forget your hands. The deftness of your hands. The yellow-haired girl crying by the door. I hadn't seen you in eight or nine years. You were *engaged* the last time I saw you.

Any child, walking along the shore, will fill her hands with shells. Sand from her hands, spilling from the corners of her dress, pulled up. A fist of the rocks that looked green in water. What is there to do but throw them out when you return home?

Arrange the broken pieces you carried back.

We dream space until shapes emerge: a wheel, mandala; confetti.

Loss is the name for the Spanish settlers who could not forget.

You say it was a misunderstanding. You say you had no idea. (I seemed to be pushing back against your pushes, perhaps the organism of me was; my body moving in the way it understood that movement begins. And ends. Betrayal: a response you cannot control. To an action you cannot control.) Bones are the only oracle.

Your hands were so quick; nimble. Cut the hands off of quick boys. The boy with quick hands jumped over the small brown girl. She never found her earrings. They got lost like I wish you had got lost. Get lost in the world. Get me out of this world.

I will whittle myself to the bone. I will triangulate. All the more to be invisible from you. All to disappear into the farthest corner. All to ruin. All to invite ruin. What else will last? In the divine way, I mean.

A rock is a desire fallen to earth. You throw your hands up, in the practiced way. A rock is a planet that has begun to divine, a planet chipped to a million runes.

I was not your ceremonial fuck, you are not the lost descendant of French settlers. At best, you are Canadian.

Afterward, you will say to the common friend: "She is just saying that now. I heard her enjoy herself."

Was I wanting it? I wanted you to see. I am not that brown-haired girl. I was never the black-haired girl that I am. I was always the brown-haired girl, except with black hair.

A rock is a winged boy fallen to earth. If I let this go, then? How long does an indentation last, then? Your name is a narrowing lake in a chain of lakes. How can everything not be an echo of what was found and lost? Of the things we understood, when we stood at the shore collecting things? And still, we got lost.

It was a reunion. Their breasts bobbing like markers in Utowanna. The tops of their breasts shimmering. The girl wanted to look nice. I was that girl. I am not that girl. Of the four Indians and one Sri Lankan in our class, only two of us returned. I should have worn what I always wore. Possibly ugly things. Loose things. Things that obscure. It is dangerous to be seen. It is stupid to think I could erase you.

A list of losses: this is a general idea of how I am arranged.

Trilobites are rocks that have already been washed and decorated in the ceremonial way.

Out of my nervousness, I asked for help.

She surveyed the map of me.

The shoes were fringed with sequins, more expensive than anything I had ever bought.

All I remembered later was that my feet were cold.

I could not walk home.

Nothing I wore that night could hold enough heat.

I wore a sweater, too thin. It was the night after Thanksgiving.

My clavicle could not speak and my arms were bare, hair rising.

Too thin for Newcastle after Newcastle.

Nothing I was could hold enough.

Nothing I could hold was enough.

My brother's wife and my mother waxed my arms, together, laughing, in the pink bathroom I grew up in, against the mirror I grew up seeing my face in. Here are the strips to lay down against the arms, thin as bones, and here is the rip of the leaving. Of the pulling away. Leaving my arms thin as branches, brushed to perfection.

A girl is a tree stripped of bark.

A girl is a skeleton, rock, shell.

A girl is a boy who cannot forget.

A boy is a girl who has learned not to see.

You told me later what I kept repeating.

I was very cold. Cover me, wrap your arms around me, be my overly friendly acquaintance; be my good brother, my hand-drifting uncle. It was Thanksgiving, for heaven's sake. I was not looking for a quick fuck. I was looking for warmth. I was looking for another you; I was looking for you. I wanted the weight of you.

Everyone else has moved on. I am still sitting here drinking coffee, listening to the garbage trucks pull up, listening to the people walking by. It is hot the way it is always hot in the city. You know how the heat comes in two directions, rising from the pavement, hard from the sun. I wanted to look nice. I did not want to be that girl I was. I drank enough fermented wheat to push her away until I could barely keep my balance. I drank enough cold beer so that the cold wasn't cold right away, so that I couldn't push you away.

I am trying to say it, to step up to the plate and claim it.

A girl is a memory pressed into stone.

You went to your reunion and then to hers. You were with her, your hand on the small of her back, when she drank too much. You told me that her dress was black and red and clingy. I was angry at you for describing her dress that way. I think that was one of the many times it became clear which way things would go, and had been going all along.

You always have a choice. Every day you have a choice about how you will live your life and what stories you will tell about the choices you made.

You had the gift, like many people I have known, of making the story you tell seem to be the only story there is. This is what you said: I just need more time. This is what I understood: I am not enough. This is what I understand now: *there is no more time.*

You are only a shell. Or perhaps you are an Apache word for metal. Or: you are a petroglyph. No one can give someone else a reason. I believe in excavation. You believe in burying. It is better to make these distinctions. It is one way that I temper my eagerness to believe that you might have chosen differently.

I forced you in the end to say what we both knew. I wanted to hear you say that you loved her. I wanted you to say to me: *I don't love you anymore. I thought I did. Go home.* Humiliate me. I wanted the final humiliation so that I would not hope, never hope. It is a terrible trait of mine, of not believing something until it is pushed into words, and of believing words long after they are useful. Words are only words after all.

I am a trilobite, a regeneration in clay, a one-way sign. You have only to say my name, and I will appear: a silly incarnation of a sixteen-year-old. I am your atavistic hope: a minor goddess with a gift for calling, for incarnating, again and again. I am your worst nightmare: a vegetarian who won't go down on you. What kind of hedonism is that?

I had no words to tell you what happened. I could barely tell myself. I just knew that it would not have happened if you were there and I wanted you to know that. I kept waking you the last night you slept next to me; I was awake and I was suffering. I wanted you to be able to read my mind, to comfort me. KNOW THIS. The girl who practiced on bananas gave better blow jobs and you knew it. I was not that girl. You chose what you had to.

I stumbled from one side of the wooden bar in its faux-NYC-loft-warehouse-look to the other, wanting your hand on the small of my back. Tonic. Your quiet laughter behind me. I would have been telling you about the kids in my elementary-school classes, about who looked different, who looked better, and who looked worse. I was saving up these stories to tell to you. Were you making a list in your head for someone else all this time? I made this into another reason to drink Newcastle.

Let me pretend you were with me all this time. I should have at least that. I would have walked you downstairs in my parents' house to the guest-room bed, and told you how to say "My name is ______" in Gujarati. *Maru nam______che.* I would have knocked into you and said, Tell me a story. You would have said, *S______, let me bring you back upstairs. You'll fall asleep downstairs. I don't want your parents mad. Come on, S_______.*

After the last time you left, I sat down and cleaned my apartment. I opened the second file drawer, the lower one, the one I had never used, and began to sort out papers. I forced myself to look through files I had not looked at in years, to make decisions about what was still useful and what should be recycled to make room for the stacks of mail and paper I had accumulated in the time I had been thinking of you instead.

I returned to the bath, trying to enact intact. I wanted to return to intact.

A rock is a moon that has fallen to earth. Its concentric rings promise one side of the horizon to the other. Each rock, even the smooth ones, carries cracks.

Given sufficient heat, nearly any type of continental rock may melt. You barely fucked me. Granite rises, another form of regret. I think you barely loved me. Below a stone = the stillness of a flute. You were a mistake. Continents form through the process of accretion. I wanted you to see me. I want you to take it back. Erase you from between my ears. *Close your mouth, close your eyes, and listen:* I was a mistake.

I tried to fit us together like a child takes the continents, pushes South America into Africa. You said, I'm no good for you. What looks like it should fit and doesn't. I did not account for pulls. Fits and pulls are different forces altogether. I did not account for you and me. I did not account for getting stuck. Or the pills that I take every day to steady me, to keep not exalted and not below. I want to take it back.

Love is the name for a burial in what is now southern Utah.

Is that what love is then, letting things lie?

Sejal Shah

Loss is a calling forth in middle Kentucky.

And my penchant for excavation? There is no name for this.

Love survives at 2:30 p.m. in middle Kentucky. These words will call forth.

We die for the smallest things. Nothing washes off—. I have died for the smallest things. Nothing washes off.

You left New York, and returned to our colder town.

But what will I think about before I sleep?

Earlier brachiopods were called inarticulates.

Following the granite-forming period came a long period of erosion.

I am a suggestion, sunk into slate, beginning to harden.

A rock is a girl rising from the earth.

NOTE. "I have died for the smallest things. / Nothing washes off," are the closing lines of Angela Jackson's poem "The Love of Travellers," first published in *Callaloo: A Journal of African Diaspora Arts and Letters* (No. 35, Spring 1988). The sentences immediately preceding hers, "We die for the smallest things. Nothing washes off—," are my echo of Jackson's original lines. I read "The Love of Travellers" when I came across it in *The Pushcart Prize XIV* in 1990. I've had those closing lines in my head ever since.

Notes on Lazarus

Rick Moody

What do we know about Lazarus? In the Eastern Orthodox Church, Lazarus of Bethany, who lived thirty years after his alleged resurrection by Jesus of Nazareth, was said, in these later years, never to have smiled—because he had seen the underworld.

"Jesus wept," it is well known, is the shortest verse in the Bible (John 11:35). This sentence describes Jesus's confrontation with the facts of the death of Lazarus of Bethany. There is reasonable consistency, among the many English translations, on this passage, although I have also found the much inferior "Jesus cried."[1] The strength of the passage is in its brevity. The brevity suggests, embodies, incarnates the feeling.

There are thirty-two modern cases (that is, cases here in the twenty-first century) of people whose hearts spontaneously restarted after they had been pronounced dead. A significant number of these "deaths" were owing to drug overdose. The technical name for a heart restarting without assistance is "auto-resuscitation." It's also called: Lazarus Syndrome.

Why is it that Jesus feels such waves of grief at Lazarus's death, when he knows already that resurrecting Lazarus is possible? Is it simply because he feels the loss that the sisters of Lazarus, Mary and Martha of Bethany, feel? Is the sibling relationship such as to suggest the pain of grief as no other does?

Maybe Jesus weeps so over Lazarus's tomb because he knows what will be commenced as a result. According to John 12, the Jews of Jerusalem plotted to kill Lazarus a second time immediately after his resurrection (in various later versions of the story I have seen

[1]Here's a good list of translations of John 11:35: https://www.biblegateway.com/verse/en/John%2011:35. The International Standard Version of the Bible gives "Jesus burst into tears."

this same intent attributed to the Romans) because they knew what the miracle would occasion in and around the ministry of Jesus.

The "grave clothes" of Lazarus are the bandages covering both face and body at the time he climbs up and out of the tomb. He is, more or less, mummified. Covering the face as the body is buried removes what's most human about it; it's a recognition of the absence of self. The body of Lazarus will be evacuated of its spirit while decaying in the tomb. And thus: when Jesus wants to reveal what is human about the resurrected Lazarus, he first has to have the grave clothes removed, meaning uncovering the face.

Why Lazarus? Why Lazarus more so than any other deceased candidate who might have been proposed among those in the Jewish community? Lazarus is selected for his excellent abilities to serve in a heroic narrative capacity. Jesus must have felt as much. Lazarus was the Rosa Parks of the New Testament, in the right place at the right time. We might say that Lazarus had an honest face. Perfect for unveiling.

In John 12, Jesus goes back to Bethany later, to check up on Lazarus after the miracle, and they have a meal together. Oh to have been a bystander! Did Jesus ask him about the four days in the underworld? Weather? Politics? That year's agricultural yield? "But Lazarus was one of them that sat at the table with him,"[2] according to John. Jesus knows, feels, comprehends what he saw! And yet the scene goes on to discuss the issue of poverty: "For the poor always ye have with you."[3] Lazarus is scarcely mentioned again at the table and yet is always present (apparently entirely without a smile).

Lazarus is not resurrected for all eternity, as Jesus promises the believers after Judgment Day. Lazarus gets his human death sentence commuted only temporarily. His is the kind of miracle that we all long for and are suspicious of, whether religious or irreligious. Lazarus is a revival-tent miracle. (After my sister's death, I remember any number of movies featuring dead characters returning, some of them profound, some of them imbecilic. I watched these films mostly with envy.) I recently heard a sermon about Lazarus that spoke to this point: *Unfortunately I must*

[2]Ibid., Authorized (King James) Version, John 12:2.
[3]Ibid., John 12:8.

disappoint those of you who, because of this story, are hoping for the resurrection of your own relatives.

And what did Lazarus feel? The eternal repose, the sense of traveling down and into oblivion, must be reassuring in a way. I think of oblivion as potentially satisfying, lavender hued. Imagine Lazarus of Bethany living at the edge of the Roman Empire, good friends with some itinerant Jew, some wandering mendicant, whom everyone wanted to put to death. An undeniable rabble-rouser, afoul of the authorities. Dying, for Lazarus, may have been a relief from constant political adversity and the physical threats of the Romans, with their superior weaponry and numbers. And then having to be raised up from that eternal repose, to face, again, contemporary political horror?

Or: maybe Lazarus suffered from the considerably rare Cotard's syndrome, in which he believed he was dead already. One can imagine, in the premodern era, when sanitation and medicine were not what they are now, when death was the kingdom at hand, that one could easily come to believe that one already had the condition. And maybe Jesus of Nazareth did what he did (as when Jesus cast out the demons, in Matthew 8:28, by transferring them into a herd of swine) simply to try to commute psychic suffering. Maybe Jesus abbreviates Lazarus's preoccupation with death. Feels it and commutes it.

Maybe Lazarus was a member of one of those ancient mystery cults, one of those Greco-Roman schools of the forbidden and secret, as with the Dionysian cult, in which *chthonic* rites were prized, at least initially (as well as rites of wine consumption). In this version of the story, Lazarus perhaps courted the underworld, according to the rigors of the cult, but was somehow lost in the process, and, at the urging of Martha and Mary, Jesus came to summon him forth from the religion of error and schism, and back to the true path. The weeping would have been, therefore, about the pointlessness of Lazarus's sacrifice.

And this cultic narrative of Lazarus would nicely anticipate his value to vodun spirituality, where Lazarus is subsumed into the wild and anarchic presence known as Papa Legba. Or what about the feast day of San Lazaro in the Afro-Cuban tradition, which conflates the

Lazarus of the Gospel of Matthew (beggar) and the Lazarus of the Gospel of John (resurrected guy). According to this tradition, San Lazaro was scourged on the flesh before being beheaded in 72 AD. This San Lazaro allowed himself to be licked by dogs too after being scourged, and is therefore the patron saint of dogs. In Cuba, there is a pilgrimage to Rincón in honor of San Lazaro, to the former leprosarium there. Now they just treat skin diseases in Rincón because there is an insufficiency of lepers.

And: the insistence in the biblical account on Lazarus reeking upon emerging from the tomb is very satisfying. In literature, descriptions of scent make a passage more indelible. There should be more biblical smells. A friend of mine who was present on the set of Scorsese's film *The Last Temptation of Christ* tells the story of Scorsese attempting to recreate the horrible smell of Lazarus in a filmic way, instructing all the extras and the cast members to recoil visibly when Lazarus came forth, but, according to this same friend, this bit was mostly cut from the finished project. It just didn't look right.

Zeffirelli's *Jesus of Nazareth* (1977) has a nice Lazarus sequence. The white-guy-with-blue-eyes incarnation of Jesus (as played by Robert Powell) feels a bit dated, and there are all those British accents to lend *dramatic seriousness* to the undertaking, but despite the telefilm-epic qualities of the project, Jesus manages to convey the immensity of his life and sacrifice. In fact, the raising of Lazarus, which miracle is heavily outfitted with a retinue of observers, is the depiction wherein I best understand the sequential importance of Lazarus to the drama of the ministry of Jesus. This raising of the dead puts in motion Christ's own execution. What's at stake is this: if Jesus can resurrect the enemies of the state, the powerless, the Jews, the slaves, the indigent, then he has to be neutralized. And therefore when Martha and Mary stop Jesus on a footpath among cypresses to tell him of Lazarus's death, you can see a real dread cross the face of Jesus. He knows.

Oh, and there's a moment of total black screen in the Zeffirelli miniseries, before Lazarus comes forth from his tomb in the hillside. The camera closes in on the blackness inside the tomb entrance, and then goes completely black. It's lovely and complete as a suggestion of the nothingness of the underworld. If I could put black screen in this essay I would. Right here.

A few more resurrections? There's "Po' Lazarus," the work song recorded by Alan Lomax, and made popular after the rerelease of some of the Lomax archive in the nineties, and again in the soundtrack to *O Brother, Where Art Thou?* by Joel and Ethan Coen. In the original (as opposed to the filmic recording), the words to "Po' Lazarus" are improvised by one James Carter with some other inmates who were chopping wood in 1959 at a certain penitentiary in Mississippi. James Carter, who therefore "wrote" the song, when presented with a royalty check after the release of the Coen brothers film (and at a point in his life during which he was working as a shipping clerk), could not remember having sung the song for the Lomax recording. He had to be convinced. He did attend the Grammy Awards, however, when the soundtrack to the Coen brothers film won album of the year. He died a couple of years later, redeemed.

So adaptable is the Lazarus narrative to the poetry and song of African Americans, so easily does it graft onto a civil rights dramatic arc, that it is possible to think of Lazarus as though he must have been black himself, and thus, perhaps, an Ethiopian Jew, which would give the whole story an arresting subplot. Because if Lazarus were black, then so were Martha and Mary, his sisters, and there's a much more resonant intersectionality about the raising from the dead, that it was to make central to Jesus's ministry the exiled community of Beta Israel, those who fled oppression, those who lived farther out in the desert. This Lazarus, the black Lazarus, recurs again and again, and his struggle with prejudice and contempt in the Jerusalem of Jesus's ministry makes his narrative that much more lasting. Jesus, after the raising from the dead, goes to have dinner with the Beta Israel.

Terry Callier's powerful and moving song "Lazarus Man" finds Lazarus with a fever to narrate his journey ("Since he bid me to rise / I ain't been to sleep!").[4] Callier, an African American folk singer from Chicago who made a number of recordings in the seventies, completely dropped out of the music business only to be rediscovered by British deejays (and Beth Orton) in the nineties, and he makes of Lazarus an allegory for renewal, both in the fact of his singing about Lazarus and in the words of his composition.

[4]Terry Callier, *TimePeace* (Talkin' Loud Classics, 1998).

Callier's Lazarus, by inference, is African or African American too, and it's interesting to think of the Lazarus narrative repurposed to describe the struggles of the disenfranchised (as the Jews themselves were in the Holy Land of Lazarus's own time). Callier's two chords here are modal in the style of Miles Davis and John Coltrane ("Lazarus Man" feels closely related to Coltrane's "India"), so the song also situates Lazarus in the heroic liberation of jazz, the kind of music they play at New Orleans funerals—elegiac, tragicomic, mnemonic, celebratory, deep.

Terry Callier's Lazarus, moreover, seems to have something in common with the outlandish Provençal tradition in which Lazarus (and his sisters, Mary and Martha) is put out to sea by hostile Jews, to drift all the way to Provence, where Lazarus becomes bishop of Marseille, after which he is put to death (he always dies eventually) during the persecutions associated with the reign of Domitian. In this French tall tale, his head was preserved.

The Marseille narrative, which gets taken up and embellished by French believers of the medieval period, is Gnostic in the way it ties up loose ends (the Mary in the Lazarus story is Mary Magdalene, even though there's no evidence for this, and Lazarus is a thief, like Barabbas, who was crucified next to Jesus of Nazareth). The Marseille narrative indicates that Lazarus is one of those pieces of the New Testament that is so powerful people want to claim it, to manipulate its particulars, to bind up its disparate material. They want to make the story so plastic that it might, somehow, continue to grow.

In the Eastern Orthodox tradition, Lazarus became a bishop in Cyprus. He may or may not have been appointed to the post by the Virgin Mary herself.

Henri Cole's poem "Hens" deals with a Lazarus: "I can't resist picking up little Lazarus, / an orange-and-white pullet I adore. 'Yes, yes, everything will be / okay,' I say to her glaring mongrel face."[5] Cole's considerable gift is for a richness of metaphor in which human struggle and human longing constantly appear recast into things observed in nature, and in the hen named Lazarus we feel

[5]http://www.theatlantic.com/magazine/archive/2009/10/hens/307670/.

both impulses, Lazarus, in tragicomic form, a figure of sport, an entrée, or a layer of eggs. As in Cole's work elsewhere, the metaphorical layering is so dense that Lazarus's incarnations shimmer multiply before us at first. Some of these layers are very funny.

At least until Cole's Petrarchan turn in the sixth line of his pellucid sonnet-like form, when again Lazarus, the chicken, bereft of smile, comes face-to-face with the particulars of suffering and nonbeing: "Poor Lazarus— / last spring an intruder murdered her sisters and left her / garroted in the coop."[6] The dread never far off, a muscular, exceedingly sober gaze at the facts of the world: "There's a way the wounded / light up a dark rectangular space. Suffering becomes / the universal theme."[7] Maybe, in this incarnation of Lazarus, his story tells a precisely human truth: that in the cycle of death and resurrection there is *eternal recurrence* of suffering.

Schubert never finished his oratorio about Lazarus.

Did you know that the site of Lazarus's tomb is contested? Like many places in and around the Holy City, it has been contested for thousands of years. There is a tomb, now underneath a mosque, the al-Uzair, which the Muslims sealed off. It was sealed off, that is, until the Franciscans cut a different entrance into the tomb. None can say for certain if it's the *actual* tomb of Lazarus or not, of course, but there have been churches in the area since the fourth century. It is more an exemplary tomb from the days of the early church, a site plausible and—because plausible—spooky. It is more exemplary than actual. The tomb, originally, was connected to Lazarus's house, or so it is said. He was buried next to his house!

In "Dig, Lazarus, Dig!!!,"[8] Nick Cave (and his Bad Seeds) reduce Lazarus (nicknamed Larry in the verses) to a rock-and-roll drug adept, a hallucinating addict, a sort of fin de siècle decadent trying to achieve satori (I'm using the Beat terminology) through deformation of the senses, and this, in the chorus—"Dig yourself, Lazarus, dig yourself back in that hole"—indicates the coming awake of Lazarus, in which Lazarus, realizing the enormity of his resurrection, the

[6]Ibid.
[7]Ibid.
[8]Mute Records, 2008.

fearsome responsibility of it, tries to return to the underworld. It's more comfortable down there.

I sort of dislike this song. It's as if Nick Cave is the Susan Sontag of contemporary music: a popularizer of other more trenchant avant-gardes. The secret weapon of the Bad Seeds, once upon a time, was Blixa Bargeld, a founding member of the Bad Seeds (and lead guitarist at one point) and former member of Einstürzende Neubauten, whose inability was his mastery, and who gave the Bad Seeds a genuinely unpredictable element. The removal of Bargeld (and Mick Harvey) made the band sort of a pop band, the way I see it, and Cave tried to resist this transition into more palatable and socially acceptable material by making the *Grinderman* album (a garage-rock side project), after which came *Dig!!! Lazarus Dig!!!*, somewhat in imitation of the *Grinderman* sound. It's a simulated punk-rock album, therefore, and the song "Dig, Lazarus, Dig!!!" is obviously influenced by New York punk. When Cave, on "Lazarus," doesn't sound like Mark E. Smith of the Fall, he sounds a bit like Richard Hell (of the Voidoids), and the lyrics allude to New York (and San Francisco), and you know he means the drugs and chaos, the energy, the *Todestrieb* of punk.

It would all seem like self-mythologizing and lyrical excess of the kind that makes for great performance, but does not withstand close lyrical scrutiny. And yet notwithstanding this simulation of urgency Cave has made plangent and memorable remarks about Lazarus of Bethany: "Ever since I can remember hearing the Lazarus story, when I was a kid, you know, back in church, I was disturbed and worried by it. Traumatized, actually. We are all, of course, in awe of the greatest of Christ's miracles—raising a man from the dead—but I couldn't help but wonder how Lazarus *felt* about it. As a child it gave me the creeps, to be honest."[9] *Traumatizing* is such a great word for the Lazarus story, and the "actually" that comes after "traumatized" here gives that beleaguered adverb a force it doesn't ordinarily have.

And so it becomes clear why there are three exclamation points in the title of Nick Cave's song, when one would clearly do the job reliably: they are Trinitarian.

---

[9]https://en.wikipedia.org/wiki/Dig,_Lazarus,_Dig!!! (italics mine).

The other way that Cave gives us access to the Lazarus story is through Cave's son, Arthur. His son, as is well known now, fell to his death in Brighton, England, in 2015, and on *Skeleton Tree*, his recent album of compositions mostly written before Arthur's passing, but recorded after, you can feel the haunting of Arthur everywhere. (The jacket of *Skeleton Tree* is the same color as Zeffirelli's black screen.) "Jesus Alone," the first track on *Skeleton Tree*, is where you feel acutely the Jesus of Nazareth who weeps over Lazarus's grave.[10] Jesus wept. Jesus wept. Jesus began to cry. Jesus started crying. Jesus wept. And Jesus wept. Jesus cried. Jesus wept. And at this Jesus wept. Jesus burst into tears. Jesus wept. Jesus wept. Jesus wept.

"With my voice I am calling you"[11] is the refrain of "Jesus Alone," and it's both Cave trying to call to Arthur across the trauma of loss, and it's Jesus alone, without the comfort of the divine, in dread of the human part of his mission, aggrieved by the loss of Lazarus, in the grief of a loss of a beloved friend, in the dread of knowing the numinous, in the knowledge of what comes next, of his sacrifice, when, after the dinner with the resurrected Lazarus of Bethany, he must enter the city of Jerusalem and proceed, well, to Golgotha.

"Evidently, this was needed,"[12] Franz Wright says of Lazarus, in a sort of a free translation of a poem by Rilke, "The Raising of Lazarus," perhaps a rehabilitation of a fragment of Rilke, a fragment that could not be completed to anyone's satisfaction, because looking accurately upon Lazarus is to be "traumatized," as Cave says, into fragmentation and silence, into failure. To know what Lazarus knew is to be *traumatized*. The antecedent of "this" in "Evidently, this was needed" is purposefully vague. The passivity of the sentence is exactly the kind of German abstraction that one associates with Rilke, and the use of "evidently" is funny and sly, because in Wright's bloodcurdling rendering of Rilke's Lazarus, it's all about *proof*, all evidentiary. As in the next line: "Because people need / to be screamed at with proof."

---

[10]And maybe there is a mystery-cult aspect to Arthur's death as well, as it was said in the press that he may have taken LSD before his fall. "Jesus Alone," therefore, really conjures this reading of Jesus, bereft and uncomprehending, at the advent of Lazarus's death.

[11]Nick Cave and the Bad Seeds, *Skeleton Tree* (Mute Records, 2016).

[12]https://www.poetryfoundation.org/poetrymagazine/poems/detail/58345.

Wright's account of the story is long on the horrors of the scene, garish physical details, and all from the vantage point of the Nazarene. Mary is a prostitute (evidently Wright is from Provence, where all the Marys and all the Lazaruses are one), and all who gather for the miracle are "Brueghelian grotesques." It's an "ontogenetical horrorshow," and we feel acutely Jesus preparing for his doom (and glory), as he raises Lazarus and removes the burial garb. But what we don't get is much of Lazarus himself. He's "the one young man"[13] who stoops at the entrance of the grave, coming forth. The fact of the poem, its reiteration of Rilke, its apparent long journey to completion, the sense of teetering on compositional unworthiness, is an indication that it's Lazarus we're dealing with. To put it another way: Lazarus is about the *telling* of Lazarus, where the dread and completion shimmer just out of reach.

Or, *evidently*, what is needed is a transit across a dialectical pairing, a Hegelian opposition, viz., life and death, a way to render the longing of the one for the other, and: I wrote these lines after spending time by the deathbed of a loved one, an ebbing out of life, and what I found in the five days before and the two days after that desubstantiating just out of reach, that particle and wave, was not a dialectical pairing, a Hegelian opposition, but rather an incremental development, in which self is pitted, mottled, interstitial, but breath continues, and then, after breath, a hovering of presence in absence, as if the other who was no longer was there again, and as I write these lines I can feel her with me, inscribed in my inscriptions. I write these lines for her. A death and not-death in language, a dissemination of fragments, a broadcasting of residuary self, a hovering into this draft. There are some ten minutes after medical death when the brain is still responsive to some stimuli, in a lavender-hued journey back and forth across the entranceway to the next place of the black screen.

Caravaggio's *The Raising of Lazarus*, which is in Sicily, where it was painted by Caravaggio after fleeing Malta because of *legal*

[13]The word choice here is powerful, because "young man" (*neaniskos* in Greek) is used in the Gospel of Mark, and, elsewhere, in the forged or Gnostic *Secret Gospel of Mark* to indicate a character, not named Lazarus, raised from the dead by Jesus, and with whom Jesus may be in love. They even, it seems, spend a night together. "Jesus wept," in this case, would have much deeper implications. This thoroughly Gnostic Lazarus might be even more revolutionary than the canonical one.

problems, has stories orbiting around it nearly as fanciful as those orbiting around Lazarus himself: for example, that Caravaggio had a body exhumed in order to paint Lazarus, and that there was a prior version of the painting, which Caravaggio himself destroyed owing to criticism that he did not like. He got an enormous commission for the painting, but some of it may have been finished by assistants nonetheless, and it wants for the intense drama of some other paintings by the master of high contrast. The arrangement of characters is powerful, though, with the women gathered around Lazarus's head. Almost exactly like a deposition. Christ looks extremely commanding, not the doubter that he would perhaps have been about the miracle. And though he looks commanding, Christ is just a backward version of a drawing Caravaggio used in *The Calling of St. Matthew* previously. As if one of the aspects of the story of Lazarus is that it features autoplagiarism.

Rembrandt's *The Raising of Lazarus* from just fifteen or twenty years after Caravaggio's, is quite a bit more unsettling. I can't tell if it's because I have already gazed at length on Rembrandt's *The Anatomy Lesson of Dr. Nicolaes Tulp* (1632), which has a cadaver in it, and which has so much intensity. (They only permitted one dissection a year in Amsterdam, and it was always a criminal. In this case it was Aris Kindt, a thief who had been executed the day before, a Barabbas character, and this you would know if you were to read *The Rings of Saturn* by Sebald, which discusses with great urgency this anatomy painting.) The arms seem to be on backward on the cadaver's body, and there's a shadow over the cadaver's face, which is the *shadow of death*, I believe, and there's something very claustrophobic about the whole. The mystery of death, the moment in which the soul flickers out of the body, is much on display here.

Should it be impossible or unlikely that Rembrandt's *Anatomy Lesson of Dr. Nicolaes Tulp* (and a later *Anatomy Lesson*, damaged by fire) could somehow have influenced his *Raising of Lazarus*, which was painted *before* these efforts? In the uncanny event horizon of Lazarus, apparently it's not impossible at all, because failure, plagiary, repetition compulsion, and nonlinear time could all easily be coincident with a raising from the dead. Rembrandt's *Lazarus* shimmers with unearthly lantern light from the left-hand margin, which shrouds Martha's face, and Lazarus, truly ghostly in white and gray, is given the vast majority of the pictorial space to be climbing up and out of the tomb, like an emissary from the underworld. It's almost as if the lessons of death, the way death is both absent and present, and most present when most absent, are catalyzed here for Rembrandt, and he keeps going back to them with the later anatomy lessons, such that his interpretation of Lazarus is affected by his collision with Aris Kindt. Even as his depiction of Lazarus's body is made more acute because of his (mis)understanding of the flesh as sketched out for the medical community of Amsterdam much later on.

Both Giotto and Duccio painted Lazarus in their preperspectival, medieval way. (The bleached, nearly cubist backdrop of Duccio suggests the landscape of Zeffirelli's *Jesus of Nazareth*.)

I am so pained by "Lady Lazarus" by Plath that I don't really know how to include it here, while giving over to it the confessional intensity that it has, the legacy of it, the importance of it to poetry by women. There are things about this poem that I find impossible to tolerate now, even as I admire it, and that is because everything about "Lady Lazarus" hurts so lastingly that it is hard to reread. It's a raw, lacerating disquiet that hovers about the poem. It is nearly vengeful, or perhaps "nearly" is unwarranted here. The threats of self-slaughter in its initial lines were ultimately successful, as we all know, and that makes it seem less boastful and more the occasion for woe, and sympathy, and dread. Which is how we know that its allegorical appropriation of Lazarus is just. I dread turning the recto and arriving at it. And yet Plath, the suicide, the one-woman mystery cult of self-sacrifice, is raised again in the popularity of *Ariel*. In the literary sense, she is raised again, ultimately victorious in the matter of eternal repose.

Perfectly articulated, with respect to Lazarus, are these lines from Evie Shockley's poem about Barack Obama's (first) inauguration:

ask lazarus about miracles:
the hard part comes afterwards. he stepped
into the reconstruction of his
life, knowing what would come, but not how.

Ben Okri's memorable, singular, highly original novel *The Famished Road* is narrated by a character named Azaro, or at least that is the name he goes by, though his parents originally named him Lazarus. Azaro is an *abiku*, a spirit child, and the long, wonderful opening of *The Famished Road* concerns the many times the spirit world refuses to allow Azaro to be completely born. Thereafter, in the years of his childhood, he continually fends off spirit manifestations around the compound where he lives, and especially in the bar of his neighbor Madame Koto, where he, Azaro, occasionally works.

Okri's novel is often compared to Latin American *Magical Realism*, but in no way does this work feel reducible to that well-traveled subgeneric distinction. On the contrary, *The Famished Road* teems with its African spirits, even as, as Ben Okri has noted, it has some western forebears as well. Azaro himself has Lazarus hovering albatross-like over his head, Lazarus's time in the underworld, and when Azaro goes *walking*, impulsively, in the bush, as he does to his parents' chagrin, unfailingly mixing it up with the menace of the spirit realm, we can feel the incarnation of Lazarus in him.

Of course, there are many other improvisations upon the story and person of Lazarus. I haven't mentioned Van Gogh, or Chagall, or the episode of *Dr. Who* that alludes to Lazarus, or some software program named after him, or the prog-rock anthem by Porcupine Tree. I haven't mentioned Aleksandar Hemon's *The Lazarus Project*, a novel that means to treat of a Jewish immigrant (Lazarus Averbuch) killed in Chicago in 1908, but which then goes farther back to speak of the Lazarus of Bethany we are discussing here. I haven't mentioned a really astonishing sculpture of him by Sir Jacob Epstein, at New College, Oxford. There are more profane examples of our inability to stop talking about him. This is not an exhaustive list.

Yet I cannot stop writing about Lazarus, adding to the list about Lazarus, which I have been keeping for over a year now, as though the intention to write about Lazarus is a symptom of the rebirth of Lazarus, and whenever I say I'm not going to write about a certain author or artist or filmmaker who has alluded to Lazarus I find myself going back and doing exactly that, and somehow adding this previously suppressed work to the list. Lazarus calls to me and I answer his call.

And, so: David Bowie's "Lazarus," from *Blackstar*, his last album, combines different strata of meaning about Lazarus, and fuses them together. The song "Lazarus" is stately and slow-moving, it is the development of change, with fragments of melody on sax and guitar emerging out of a dirge of bass and drums. The first verse is narrated by a Lazarus-like figure from heaven and indicates some of the contradictions of a heavenly repose ("Look up here, I'm in heaven / I've got scars that can't be seen").[14] But the second verse seems to frame "up here" more as a place of isolation, perhaps the latitude of fame, and of danger ("I'm so high it makes my brain whirl"), which in the significantly heartrending video for the song, is the space of the clinic, the space of illness, the place of physical destitution, like Lazarus's grave.

Then the song rises up into some sort of chorus/bridge, which only occurs once (for such a rhythmically straightforward song it is structurally rather odd and fragmentary), of the kind, in the Bowie catalog, that invites biographical speculation. It's never clear whether this song is *actually* autobiographical, or just has the veneer thereof. What does "Then I used up all my money / I was looking for your ass"[15] mean? The easiest interpretation of Bowie's "Lazarus" would be that it articulates Bowie's feelings after his onstage heart attack of 2004. He did brush up against mortality then. But the video for "Lazarus," with its hospital imagery, seems more to describe the mortality of Bowie's later battle with cancer. It transcends illness by celebrating illness, by speaking openly from within the space of the clinic.[16]

You could also argue that the song has a much deeper purpose. You could argue that its purpose is to describe Lazarus, the guy who died and who was raised from the dead, in all his complexity, in his death and non-death, with all the mixed emotions, the awe and confusion and dread and trauma, that attend upon the Lazarus story. The "Lazarus" video is rich with irony, and the "I'll be free" out-chorus of the song seems especially ironic, and meant to convey just the

---

[14]*Blackstar* (ISO Records, 2016).

[15]Ibid.

[16]And this corresponds with the most recent time line of *Blackstar*, namely that Bowie didn't know that his cancer was untreatable until after the album was recorded. In fact, apparently Bowie didn't even know his cancer was terminal until he began filming the video for "Lazarus."

opposite sentiment. Freedom and nonbeing being both identical and inimical to one another.

In Bowie's portrayal of Lazarus, he's the character who occasions irony, as if irony is a thing that is best understood by those who have experienced death, as if irony is the inevitable style of those who have been to the other side, those who have come back to tell of it, like Virgil and Dante. (I'm betting Tiresias understood irony, having been both woman and man.)

David Constantine's remarkable poetical sequence "Lazarus to Christ" and "Christ to Lazarus" goes to similar lengths in seeing into Lazarus's complex impressions of his heroic journey. I admit that I also really love the voice of Christ here, but I also feel I *know* that Christly dramatic reconstruction—full of anxiety about his own resurrection, given to complaint about being abandoned by the apostles. I can get to that impersonation of Jesus, but Lazarus's voice is more complex, because more surprising:

> Even you, who wept for me and of whom it is said
> You know all things, what I mutter in nightmare
> I believe you lie awake to overhear.

This beautiful perception gets us much closer to the fearsome mystery of nonbeing. Why is it that we need a redeemer, you ask? What is it about this trudge through the abattoir of the contemporary, with its stringy bits of gristle dangling everywhere about, that so leads the human heart to need a redeemer? It's what Lazarus said, it's what he mutters in nightmare, it's the black screen from the Zeffirelli, it's nonbeing. In the end of his section, Lazarus says (according to Constantine), further to the point: "However I wash / I cannot get the foist out of my flesh." What a luminous, immemorial line, one that causes us to go back and think about *foist* all over again, with its Dutch reverberations that have to do with palming false dice.

Jesus of Nazareth is supposed to have descended into hell, or to have *harrowed* hell, during the period between the Crucifixion and the Resurrection, weeks after Lazarus was raised, but there's almost no real scriptural support for the trip. There are sermons about it from the second century, and there are epistles that mention it or allude to it, during the period of the early church, but there is no real scriptural support. Why did he have to do it? Because all *humans* have to do it, experience death and the afterlife and irony and trauma, death and not-death, the black screen, and Jesus of Nazareth was, lest we forget, one of us.

Did Jesus know what Lazarus knew? Did Lazarus tell him about it at their dinner? And what does Lazarus tell us about death, in the end? If he could talk to us now, in our tongue, what would he say? That death is not the end, that life is not the end, that life is in the oneiric realm, full of deaths and endings that are commuted into beginnings, and beginnings that become endings, and that the feelings one has about all of this are of loss, and trauma, and regret, and humility? About what Lazarus knew, one weeps.

Or: Lazarus didn't smile, and got decapitated for this and for other crimes, scourged, for the traces of his story, for the retelling of his story, for the implications of his story, for being a bystander to Christ's ministry. In his bearing witness, again and again he is reborn for us to retell.

Two Inclinations

Maud Casey

THE INCLINATION TO BELIEVE

Is the story of Geneviève we have provided the truth? We are very inclined to believe that it is.

—*Iconographie photographique de la Salpêtrière,* Vol. 1 (90)

Figure 32, Plate 15. Photograph of Geneviève Basile Legrand by Paul Regnard, Iconographie photographique de la Salpêtrière, *Volume 1, Paris. 1877.*

YOU EMERGE RELUCTANTLY on the photographic plate. Your hair parted in the middle; long, lumpy braids punctuated by thin-ribboned bows. A third bow perches on top of your head, an afterthought. Your flat mouth. Your crumpled chin. One eyebrow interrupted as if you shaved a line through it to stop its progress. Earrings dangle from your small ears; once, someone thought it was a good idea to adorn you. In this first photograph, you don't yet know they have a name for your pain or that the stages of hysteria are called, collectively, the Passionate Attitudes. With great effort, you summon a body for the photographer.

You weren't the photogenic one. That was Augustine. Still, there is the fortuitous coincidence of your godliness and your hometown of Loudun, famous for its demonic possessions. In particular, Joan of the Angels, mother superior of the Ursuline order, to whom Saint Joseph appeared after a final rough exorcism. That you walked the same earth as Joan of the Angels is useful; you hear the promise it holds in the way the doctors discuss the *she* who is *you*. Serpentine sentences laced with optimism wind themselves into a shape, a science. With your birth in Loudun, the doctors make sense of your life; with that detail, your life becomes a story with a beginning, a middle and, somewhere up ahead, an end.

In the photograph, you look sideways out of a face a paler white than your blouse, which looks more like a billowy straitjacket but that comes later. You may not have been the pretty one but soon you will be known as the Houdini of the city of incurable women; it was said you could rip a straitjacket to pieces with your teeth.

Figure 35, Plate 22. "Terminal Period: Ecstasy."
Photograph of Geneviève Basile Legrand by Paul Regnard,
Iconographie photographique de la Salpêtrière, *Volume 1, Paris. 1877.*

You can't remember them all, the various stages of hysteria. Ecstasy, though, you know by heart. You have never not known it. The pose blurs your face, plumps your lips, ungrims the line of your mouth. Your hands clasped in prayer, you look up in the air but you are here on the ground, filling your body like a sail. The photograph makes a body out of your godly imagination. Your inclination to Ecstasy was your ticket out of the ragged stench of the room full of other women, slipping you between clean sheets in a private room with a window you can open or close. Surely, they thought, everyone would want the sort of quiet space in which one's thoughts might wander.

Where did your thoughts go?

You were an orphan, left in the deposit box for babies at the Loudun Hospital on January 2, 1843; your parents too poor to care for you; or you were a scandal; or maybe everyone was dead. Of 181 children born in Loudun that year, only half survived and one of them was you. You were the first entry of that year in the town's registry. An *enfant trouvé*, a found child, a foundling, which suggested a place you were supposed to be but weren't. You would be lost then found then lost again. Later—after the foster families and the nuns, after the stint hauling coal and wood in the home of Monsieur L.—your belly began to swell. You threw yourself around the room and hoarded belladonna pills but they brought you back from death to save the child who turned out to be imagined. Lost then found then lost again, you began to walk as if you could walk right out of that body so insistent on living.

Expert fugitive, you walked from Paris to Toulouse; when you returned, you were pregnant again but this time the baby was not imagined. You called her Desirée, the desired one. You walked from Paris to Avallon to visit her after she was adopted as a foundling though she had never been lost. How far is it, you wonder as you walk to find your daughter, the distance between lost and found? For miles, your feet step and step and step as you consider the way lost suggests you have disappeared altogether when aren't you still somewhere, the way so often you're somewhere else not here, or here, or here.

You were detained by Prussian officers and Desirée remained found in another town, unreachable. Who knows how many miles to who knows where, after which you returned, who knows why, with a very small dog. You walked from Paris to Loudun, to walk again the same earth Joan of the Angels walked over two hundred years ago. Most of what you know about Joan of the Angels the doctors told you—the handsome ghost spotted in her chambers; the writhing on the ground shouting obscenities until her sister nuns saw similar handsome ghosts, until crowds gathered to see the satanic possessions; the way she wasn't content with being possessed by Satan, and so the iron-boned, shape-shifting beast Behemoth, who arrived as a rhinoceros or maybe even a dinosaur, and Leviathan too rose from the sea. Chaos monsters filled her until only an exorcism so rough it nearly killed her could expel them. Once she threw off the demons, she accused a local priest of acting as Satan's accomplice. Before he was set on fire, the doctors tell you eagerly (it is your history, they want you to know!), his legs were crushed with Spanish boots, those divine instruments of torture. For years, the priest had seduced local widows and unhappy wives (except for the old and ugly ones). There are miles on the road back to Paris from Loudun when dusk light flickers its admiration through the trees at the way Joan of the Angels conjured the chaos monsters, then became one herself.

Because you were born in the same place as that conjurer of chaos, the doctors are able to make a shape of your life, one that can be seen from a distance; from deep inside this thing called your life, there is no shape. There is never enough stillness to make a shape; there is only spilling and more spilling, and pouring back and forth. When Joan of the Angels toured the country with her sacred shirt stained with Joseph's ointment—even its ancient smell couldn't save her from the chaos monsters—the pilgrims fell to their knees. When you touched the dirt where Joan of the Angels walked, you fell open. You spilled over and you spilled over.

You gathered a handful of that long-ago dirt trod by Joan of the Angels, tucked it in a pouch, tucked it into your skirts, walked it back to Paris, hid it under your bed, tucked it back into your skirts, walked it from Paris to Quesnoy, from Quesnoy to Bois-d'Haine, walked it all the way to the cottage of the girl stigmatic. She, like you, suffered from what the doctors called the disease of faith. They called her the Belgian mystic; you called her your sister. Her bruises matched yours from being thrown around the room by demons; like you, she was visited by the chaos monsters, who one night cracked your skull on the foot of your bed. Like you, she had always known Ecstasy by heart.

In the photograph called *Ecstasy*, you clasp your hands in prayer, palms warm with the miracle of your own blood. When you clasp your hands, you clasp the miraculous hand of Joan of the Angels, and all the hands of the pilgrims who traced the names—Jesus, Mary, Joseph—etched into her hand; you clasp the bleeding hands of the Belgian mystic, your sister. When you arrived at her cottage, they wouldn't let you inside. Why should they care you'd walked all that way? There were pilgrims who had walked farther to be in her presence. But you didn't need to go inside to do what you came to do. When it was dark, you pulled the pouch from your skirt, sprinkling that long-ago dirt trod by Joan of the Angels outside the cottage door so all of you could walk the same patch of earth.

The ghost of Louise rising up in Joan, the ghost of Louise rising up in you, risen and rising still; all your bodies, ghost filled. Bodies, you think, are like haunted houses. You walk and you walk and you walk in your body so insistent on living. You walk as if you could walk right out of it but bodies we are in them.

Figure 36, Plate 39. "Hystero-Epilepsy: Succubus." Photograph of Geneviève Basile Legrand by Paul Regnard, Iconographie photographique de la Salpêtrière, *Volume 2, Paris. 1877.*

You are a quick study. By now, you've learned in order to be a star at the Salpêtrière you must not be cured. A star performs. The illness written on your body for everyone to read; to keep your private room, you will write it and write it and write it. You will carve the names into your arm as Joan of the Angels did—*Jesus, Mary, and Joseph.* Or perhaps, simply, *Desirée.* Your daughter is gone but aren't you the desired one now? If you need to, you will bleed and bleed. There may be a cure in curiosity but there is no cure for it. The doctors write a chapter about you for their book called *Succubus.* A chaos monster in beautiful woman's clothing who fucks men while they sleep. You are an extra-special succubus, possessed by an incubus; incubated by the nocturnal lover Monsieur X. with whom you describe long nights of talking and kissing and voluptuous sensations. *Your sick imagination,* the doctors write, *has created an entire novel.*

In the photograph, you cast your eyes down. Wearing a black veil, you hold what appears to be a box of light. Your mourning disguise, one more escape. You were not the photogenic one but in your costume of grief, you are beautiful.

There you are.

Are you there?

Then you are gone.

Maud Casey

HER GODLY IMAGINATION

Death of a Queer Being

From *London Truth*, reprinted in *The New York Times*, September 18, 1883

Death has just put an end, at the village of Bois-d'Haine, in Belgium, to the sufferings of a strange being, Louise Lateau, whose singular case has puzzled many a doctor. She was called "La Stygmatisée," the Catholics declaring that every Friday blood flowed from wounds visible on her hands, her feet, and her side in remembrance of the Crucifixion. This "miracle" attracted innumerable sightseers, whose contributions were sufficient to enable the practical showman to rebuild the little village church and parsonage in a most luxurious style.

Louise Lateau

From a letter dated *August 12, 1876,* from Dr. Decaesseckey of Quesnoy-sur-Deuele to Dr. Jean Martin Charcot of Paris, as translated by Asti Hustvedt in *Medical Muses: Hysteria in Nineteenth-Century Paris* (W. W. Norton, 2011):

Dear Sir,

I am taking the liberty to write you on the subject of a patient who interests you very much: I am talking about the hystero-epileptic, Geneviève L. As she was traveling through Quesnoy, she was overcome by an attack of hystero-epilepsy that lasted from six in the evening until one in the morning and was only stopped with ovarian compression.

Before her attack, she had stopped in a cabaret, where she had, I am told, made some untoward remarks, and, because she had been drinking about a half liter of beer with people of even looser reputation than she, this was enough, in the eyes of the village inhabitants, for her to be taken for a drunk, for a woman who deserved not the least pity. This impression was in no way helped by a doctor who had little knowledge of nervous ailments.

When I saw her, she was in the throes of one of her attacks, with swelling of the abdomen, intermittent contractures, delirious reason, hallucinations, etc. I quickly ruled out pregnancy and epilepsy. It was by recalling your wise lessons that I was led to practice an ovarian compression.

Rapidly brought back to herself, Geneviève narrated her history to me, and I was happy to have spared this girl the humiliation and the more-than-malicious criticism that had buzzed in my ears. Given the cruelty of some people's ineptitude, it is satisfying for me to recount to you this incident, to prove to you the devotion and interest that you inspire, and to take this opportunity to acknowledge my debt to you.

Geneviève remained with me for one day, and despite my insistence that she return to Paris, she said that she wanted to go and say hello "to her sister Louise Lateau" as she called her, not without reason.

After you were denied entry to the famous cottage, you decided you would sleep under a nearby tree. The little cottage in Bois-d'Haine where she lived with her mother and her sisters was like all the others you'd passed between Mons and Charleroi—whitewashed, green shutters, red-tiled roof. You'd walked all the way from Paris; still, how could you sleep with the whisper of blood seeping from her holy feet, tunneling through dirt? The heat of your back drew it up to you. Lying under the tree, you watched through fall-stripped branches the clouds make the shape of her wounds—on her feet, her hands, her wrists. The most recent one on her shoulder signified Jesus's burden as he carried the cross to Mount Golgotha.

When you arrived earlier that afternoon, the curé asked for your letter from the church. Pilgrims are required to make written requests, he explained. You suspected every word out of his mouth—*pass the salt, it looks like rain, amen*—sounded like an explanation. He nodded his head in the direction of the other pilgrims tiptoe-peering through the window, lumping you in with the other letterless people. *My sister, my sister*. You didn't speak the words out loud but you thought them in the direction of the cottage. You hadn't yet figured out what else to say though you had searched for words as you walked north through cities and villages and then you were in another country. *My sister, my sister*, the rhythm of your feet. She was renowned by then. The doctors told you the stories everyone knew. You told them to yourself as you walked. She was born into the same wrong world seven years after you. In the midst of dying all around her, she was always almost dying. Twelve days after she was born, her father died, peeled away layer by layer by smallpox until there were no more layers. When she and her sisters and her mother fell ill too, the neighbors fled, afraid. Weeks later, a man who had worked with her father at the foundry discovered them; she was the half-dead baby girl wrapped in dried-out bandages. At age four, she nearly drowned in a pond. At eleven, she ministered to the sick with her sister Adelina. This was after she'd mastered the catechism, after her first communion. She and Adelina watched over the neighbors, who, after fleeing, returned to the village and fell ill not with smallpox as they'd feared but with cholera, which had not even occurred to them. She and Adelina carried their neighbors' coffins on their backs to the cemetery. At fourteen, a cow trampled her back into crookedness. Before she was eighteen, she'd had the last rites administered to her three times. When she was finished almost dying, she began to bleed. She never bled the way other girls bled; instead, a holy faucet.

My sister, my sister. Near the end of your walk from Paris, though still there were only those two words, they meant more. What other words were there? That's what you'd come here to find out. *My sister, my sister*, past the village of Manage, skirting the borders of the great Belgian coalfield, past the railway station, through orchards and gardens until the cottages became scattered and there were no regular roads. Now there you were on your back underneath a tree watching cloud wounds, straining to hear the words in the blood whisper seeping into the dirt while *your sister, your sister*, she who ate nothing but one communion wafer a day, peed two teaspoons in a week, never shat, never slept, stood barefoot on the beaten-earth floor, which was the very same earth against which you pressed your back except the house built around where she stood said this is now a floor. Her sisters Rosina and Adelina were there, her mother too. *My sister, my sister*, you sent the only words you had into the ground, willing them up through her feet where she stood bleeding in the ten-foot-square room built especially for her. She had abandoned her sewing machine hours ago.

The first Friday it happened, pain in her hands and her feet; a tingling encircled her head. The second Friday, the local priest to whom she confessed the pain and the tingling and the drops of blood said, Put it out of your mind. The third Friday, the blood flowed freely.

Tell no one, the priest said so she told her mother, who worried did it have something to do with the trampling cow? She loved her mother but often she wondered what she was thinking. She looked at her mother as any eighteen-year-old girl would. Every Friday since, she bled from her palms, her feet, her sides, her forehead. She bled and bled. She had been bleeding for years. She bled until there was no one who didn't want to hear about it, even, especially, the local priest who said tell no one. Tell everyone is what everyone did.

Only pilgrims with letters from the church are permitted, the curé repeated when you looked at him the way she'd looked at her mother when she asked about the cow. Did he think you had lost your hearing as well as the letter? You suspected a fee. There was usually money involved when women bled for God. But you didn't open your mouth, fearing it was also your alleged beer breath that had him lumping you in with the letterless pilgrims. Why waste what remained of the taste of beer on your tongue, never mind your breath, on this godless man of God? You weren't drunk, you'd protested in that tavern a town or four back. They suspected every word out of your mouth—*hello, nice weather, I love you*—sounded like protest. Whether you're drunk or not isn't the point, said the man who threw you out. What was the point? You really, really wanted to know, you said. A woman alone, he began but he didn't finish his sentence. These men explaining things to you had started to sound alike. *Pass the salt, it looks like rain, amen.* All those miles, you had dropped the point on the side of the road, somewhere in the dust, when you squatted behind a tree to pee. Maybe the point was the dust. You didn't tell him any of this. He had shut the door at the end of his unfinished sentence. Even if he hadn't shut the door, you wouldn't tell him the way you wouldn't tell him about the pouch of dirt you brought from centuries ago, dirt touched by the feet of Joan of the Angels, feet blistered from the fire that burned her from the inside out. The doctors—*Pass that salt. Look at that rain. Amen*—so determined to find a point so dry all you had to do was look at it and it went up in smoke. In search of that point, theologians and scientists put ammonia up your sister's nose, shouted in her ear, ran needles through her arm, shocked her with volts of electricity. The vicar general of the diocese wrapped her gloved hands in linen bags tied with rope to show it was not a trick. It was not a trick. *My sister, my sister.* She bled and bled.

Through the fall-stripped branches, rings of clouds made the blood-beaded coronet that appeared every Friday on her forehead.

The beads that fell and bloomed on the fabric underneath the sewing machine over which she bent her head, as she had been instructed to do by the observing theologians. *Continue work on the days of the week that aren't Friday, and on Friday too. Ward off Ecstasy with the power rendered powerless by Ecstasy, proof of the irresistible lure of Ecstasy.* You didn't need proof. *No salt no rain amen.* You too lived in a body that filled weekly with holy yearning and a desire that unbound you from the world where the theologians and scientists lived. It unfurled you tender into a place where there were no words except those you made with your body, irresistible as the place itself. You knew what it was to tumble back again from the risen other world into this one, to land stiffly, arms locked at your side, icy hands, face pale and cold with sweat, your pulse thrillingly undetectable. The death rattle in your throat never lasted the fifteen minutes the doctors who loved to count the minutes reported hers had; still, she was your sister.

And so, when he turned you away, you said nothing to the curé. You would not waste your beer breath protesting in the name of devotion or love. *Hello, nice weather. I love you.* There was a time you wanted to be as complete as the photographs the doctors took of you but from within the endless spilling that was your life, you had come to understand that aspiring to be still as a photograph was to fail and fail. And yet you were beginning to suspect that aspiring was all there was so why stop? The distance from inside your spilling to the spilling inside other people was the distance you'd walked from Paris to the cottage, multiplied by your lifetime and theirs.

You'd walked at least that many miles trying to explain to the doctors the visits you'd received from a certain Monsieur X. (the name the doctors gave him) who visited you in the middle of the night to conduct medical experiments, which caused, as he explained (*Amen, it's raining salt*), genital sensations. You required no explanation. You just said thank you. (*Hello! Nice weather! I love you!*) Sometimes you and he had violent quarrels. Sometimes you got along well. According to the doctors, Monsieur X. was imaginary. What you knew was there was more pleasure with him in the middle of the night than you'd ever had with any man. The doctors said they admired your imagination. If it was your imagination whose fingers stroked you slick until you came, then you admired your imagination too. When they continued to ask what was the point of this imagined lover, you just smiled.

No sharp edges, blood rolls around and over all the points. *My sister, my sister.* She went to church every day except Friday; on that day, the Blessed Sacrament was brought to her on a platter held aloft by the local priest who had said tell no one.

When the curé told you to leave if you couldn't produce a letter from the church, you didn't tell the curé that you wouldn't be able to distinguish true holy oils from fake ones either if they were waved in front of your face, nor would you be able to detect the fragment of consecrated host in a priest's pocket or the snuck-in sacred vessel or the sacred relic—the finger of a beloved saint wrapped in a bow, for example—tucked away in a satchel. Joy trembled your body too but why put a ribbon-wrapped sacred finger in a satchel? Why wrap a ribbon around a bone in the first place? Though it did give you good ideas for your funeral. You wouldn't bother to ask, the same way you wouldn't explain how when joy trembled you nearly to death there was no asking or explaining, no pitiful effort at words. *My sister, my sister.* No words for the no feeling at all of their needle passed through her arm. *Do you feel this?* Or the sensationless sensation of their hot wax not burning her flesh. *Do you feel it burning your flesh?* Declarations with question marks placed at the end for the sake of the audience. The doctors knew exactly what you would say (*I feel nothing*) the way the theologians knew what your sister would say when she returned from Ecstasy (*I remember nothing*). Declarations with question marks at the end of them for the sake of those pilgrims who had letters telling them this was God's work. The body upon whom God was working? That body was for no one's sake and forsaken.

At the end of your walk from Paris, when you arrived at the cottage like the other cottages but this one with your sister and her whispering blood inside, it came to you. You would stand before her. You would announce, *we are the same.* You would hand her the pouch filled with centuries-old dirt trod by Joan of the Angels' ancient feet. Joan of the Angels was the same as both of you. All of you, born into the wrong world. You longed to bring her this news but you heard in her blood's whisper the way she already knew. No explanation, no protest. No pitiful effort at words required.

As afternoon turned into evening, the curé grew exasperated with the letterless tiptoe-peerers, their faces fogging up the window of the cottage. This is a house of God, not a cabaret, he shouted. By then, you'd already done him the favor of banishing yourself to lie underneath the tree. You were exhausted by the endless division of the world into the high and the low, the this but not that, the that but not this. The house of God or the cabaret, as if God lived only in one place and never went out for a drink and some company. What kind of life was that? When Ecstasy overtook you, when it trembled you the way Monsieur X. trembled you so well, you knew God filled you the same way he filled the men who offered you the last of their beer the way he filled the man who kicked you out of the tavern the way he filled the curé insisting on a letter to grant you an audience with your sister so full of God she bled all Friday long.

The cloud wounds have seeped into the sky, absorbed into darkness like her blood into the earth. You read an article once in which she was described as an untutored peasant girl. *Imagination she has none,* it said. After the curé shooed away the pilgrims who lacked letters, after he went home, you slipped through the dark to the lip of the famous cottage you were never permitted to enter. You opened the pouch and, ashes to ashes, scattered the dirt trod by Joan of the Angels on the threshold.

How could you possibly have slept underneath those fall-stripped branches? Your sister, your sister, the whisper of her blood was not made of the pitiful effort of words. It whispered the grit and silk of pond water between her fingers, her toes. It whispered the soft fabric held in place with the tips of her fingers and the prick of the sewing machine when her attention drifted. It whispered the smell of Adelina's neck where she burrowed as she went to sleep though always she woke up on the other side of the bed, legs entangled in the legs of Rosina, who chewed her fingernails even in her sleep. It whispered her hair waving like the plants on the muddy bottom of a river. It whispered the musky warmth of the cow's slow, heaving side where she and her sisters buried their faces when it lay on the ground. It whispered the sky swallowing itself in darkness and the cloud wounds turning into stars. All through the night, it whispered love and countless other things for which there is no translation.

NOTE. Plates 15, 22, and 39 are reproduced courtesy of the Harvey Cushing/John Hay Whitney Medical Library at Yale University.

House of Virgins

Samantha Stiers

SILENT

DISPATCH NEEDS TO CLARIFY. Several virgins held hostage by their own desire? Yes, we will send someone right away. But we need to know. Please, try to stay calm, ma'am. Is this a purely physical desire, or is it a desire for spiritual union as well?

The caller says that only a man could dream of separating the body and the soul.

The emergency response team is silent on its way up the canyon of tall gray stone and still green leaves that holds the house that traps the virgins. Even the flash of sirens is silent. It is the silence of a virgin touching herself in her narrow bed in her parents' house late at night, her body rigid in efforts to suppress even the softest sigh, the creak of the bedsprings.

The men mute the sirens out of respect for the virgins. Passersby, rubberneckers, know such a long line of ambulances can mean only one thing: that more girls, for whatever reason, have been starved as surely as anyone deprived of food. And starvation is always a most private thing.

VENUS OPPOSING SATURN

In the house there is one virgin who is fat and dirty, not like the others. She does not want to be beautiful. She wants to survive. While the other virgins lie on the swept-dirt floor and moan about being virgins, she pleasures herself with grunts and cries, sounding more grief-stricken than pleasured.

Another virgin, tall and thin and severe, who will later become a stockbroker, lies in her white gown and contemplates the actions she could take against the fat virgin—petitions, signs, rallies. The stockbroker virgin is not cut out to be a virgin. It is her parents' dream for her. Her virginity is a life stage she has to get over with before moving to bigger and better things.

HOME REMEDIES

Tinctures, bought once a week at the little store in town. Catnip, skullcap. These are general nervines, calming potions.

The long-term virgins inject lidocaine up themselves to numb their desire. There is a black market for desire treatments, most addictive—perpetuating their own use, they relieve nothing. The lidocaine is more useful, injections that sting, but the desire never fully goes away. It is because the girls cannot find the source—they would have to inject their brains, souls, hearts.

SUGAR-CUBE DESIRE

Most of the virgins do not admit any desire. Their desire is a sugar cube removed from their bodies and hidden in an unused portion of their brains, sectioned off with police tape.

The stockbroker thinks that is nonsense. She is matter-of-fact about it. She has desire, yes, but it is *well managed*. Who or what does the managing, or how well they do it, she cannot articulate, but that is what she repeats to herself all night—*well managed, well managed*. The noise of the fat virgin, though, reminds her of a time when she was not so well managed, that ill management, as a concept, might exist.

MEMORY

The collective soul of women remembers with horror the sexual famines that swept the land in their mothers' time, how even the bees died, and how in newly made deserts their mothers sat in relief tents and submitted to desperate experimental treatments: blood transfusions from those who had just made love.

But it was no use. Joy and comfort were not carried in the blood. The virgins who died were autopsied. Their brains were enlarged, their hearts shrunken, their dopamine and oxytocin depleted. Supplements were given to the survivors: they made no difference.

TRUE STARVATION

The EMTs want to respect the privacy of the virgins, although it may be privacy is what they had too much of—still, they must be allowed their secrets, particularly their secret hungers, they must not be taken from the darkness straight into the light, or the pain of exposure will be too much, and they will die in their own way, not as blatantly, not as physically, as those suffering "true starvation," the only kind of starvation allowed on men's news—oh, if women ran the news, how many kinds of famines, of epidemics, would make the headlines—not only the deprivation of the stomach, but also the plagues of forced virginity that descend on many lands, and the many illnesses that result from them and are attributed by male doctors to female irrationality.

UTERINE FIRE

The men are businesslike in the back of ambulances, assembling IV drips, tubing, masks, and siphons. They see thwarted desire as a mechanical problem only. They have been trained to see it as mechanical, because they are professionals. A professional man does not feel desire for the slender virgin in tattered white cotton whom he lifts from her own uterine fire. There can be a certain detached tenderness, but once the virgin has been taken to the treatment center, intubated, her hormone levels balanced, the professional man must look away. The place between her legs is so small and smooth, and he tries to pretend that the many nights she has held her desire tight within herself have not given her a certain scent, and he pretends he does not smell it as he lifts her gown. This is being a professional. Her wound may tremble as he dilates it to prepare her for whoever will break the seal, but it is not like the trembling of his lover. The virgin's trembling, the EMT knows, is from fever, serious illness. He must not be aroused by her suffering, although it looks like joy. Virgin bodies do not operate like ours. They need different nutrients, they are prone to different diseases. Their pain and their pleasure look the same.

One man is scared. He has never liberated a virgin from her own desire before.

TOURMALINE CRYSTALS

The virgins await one of two things, their rescue or their rape. There are men who trawl the mountains looking for caches of virgins to rape. Then the women would not be virgins, although there was a group of women who claimed otherwise. Their virginity had shattered during their rapes, been ground to dust and borne away on the night breeze. Now they found their virginity in the minerals of the sea, in tourmaline crystals, in the moon's cool light. They gathered up its shining dust and put it in their beds to prevent nightmares.

That's not real virginity, though, sniffed the unraped virgins. And that was the great schism of 1912, between virgins who believed virginity to be a purely physical phenomenon, determined by men, and virgins who believed virginity was a state of mind, a state of spirit.

MADNESS

Whatever the condition of the fat virgin's hymen, surely she is satiated, the virgins think.

What no one knows, not even the fat girl, is that her hunger only grows each time she touches herself, because her body recognizes echoes of love empty of substance. This drives her wild—recognizing the reminder of what she wants, but seeing the actual thing nowhere to be found. The substance in her blood that desires love rises with each futile, desperate touch, driving her near madness, the thirst of a sailor drinking seawater.

And so she starts ordering in.

ASPIRATIONS

The other virgins had imagined their virginity from childhood. Before they knew what a virgin was, they poked and prodded at themselves, hoping to make themselves into virgins. They knew a virgin was a special and pitied member of society. They and their sisters dressed up in nightgowns, playing the virgin game, waving their dolls and yelling out the window, "We're virgins, we're virgins, save us!" until their embarrassed mothers made them shush and get dressed, it was almost noon.

In adolescence they dreamed of being on the news, in the papers, on made-for-TV movies and after-school specials that warned girls to lose their virginity, yes, not too soon, but also not too late. They wanted to be interviewed from hospital beds with tubes running up their noses, white, white, the hospital beds, their faces, their gowns, everything white.

CLINICAL SIGNS

What are Virginity Treatment Centers like?

Virginity, like starvation, leaches nutrients from the body. What are the body's and mind's reactions to such deprivations? The clinical signs?

These days there are telethons for virginity relief efforts.

DESSERT

The first time the virgins hear a knock on the rickety gray wooden door at night, they tense. It is either the rescuers or the rapists.

But it is only a restaurant delivery boy. The virgins are confused, because no restaurant delivers this far up in the mountains. The house of virgins has no telephone, no Internet. But here is the fat virgin lumbering up to answer the door—naked, her long teats swaying.

The minute she accepts her order, the other virgins wish they had ordered some too. Not because they want her food—a glass platter bearing a three-tiered cake with pink icing and a maraschino cherry on top—but because the delivery boy sees her nakedness and her hunger, and treats her so kindly, treats her as though she were human, instead of the ball of need that she so obviously is, that all of them are.

The cake itself scares them. It looks like their insides laid bare. It looks like the parts of them where their virginity and their hunger dwell. And yet they can see a sort of innocence that the cake has, the way it displays its cherry so openly. The cake only wants union, it only wants to give pleasure, and in that way, it is much like all of them.

"This is exposure therapy," the fat virgin tells the delivery boy when he comes by again, and she answers the door again, naked. "I'm exposing them all to the idea of food."

PREGNANT WITH THEMSELVES

It is fullness the virgins crave. Nightgowns ripped off, the hard bite on the nipple, things rammed up them until their insides are annihilated into smoothness, the hot squirt of vital liquid in the vestibule of their innermost chamber, the deep itch finally scratched, and then, the hard, tight drum of their stomachs as a baby begins to grow, and in a reverse of the process, the birth, the destruction of the pelvic wall.

"Screw that," says the fat virgin. "It's called eating. Makes you full."

"You've just given up," says a virgin. "You've given up on our rescue."

"Are you a Disney princess?" says the fat virgin. "What I do, girls, is called self-rescue."

"I think it's called self-abuse," someone says primly. "In both senses of the term."

But after this, the virgins realize they are running low on the fantasies they deny having. Each one is sick of her same old fantasies. So they write down their fantasies on scraps of paper, mix them up in a glass jar, and each virgin draws a new fantasy and shares it aloud.

The virgins discover they dream of heated dildos, nipple clamps, being fed with a baby bottle through their cunts. (That last one is weird, all the virgins agree, except for the fat virgin, who thinks it is the only halfway original one.)

FORECAST

There is only one bed in the house of virgins, and the fat virgin commandeers it for herself.

She was raised by a mother who kept her in bed at the slightest sign of illness, and now she believes that beds, carved mahogany four-poster beds, beds with white muslin sheets and canopies of mosquito netting, are powerful tinctures, not only for the body but for the soul. And she knows that something in her is very, very ill, and so she gets into bed and stays there.

Soon the other virgins have to be in bed too.

They build beds for themselves out of whatever they see, sun-bleached rocks and twigs they gather from the woods. It is difficult to lift the heavy stones with their starved, parched white arms, and they often enlist the fat virgin to do it for them.

Under the stones a flat space has been made in the damp, rust-colored pine needles, crawling with ants and grubs.

It is true, the virgins are ill. Ill with a disease they nickname *the purity nettles*, a disease that makes them feel their insides pricking with messes of dry nettles. Because homeopathy is the rule of the mountains, the virgins gather nettles in their white skirts and soak them in well water along with flat stones to make an autumn tonic.

The tonic strengthens but does not soothe, and the fat virgin suggests something different—peppermint tea, and the last of the ripe, juicy strawberries out back. The virgins are afraid to eat the strawberries, afraid something so wet and red might compromise their virginity. If like cures like, the fat virgin reminds them, surely like will preserve like.

The virgins fall for this and eat.

The virgins need to know when. When their lovers will come.

The fat virgin will not help them divine this. So they gather in a clearing in the woods and hold hands around the flattest, most sun-drenched stone they can find to call a sundial. But they do not understand how to read it, how to mark time upon it, and at high noon all they see is the eternity of stone awash in sun.

So that is their answer, they think. Their virginity is eternal and hot and scalding as the noon sun. They go back home and weep.

SURVIVORS

The famine survivors who became our mothers rejoiced that we would not be deprived. Imagine their horror when a generation of us, carrying memories picked up in the womb, played "virgin" with our dolls, tore our white nightgowns to look like the victims. Our mothers hit us and only bought us colored clothing.

What are the long-term effects of virginity, ask scientists, psychologists, gynecologists, suicidologists. We have discussed the starved ones who forget to eat. They live as invalids. The tragedy of virginity, all agree, is that it can last a lifetime, but does not kill its victim.

Old women confess to senile husbands that they were once virgins.

STRUM OF JOY

The fat virgin, unlike the other virgins, does not much care for nature. As a child she had been carried away by its beauties, but ever since her body had changed, a numb white haze covered all her feelings, including the strum of joy that used to shiver across her lower belly when she heard aspen leaves rustle. When she and the virgins go gathering nettles, she always finds herself far behind, sweating, needing to rest.

Sometimes a virgin will be polite and show her a broken bit of glass they found at the old hippie camp, or the first strawberry to turn red, insisting she taste it. But the fat virgin knows these are false, pitying kindnesses, brought on by the warmth of sun on the virgins' thin arms, warmth that soothes their desire, desire that often makes them so cruel, snappish like creatures in pain.

A WEDDING UNDER AN ASPEN GROVE

The virgins are not without comfort. There is the earth itself. They run outside in summer, in clean muslin nightgowns, barefoot, and sit under the aspens.

The virgins love the trembling aspens. To sit in a grove of them, peel off their bark, breathe the scent of their shivering leaves. *Our men,* they call them. The virgins are tall and thin and white too, with heads that tremble. They will make a good couple, the girls and the aspen grove.

INSIDE

The virgins' eggs are freshwater pearls. They harden into gnarly, glossy iridescent knobs, and the pearls are not sad, not sad at all, that no seawater moistens them.

SCAR TISSUE

And there are those who claim no desire, who remove it with coat hangers and quinine, who give their money to a man who claims he can make them never yearn again, but later, deep in pelvic scar tissue, find it again, buried and therefore unable to ask and therefore unable to be sated; the starving person who does not feel hunger is in the worst shape of all. The therapy then is to cut back the scar tissue, uncover and nourish the desire. This is terrifying to the victim because she knows she may feel it in full again, and, as before, be unable to satiate herself.

FOR THE SAKE OF SCIENCE

In order to learn, scientists perform autopsies on virgins. They find the muscle of the women's hearts stiff and gray, having never been made to beat hard at the promise of love.

COURAGE

The virgins bear up bravely, in the way that women do. They do not lie abed after waking: to do so would be to invite disaster. Instead they march down to the spring. They wash in the cold water under the pearlescent sky. They try not to look at each other's naked bodies, as suppressed desire has a way of diverting itself onto new objects.

The cold water helps a great deal. They make sure their muslin dresses are stiff and clean and starched, having hung over the clothesline, scratchy and smelling of mountain air. They take very little for breakfast, some roots, and sarsaparilla. They brush their teeth with goldenseal. They make all the beds in the house tight, changing the linens daily. They send the virgin who seems to be struggling most down to the stream to wring the washing by hand.

After all this, they are satisfied their bodies have been taken care of, in all ways except the one that is needed most.

The long, hot mountain summer days are dangerous. They are languid. Hummingbirds zip past, linger over a flower. It is unsafe for the virgins to have nothing to do.

Really, their whole house is perfect except for the fat virgin, who sometimes interrupts their mooning by stomping past for something to eat. She is desire itself, and not a beautiful feminine desire, but a raw, messy hunger. She reminds them of their own festering needs. They pretend she is not there.

This whole virgin ideal would be so elegant and tragic if not for her.

NEWS

The headline in the typo-prone *Mountain Times* read: "'It Was Wounderful,' Says Human Touched by Another."

The article told about how a human had been irritable and depressed, and resigned to living this way, thinking he was happy. And then another human had offered regularly to touch him in places that it had not occurred to him needed to be touched, and when she did so, he became much happier. And he did the same for her.

The virgins thought it was a fascinating article and tacked it up on their wooden wall. But they didn't understand why they liked it so much.

WITCH BURNING

Afternoons, the virgins sit on the porch and whittle. The things they whittle come out firm, smooth, long, comfortable looking. They fit the hand so nicely. *Help sticks*, the virgins name them. They carry their help sticks everywhere. To dinner, where they sit beside their tin plates, dressed in quilt scraps. Even to bed the help sticks go, the way girls in olden times carried hot irons to bed with them at night.

There is peace in the house of virgins.

Here Stockbroker Virgin draws the line. Voodoo, she calls the help sticks. Are you virgins or witches, she demands. "Virgins!" sob the ever-hormonal young girls. "Oh virgins! Always and forever virgins!"

"Then bring your little dolls and follow me!" cries SV.

Numbly, hysterically, the girls walk out to the dirt out back where Stockbroker Virgin has built a bonfire. They tremble, recoil, clutch their help sticks tighter as they see what Stockbroker Virgin wants them to do. And then the first virgin steps forward and casts her help stick into the fire. They all do it, and their tears blur with the blurred heat of the fire, their bare feet kick up plumes of black dirt.

Samantha Stiers

GLOWING IGLOO

It was pain. None other than pain, hard pain, against the bone.

The fat virgin was not as young as the others. One night, above the tin sink and scratched mirror, she found streaks of white in her black hair, and knew that hard want had aged her body prematurely. Where had her youth gone? She had spent it here, eating, building circles of fat around her core, a body igloo, impenetrable. In the center of the igloo may glow firelight, but who can penetrate the bricks of white ice?

The other virgins were glowing igloos too, although their bodies were thin.

That night she joined the girls for their meal of sorghum and bone broth. They eyed her wearily. Without bags of white flour and brown sugar, the fat virgin's desire grated, bone on bone when the ligaments are worn away.

LIBERATION

If want cannot be satisfied, one solution is not to want. If one cannot stop wanting, a solution is to remove desire at the root.

Virgins sharpen shards of tin down by the stream. They sleep with them under their pillows, running their fingers along the jagged edges, pain that distracts from the impacted desire and helps them sleep. They think about the day when, with blood and pain, they will be free. When the ones who are not strong enough to free themselves will be held down by the others, legs spread.

They will clean each other's wounds with cold spring water, hold rags to stop each other's bleeding, stitch each other with spiderwebs, and finally the virgins will look upon each other with tenderness, and, in injury, each will be touched.

STERILIZED IN FLAME

Because it is more acceptable for women to hurt than to desire.

Some of the shards are sharp enough now, ready to be rinsed in the stream and sterilized in flame.

The fat virgin, in secret, calls the authorities.

AT THE RESCUE

The EMTs are tender with the virgins.

"Does—does it—hurt?" an EMT asks.

"Does it hurt?" repeats a virgin, confused.

"Does it hurt to be a virgin?"

CRONE

He means, they suppose, is it lonely.

It is taboo to ask a virgin about loneliness. It is offensive, invasive, and in poor taste. Like asking a circumcised woman the exact perimeters, the exact secret physical effects, of her wound. We are supposed only to empathize, to hide our morbid curiosity. But of course, how can we truly empathize with virgins, we cannot begin to imagine, we who have not had our tender inner places scorched by purity's white fire. When we see virgins walk down the street, we can't help but speculate about their loneliness, for this itself is the horror and the thrill of virginity. When a woman has made love, she forever carries a part of her lover inside her; no matter what happens later she is not alone in her body.

Virginity is a "purification chamber" where women's inner parts are held over solitude's white flame, and their hearts too, and the resulting nerve damage is called "loneliness." When a virgin has been tortured by the flame (which is her own desire) long enough, her flesh withers, until she is only smooth bone, and does not feel "loneliness" anymore. The other virgins envy and fear these crones. The younger virgins have taken on whiteness as a sort of spiritual fashion statement, but the crones have become white. The girl-virgins, despite their pale skin and white gowns, retain some juicy redness in their hearts and other parts. The crones do not.

How do the virgins survive it? Some of them take the pulpy redness of themselves, tenderized by salt, dip brushes into it, and make art. Some of them do not survive.

If touched, can a crone regrow her flesh? Can bone feel again?

PROTOCOL

The EMT who was nervous becomes even more so as he kneels beside the first virgin. Provisions are limited. The team did not anticipate this severity. What would he want, he asks himself, were he a virgin in this condition?

He would want the rescuer to say he was trying his best to get her what she needed. That he was going to stay with her until more help came. That he was so sorry he could not give her that help. He would want his rescuer to cry with him.

He does all these things. But they do not work. So, near evening, out of sheer desperation, he designs his own experimental treatment for Stage III virginity: he holds her. He does not get the idea from any treatment manual. It comes to him when he is too scared and exhausted to think of anything else. And somehow, although he has none of the requisite siphons, tubes, and supplements, the holding seems to stabilize her.

All that night, he moves from virgin to virgin, holding each for three minutes, then starting at the beginning. Contact rations. During a break, in a moment of grandiosity, he imagines naming his new treatment after himself—designing studies, writing up his holding protocol in journals.

THE WEDDING

Virgins are not the only ones with dreams. EMTs have dreams too, especially the anxious ones.

They dream of virgins, of taking one virgin, and making her a bed. Of building it with their own hands, smoothing the cherrywood posts in the lathe until they are curved and smooth, of hammering it together, the warm, fresh scent of hurt wood, and even washing the muslin sheets in cold water, for their virgins, their very own. They will have their own houses, shining cherrywood, white goats out back, carved hope chest in the corner, cool stream.

The virgins will lie in the beds first, and it will not even occur to them to invite the EMTs in. But night comes, and there is nowhere else for them to sleep.

SPRING AGAIN

"Get up," the stockbroker tells the fat virgin. "It's the rescue."

"I don't care," Fat Virgin sobs.

"Fat Virgin," says one girl. "Don't you want—don't you want—"

"No."

"You don't want it at all?"

"No."

It is spring in the mountains now, because during virginity plagues the seasons follow the minds, bodies, of young girls, change quickly, and are what certain men call abnormal.

Green leafy breezes blow in through the open windows.

UNION

The stockbroker virgin also refuses to go outside. She does not need to be carried on a gurney. She will not lose her dignity to EMTs barely old enough to shave. What do those men know of her desires?

The fat virgin weeps in the big bed. The house empties as the virgins are carried out on gurneys one by one.

Never again will the fat virgin know the scent of muslin and sarsaparilla.

A breeze shudders through the house, the breeze of still chilly spring. It is sunset. Time for the fat virgin to become who she has been all along, the goddess of the sunset, the goddess of the blood light that illuminates worlds through dark transformation.

Stockbroker Virgin barely notices. She is preoccupied with her own trouble. *I've forgotten my name,* she whispers, and she paces, her long, narrow feet bare for once, over the smooth gray floorboards. She paces in circles. *I've forgotten my name.*

In the early hours of the morning they lie beside each other, the women who have shed their false names and now have nothing, their phalanx of virgins no longer shielding them from each other, their hatred and hunger burning out until only love remains.

Ruth

Forrest Gander

Her husband lifeless
in chair facing
TV, whole days
mute, her own mind,
her hearing,
shot. *And it won't*
get any better. Absolutely
nothing to look
forward to, she says
to whom if
not you?

Wearing two identical
left shoes. *No one*
believes I don't
dye my hair, she remarks
for the umpteenth
time. Point taken, I'm
grayer than my
mother though
in the mirror I see
her face, her small
dark eyes.

Five states north, he
wonders what
causes the
swishing
he hears behind
his mother's
voice: she must
be down on the
floor, the phone
in one hand
and with
the other
must be
scratching the
tumorous dog
whose paw
convulsively
rakes the carpet.

green case on the nightstand
glasses on a Redskins lanyard

green glasses case
containing one hearing aid

minus its battery on the nightstand
glasses on a Redskins lanyard

in the green grass
under one of many bird feeders

in the backyard thronging
with blurred mute birds

Occasional muculent chortling
or choking and steady
beep of the EKG.

The beak-hard
determination to
be a good person,
what happened
to that? How
is it true
I have to
go now? For her, the
occasion of my
presence begs
more. Who is my
mother now I am
unspoken for?

So take her hand, walking in
the garden: an animal moment of warmth
she won't recall after our sit. Voracious
starlings ride a swinging cage of suet.
That signal enthusiasm in her eyes
muddles with torment. Choose whatever
you will and the disease
still wins. Like a heavy shawl,
the shadow of cloud drags across
mountains on the horizon. Maybe I've
misread her expression.

To plunge into love as into a sidewalk.
Came awake as though I were a siren going off.
The ugliness of putting food in my
mouth, my belly gurgling
like so many horseleeches. And so
days-to-come will crack open without you,
dropping their yolk over places you walked.
And the white lowly primrose will foam
wild like some scrap of your happiness
refusing to abandon me. Blah blah. The
mirror in the shrine is memory. All
you lived adjusts now and is lived back
in me here on earth. A flock of geese
sifts through the barrow pit. Postpuke
acid sears my throat.

To find the present breaking itself
loose from the sequence of events, bolting
through gaps in the corral of context and
carrying its befuddled rider
into an expanding plain of brumous outlines.

* * *

How she fights the sleeping pill, to stay up with me as I drive back from the beach, to keep talking, to speak and be spoken to: the assurance of voices, even her own now druggy iterative slur, which is like low birdsong, a blind inquiry in twilight—*is someone there?*—and a claim she is alive, here in the seat beside me, her seat belt around her, overcoming the pill, the devious obstacle course, the drowsiness I administered in order to drive her four hours home this evening, to concentrate on driving, to save my pollen-swollen and mucus-inflamed throat from the overtime shift of talk, to stay the repetitive questions, her struggle among scraps and familiar names torn from faces and feelings, the cipher-names of her husband and her grandchildren, a language of blanks, I drive with my left hand on the wheel, the other massaging the loose skin of *her* hands, feeling for the tightened cords in her palms, bands of fascia that curl her fingers forward, and when I think she's finally fallen asleep, her face uptilted and drawn, as we cross Indian River Inlet where she would, with my father, fish for flounder from the Grady-White whose single outboard, pumped and primed, had been startled into coughs of blue smoke in the canal back in Bethany dawn hours earlier and piloted, always by my father, through the gauntlet of buoys—*red right return*—that drew it through Assawoman Bay, past Harpoon Hannah's, and into the yawning Atlantic, when I start to pull my hand away, she tightens her grip, not opening her eyes, maybe in reflex, holding on to her will to be awake with me, her son, whom she knows, whom she thanks now in her almost sleep, her narcotic fatigue, in the spreading murk of the pill I coaxed her to swallow so that the trip might be easier for me while she rides beside me, holding on.

* * *

Sitting on the edge of the bed with her shirt and pants off, she reaches behind to unclasp her bra. I help her stand and draw her underwear down and she lists to one side in pain, though she doesn't complain.

This is how she wants to go to the bathroom, naked, before we put her pajamas on. Never either shy or proud of her body. Even in my childhood, I understood she regarded the body as implement. Whatever the psychological traumas my sisters and I metabolized, we grew up at ease in our bodies, unembarrassed by nakedness.

Before me, my mother looks plumper than she does in clothes, but staggering toward the bathroom, reaching for the doorknob, she is a splotched drama of mortality, her buttocks collapsed into folds, the scar from her vertebroplasty lost in a constellation of liver spots, her waist overcome by sagging flesh.

A memory: in La Paz, I saw the Aymara wave backward over their shoulders to speak of the future. And to reference the past, make sweeping forward motions with their hands. The Aymara word for eye, front, and sight denotes *past,* while the word for *future* means back or behind. In my mother's body too, her front is the past and her back is our future.

She sits and I bunch pajama bottoms over her feet, one at a time, and pull them up as she bends forward to stand in elaborate slow motion. Another world's wounded crane.

* * *

To listen to each repetition with renewed attentiveness as if it were the first occasion, to forget you've heard it before and to receive her words as her first words or her last ones, for she repeats things not only because she's forgotten but also so they will be remembered. To come into a rhythm of farewell with her, marking it, relishing its periodicity, in order to crack open another kind of love inside the old, familiar love, a vast of acceptance, without condition, akin to what a mother might feel for her child.

Want to but can't. I can't die, she says, and her eyebrows
furrow, expatiating the point. A chiming
of patient monitors like electronic crickets
in perpetual night. Or a subaltern intelligence. Code
red is clear. Did Karin put lipstick on you this morning?
A quarter turn of the petcock on the O_2 tank. We brought
dinner from the Quotidian Pain. Outside
the hospital window, stars glowing in the ultraviolet
light of the Prawn Nebula. *It's you who are.* What?
A hummingbird, she says. My lord, in heart, and let
the health go round. Though I am so far already
in your gifts.

Playing the Whip

Kristin Posehn

I WOKE UP ON THE PORCH SOFA. It was the hottest day of the year. The air stood still, the light was precise and tinted blue. I'd lived in Seattle for years, but couldn't pick out a house on our street from a lineup. Everything was overgrown with crowns of colored leaves, Japanese maples thicker than a man, ferns and white-tipped flowers pouring down onto cracked ribbons of sidewalk. Mattresses sagged against pine trees and fence posts. Half-clothed boys lounged on the curb, skimming their phones, dimpled in shade. For the rest of the day I planned to do X, where X equaled cleansing and rejuvenating activities, plus slip out to purchase a bikini, then begin a new phase of life by exposing my plenitude to radiation on the banks of Green Lake. Excited by my plans, I sat on the steps until my shoulders were sunburned and went to a party.

In a living room several blocks away, a burgundy armchair and flocked sofa met at right angles. Street light shaded the blinds a mellow orange. I slunk into this situation wearing shorts and raffia sandals, an ensemble motivated by the weather but mortifying to me. I stood next to sweating men with beards, smokers, and pretty dykes. We looked at each other's hairstyles and types of legs.

I felt unshapely and warm. My left hip ached. I settled on a coffee table and slipped my fingers into the crevice behind my knees, where sweat trickled as if from a spring. Someone danced with a cutout picture of a hamster nibbling cake. People played the paper-bag game. If I heard a rumor I passed it on.

"I've stopped exercising," I told someone whose name I couldn't remember. "I'm on a high-fat diet. I'm drinking beer through a straw. Have you seen that painter who does landscapes on curtains and folds them like origami? What if we all carried squirt guns in our wallets? I'm going for more drinks," I said. A girl stabbed me in the butt with her purse covered in spikes.

Just then I saw my friend Mort by the drinks. Mort sold leather jackets for his livelihood. He had a prosthetic arm and feathery hair I admired. All winter he wore two leather jackets at a time, in contrasting colors and textures, adding substance to his long and angular frame. Once he told me his genome had been sequenced, and that it said pirate heritage. Typically we drank beer in rooms that looked like an uncle's basement, while I watched him sell the jackets off his back.

"What's that noise coming from the kitchen?" I asked him.

"An electric meat slicer, by the sound of it," said Mort, as he dropped carrots into the dip. "Eating is a repulsive activity and incompatible with the early stages of attraction. Is that sour cream?" He was into ugly food, which he said was a thing.

"I'd like to educate myself with liquor" is how I replied. "What I mean is that, when I can't finish my third scotch and soda I'll put it in the freezer with a stick, so I have a scotchsicle for tomorrow, but when it unthaws it tastes pretty much the same, due to my undeveloped palate, and that's something I'd like to change."

At that moment Jessifer swept by, sat me down on the couch, and told me she had a brain lump. She had shoulder-length dark-blonde hair and was doing her dissertation on blocked messages. We were sort of friends. She took my hand in hers and led me through her hair, coarse and oiled at the roots, until my finger rested on a hard protuberance at the back of her head. She talked about her fears, the malignancy, and so on.

"I havc a skin-on-skin rash between my thighs" is what I said, retrieving my hand. "Most likely due to the weather. But in no way is that a brain tumor. That's your skull thickening. A known thing. It happens with age, or maybe overuse of the lobes. A person can have a wavy skull, no problem." I was too drunk to manage anxiety with my normal aplomb.

At home, I studied the fingerprints on our fridge and ate my housemate's peanut butter from the jar with a knife. The building gurgled in a digestive manner. To the extent that a house can be unpleasant, ours was.

I lay in bed and listened to the freeway. Mort had installed a single bulb on a red extension cord as a kind of chandelier. A nail left by a previous tenant livened up the stucco wall. I watched the glass of water on my nightstand as it rippled in tune with the vibration of traffic.

I was having such a plump day. My left hand plucked at the elastic of my shorts. I chastised myself for doing nothing I'd planned; for the wanton sunburning of my shoulders, which began to itch; for consuming beer and peanut butter as if they were meals, in addition to meals; for my inability to dress or do anything useful. My hand went about poking myself for some time, trying to gauge the extent to which I'd swelled. I forgot if I'd changed the topic of my thesis, or what I'd changed it to. I wondered why I was still in school.

Deep in my mind, like a groundhog snuffling toward the sweetness of light, it dawned on me that when I poked myself in certain regions I didn't feel myself. I pressed my fingers into the flesh of my hip where it ached: I felt the skin, but my hip made no reply. There weren't any nerves. My lumpy swelling lacked sensation. In fact it was rather round and symmetrical. The ache came from deep inside, as if something pressed on the bone. For a few moments I pinched and kneaded in a stupor. Then the pieces fit together, and I realized I didn't have a womanly curve. I had a tumor.

"Mort, I'm leaving you this voice mail because I can't bear to speak with anyone yet, also you're probably not awake. I'd like you to know that I found a tumor. It's big, in my left leg, and I'm on my way to see a doctor. I don't know what to think. I'm existing in a strange multiplicity at the moment. A bumper has compromised the intimacy of my left flank. I thought I was extra fat right there, but it's weirdly symmetrical and I can't feel it internally. Picture a small orange sliced in half, a chunky diameter smooshed into the hollow of my hip, a small tertiary boob. It's probably made of peanut butter. Don't ask me any questions. I can't believe this is happening to me." I hung up the phone and got on a bus.

The medical complex was in an unfamiliar part of town. I had health insurance through the university, but always assumed that was for when you broke a toe. I wandered through courtyards bordered by grassy mounds, feeling newly motivated to please my adviser.

A television set to a cooking show dominated the waiting room. One man sprawled across two chairs, picking at his nails. A young woman hunkered down in the corner behind a moat of shopping bags. Over by the pamphlet racks, a well-dressed father read to his children. I approached the check-in desk with my paperwork, earnest and prepared to explain myself. A heavyset man in scrubs picked up a clipboard and asked the receptionist across from me, "Who's taken care of Yao?" She gestured with a blank look toward a colleague, who rolled his eyes.

I showed the doctor my hip and told him it ached.

"You do know what it is, don't you?" he said.

I sweated.

"It's a fatty tumor. We call it a lipoma. Completely benign." He waved a tape measure in the vicinity of my hip. "You have some extra there," he said, chuckling. "It's one inch. I'm referring you to plastic surgery and they'll excise your little lump."

Thirty seconds later, I was alone in the examination room, ripping off a threadbare gown that opened at the back. One of my socks had a green toe, and the other dancing Santas. They both had holes. He got the size of the lump wrong, I thought. Then I heaved myself away, feeling stupid and ashamed.

For several days I couldn't recall the word turquoise. My hip became a constant throb.

The air changed. I set alarms for myself, kicked around the duvet. My guts were in knots, my nose stuffy, my hair perpetually dirty. I wore too much gray and felt like a combustion chamber for the lower gases. I lost hours working at my desk, wearing a short dress and black tights with a ladder on my camel toe. It was time for a total and comprehensive reevaluation of my life.

I met Mort on the stools at Shorty's, his favorite bar. The place had a whiff of nostalgia and dread. Some chick in a low-cut, ice-blue tank nursed a bourbon while reading *Criminal Procedures*. A wan curtain hung over the door. Extracurricular activities of the street drifted by. I wanted to be inarticulate and sexually simple, if only for a night. Instead I dragged the embarrassment of my self-consciousness into these rooms, the acute awareness of my thighs, my malaise, the flap of skin on my left thumb I'd nearly cleaved off.

I told Mort about my near-death experience. "I have a lipoma," I said. "An encapsulated ball of fat inside my fat. It's a benign thing that doesn't spread. Maybe it's been there six months, or ten years, slowly expanding in accord with a mutant cellular logic. All that time, I never imagined I harbored a growth. Even while I had one under my nose. Why didn't my body bring this up sooner?"

"That's terrifying," Mort said, in a congenial tone.

"The doctor was insulting," I continued. "First, he didn't take a moment to compare my left and right hips. Second, he said the mass is only one inch, and he had the audacity to ascribe the rest to my plumpness, which he seemed to think is funny. I'd like to strangle him. Plus I think he's wrong. I guess it doesn't matter, because he referred me to plastic surgery, and they're going to remove it. I heard they make a small incision and vacuum out the tumor. While they're in there, maybe they can get more stuff too."

The bar was chilly with street air. Mort loaned me his outer jacket, a slouchy chestnut bomber. He'd used wood glue to seal the pockets shut. He was forgetful and had a tendency to anchor his prosthetic arm, which ended in a metal claw, anyplace convenient. Every so often I asked him why he didn't upgrade arms. He said he liked this one.

"Given the stress, how's your eating and sleeping?" he inquired, opening and closing his pincer around a stray nut.

"I'm on a health kick. I had a can of beans for dinner. Also a pound of figs and some pickles, thanks for asking. I want to sleep when I have to wake up. For work, I pretend I've been body-snatched, like I'm infected with a foreign virus that causes an inescapable compulsion to sit in the library." I nodded at the bartender for another round.

"How's the junk shop?" I asked. Mort spent his daylight hours in a rundown shop front on the fringe of town. He limited the merchandise to leather jackets and objects his wife didn't like.

"Mostly idle, as you know. Today a guy came in looking for an ice bucket, which I didn't have, so we talked. He described himself as a former engineer who'd shaved his head and quit his job to become a musician. I thought of you, because you remind me of an artist I once knew. Although I'm not saying you should shave your head, your hair is nice the way it is. I showed him the stash of homemade pornography I found when I moved into the place, and that saint's knuckle I got through a friend of a friend. He purchased a leather hoodie and a tan suede trench."

Days and nights went on like this. I sent my brother Howard a picture of the potted thyme growing in our kitchen. A tendril had broken away from the pack, probing toward the sun like the sound of flutes. Then I locked myself out of the house.

Maybe I could pick apart my life, I reasoned, into sensible categories. Everything I did descended into clutter. Despite my best intentions, I kept generating the squalor in which I nestled. I was a mess I hopelessly made.

If I could observe and articulate my mind, it would have a shape. I thought about sweaters and how they fit; the accumulation of doubled-over napkins in my bag; the different ways people responded to my greetings; the noises I made in my environments; my long, suspenseful exhalations; how it felt to have a mild pain in my hip that never stopped. I desired mercilessly for peanut-butter-and-jelly sandwiches;

for Arjan, the moody TA; and Tioga, my housemate's best friend. As I imagined, Arjan would be in my room, helping with my dissertation, then I'd invite Tioga in to hang a picture. As they met for the first time—affable, tapered, and oafish—I would turn my back to them and stand at the door, slowly turning the lock until it snapped. These were my incorrigible things. I didn't know who I was, but I thought I knew what I should be.

When I felt most burdened with experience, more arrived.

One month later, I received a slip of paper in the mail with an appointment for a scan. I called the doctor's office trying to figure out why: Did I really need to waste a chunk of my day? How much would it cost? Was it urgent, should I be concerned, could we move the appointment up to tomorrow? After an extended hold, the receptionist came back on the line saying it was a formality, that plastic surgery had a reputation for being detail oriented.

"I'm going to be so cool and collected this time," I told Mort. "It's a formality, so I'll wear a dress and I won't even have to change." Also, my jeans were snug.

It rained hard before the appointment. The lawn was lashed flat. I advanced farther into the hierarchy of waiting areas. The second felt crisp and clinical, with better chairs and a vast television. The scanning technician who called my name had dark hair with a blond streak and seemed particularly concerned for my well-being. He ushered me to a windowless room filled with machines, where the only decoration was a hazardous-warning label in the middle of the wall.

"Is it still raining outside?" he asked, eager for news. I lay down on a platform shaped like a spit and described the clouds, thick and ominous as sheets of quarried stone. He wrapped me in a warm blanket, taped my toes together, and retreated behind a half-silvered wall.

With a jerk and a glide, the machine swallowed me into its scanning tube. I lay motionless inside the cylinder, breathing my own hot breath refracted from a ceiling mere inches above.

The strangest noises I'd ever heard commenced: magnificent, titanium-laced arrays of clankings and zaps, piercing every inch of me. Several times a second, an electrical current ripped through the metal coils into which I'd been slotted. On each pulse they expanded with a bang, generating an electromagnetic field around me ten times greater than the earth's, causing the protons in the hydrogen atoms of my water molecules to emit faint signals, and in this sense I was perceived by the machine.

My hands lay clasped on my chest. My thighs sagged; the tape bit my toes. I held my breath when asked and fought an urge to beat the walls. Under my left hand I felt a throbbing in time with the clanks. A metal bobby pin had hooked itself to the knit of my dress and danced a magnet-driven jig, like a mad puppet restrained in my palm. Terrified that I'd ruined the scan, decalibrated the machine or worse, I stared at the arc of my beige plastic cave and said nothing.

Every few minutes, the tech pulled me out of the tube to ask a question, then popped me back and trotted away. I assumed he was trying to flirt with me.

"Have you been scanned before?" Only at the airport.

"Do you have pain? Energy?" Some, not much.

"How far did you drive today?" I took the bus.

"Great job!" he said, complimenting my ability to lie still without breathing. I felt like a sausage in puff pastry. "You're doing so great! One more three-minute composition!" he called out, returning to his den.

As a consequence of my morbid obesity, I wrote on the intake form that my weight was 143, although I probably weighed 159, because if I ate one apple, one yogurt, and a meatless burrito bowl for twenty-eight days, as I fully intended to do starting tomorrow, I'd weigh 143, which is the weight I should have been. I have fat cancer, I thought.

As I left, the tech said, "Good luck to you."

In my free time I searched for an ikebana sensei, imagining a petite woman for whom I'd sanitize buckets and sweep fallen leaves as I learned the ancient art of flower arrangement. I signed up for a wilderness navigation class, but forgot to purchase a compass and had to cancel. Every other minute I prodded my hip, trying to guess its secret dimensions and rate of growth.

On my follow-up visit, a different doctor entered the exam room twenty minutes late. I smiled nervously and shook the hand of a brusque woman with a large nose who seemed kind. Feeling optimistic, I summarized while she browsed her computer.

I've been having terrible period cramps, I said, so a script for pain meds would be nice.

Her eyes narrowed. She paused.

Your tumor illuminated on the scan, she said. What an extremely rare event. In twenty years of practice she'd never seen a fatty tumor brighten up. She didn't have any suggestions about what to do next, but I was in the system, she reassured me, and due to receive a letter with instructions in two to three weeks. Without a doubt, she said, the cure for menstrual cramps was to abstain from hot foods and beverages.

By the time I'd reached the elevator, my world had narrowed to logistics plus obsessive fantasies about the worst possible outcomes. Obviously I had cancer in my hip. Soon I'd be broke and dead. A waft of adrenaline propelled me forward. I called in favors with medical friends and aggressively shopped for cancer doctors in the university system. Seventy-two hours later, I took a tram up the hill to meet a famous oncology surgeon.

Hundreds of people coursed through the hospital lobby. Polished tile branched in every direction, glowing from windows high above. A woman in front of me wore metallic pumps and peeled an orange. I couldn't remember if I'd showered. People carried cups of tea, take-out containers, swaddled children, and bags. They rested by the karaoke station on crutches or in wheelchairs. It felt like I passed among everyone I hadn't met—my future neighbors, acquaintances, and strangers I'd find again one day, on the other end of a call or across a desk. They ambled, strolled, and minced, with contusions and stitched wounds, sunk in the depths of their circumstances. Worn or hopeful, everyone belonged. Two men raised their hands to greet each other. Everyone spoke softly, and all of these things mixed.

The exam room was ratty and thin walled. I perched on a plastic chair, rehearsing what I'd say.

"Have you seen it yet?" the surgeon asked me, striding in without a lab coat, wearing a plaid shirt that hung from his shoulders and khakis faded to velveteen. He was thin and tanned in a speckled way.

I'd barely said no when his long arm snaked toward me, grasped my chair, and pulled it toward him across the linoleum floor. His eyes were dark and shallow as skillets.

"See, here on the screen. It lights up," he said.

There I was, framed in the monitor, naked from pelvis to mid-thigh. I gaped. My tissues were spectral, my bones black, my organs cradled in galaxies of muscle, my borders sealed by a thick rind of fat. I couldn't stop staring at my left side and its massive, shining, mango-shaped blob.

"Your tumor measures thirteen by seven by three centimeters. That's roughly five inches long. It looks like a liposarcoma, a cancer of fat cells. I can't be certain. You need surgery." He started typing.

I struggled to absorb this information.

He swung toward me and asked to see my hip.

"Can't you do a biopsy first?" I said, still examining the scan while revealing my bathing-suit bottoms.

"A biopsy is pointless," he said dismissively, returning to his screen. It appeared that every aspect of my condition should be obvious. "The mass is very large; maybe only portions are cancerous. A needle samples a tiny fraction, at best. The only option is to remove it surgically and have it examined by a pathologist."

"Will this affect my pole-dancing career?" I asked.

"I'm not a plastic surgeon. My job is to keep you alive." He spit these words out with disdain and a flick of the wrist.

I swallowed and felt hollow.

"How about surgery tomorrow?" he said, a bit cheerful at the prospect. He typed my medical-record number into the calendar.

I went home, put things in a bag, told people, and freaked out. The next day, Mort and Howard took me to the hospital and waited with me as I was ritualistically prepared. I removed my clothing, changed into a flap of sterile cotton with a string tie, and relinquished my belongings. I was questioned, weighed, measured, issued identification, laid out on a gurney, and stuck with needles. The anesthesiologist introduced herself. The surgeon drew on my hip with a Sharpie. Then he wheeled my gurney to a part of the hospital that you're not supposed to be awake for or remember, where the corridors were thinner, older, and mazelike. He pushed me into a small room outfitted like an industrial kitchen, and my body was transferred onto the stainless-steel table.

I remember the anesthesiologist untangling my hair as she placed a mask over my nose and mouth. I felt the soft crush of her fingers, and I counted down the planets: "Mercury, Venus, Mars, Earth, Jupiter . . ." When I got to Saturn, I didn't fall asleep. I simply became lighter, my hearing sharper. I felt her presence behind me, and the surgeon to my left, but in my mind I stepped into waves on a black-sand beach. It was twilight; the waves at my knees were glossy, crystal clear and weightless as air. They grew higher and came faster. On their peaks and troughs, which hit so fast and sudden they almost couldn't be distinguished, I glimpsed moments of sound and vision: the green fabric raised over my abdomen, the tinkle of instruments and voices, the motions as they rocked me like a ship. These were the waves of my consciousness, lapping into me, eager as tongues, slowing to the click of wheels in dark halls, until I turned away from the horizon and saw the clock above the nurses' station.

I received my body back.

Mort took me to see the surgeon for my one-week follow-up appointment. Pine needles stuck to our shoes and gathered in piles on the floor of the tram. I was distant, preoccupied, packed tight and pepped on Vicodin. I hadn't showered in seven days. My six-inch incision was stapled shut; my hips were bound with gauze and bandages. A slim plastic tube emerged from the skin above my pelvis, slowly vacuuming fluids from my wound to a jar pinned on my sweats. I hurt in such a deep way I didn't feel it. All I could think about was the pathology report and what it would say.

I snapped at Mort in the hospital foyer when he wanted to try the karaoke. He slung a jacket over the back of my chair in the oncology waiting area, while I tried to distract myself by memorizing the Hippocratic Oath. When the nurse finally called my name, Mort squeezed my shoulder and said, "Good luck, muffin." He was midway through a demonstration of his arm to a group of bald kids.

I sat alone in the fluorescent light of the exam room, waiting.

"That was a big one," the surgeon mentioned as a greeting. "Fourteen centimeters. Bigger than it looked on the scan. Creeping down your leg."

With his long arm he nudged the door shut and swiveled toward me on his rolling stool. I looked at him expectantly, trying to gauge his mood and tone for clues.

"Look at this," he said, as he opened his mouth and lifted his tongue. I froze. The underside of his tongue had been partially severed, perhaps years ago—the slippery pink muscle had healed into a thick white scar. He laughed and said he was a little too driven by his work.

"I have so many questions for you," I said, single-minded and undeterred. I might have been afraid of you last week, I thought. Now all I want is to know.

"No, you don't," he said.

My breath caught in my chest. How long had I carried a fucking tumor in my hip? How could I have been so ignorant of my own body? Was it cancer? Was it all gone? Would it ever come back? Did I do this to myself?

"No!" I blurted out. "I don't care whether you have five PhDs and a thousand academic citations, plus whatever nutcase thing you've done to your tongue. I have a lot of questions," I repeated, more calmly now. "I just haven't asked them yet."

"Very well," he replied, with a faint smile. "Before we discuss the results of your pathology report, the nurse has something to show you." Then he turned on his heel and disappeared.

A young man brought in my tumor on a stainless-steel tray. Flecked with blood and stray hairs, it splayed across the platter in a sallow, fleshy mound. Nodules and bumps protruded at the edges. It seemed to grow in size with every step he took toward me. As he came closer, I saw it more clearly, until I realized that its folds were features and the whole thing was a grotesque, almost inhuman, abhorrent face.

I gazed at this without blinking, without fear. A deep sense of calm washed over me. We had divorced each other, myself and I, and now we saw each other, as if for the first time.

The Body of the Great Writer and the One Hundred Yiddish Writers Who Kept Watch

Nomi Eve

In every Jewish house in the shtetls of Europe, two-thirds of the kitchen was occupied by a huge brick oven, large enough to accommodate burning logs to one side and with room for as many as eight loaves of baking bread and a few cooking pots. On the upper level, above the oven, was an opening about four feet high, seven feet wide, and five feet deep. This place was known as the pripetchik, *and during the long winter months, it served as a warm gathering place for the small children. This was the only heated place in the house and they often fell asleep there.*

* * *

1915
Noviye Mlini
Chernigov County, Ukraine

Everyone knew that Baker Loew's *pripetchik* was haunted. A descendant of the Maharal who conjured a golem to save the Jews of Prague, Baker Loew had a familial predisposition not only to believe in spooks, but to think them good company. As he rolled a dough or reached down into the bucket for a bit of sour for rolls, Baker Loew would boast that the ghosts above his oven were none other than the souls of seven centuries of dead bakers. "They give me advice and, most importantly, they regulate the temperature of the fire. Without them my dough wouldn't rise, and local matrons' Sabbath stewpots would burn. Yes, we should be grateful for the ghosts in my *pripetchik,*" he was apt to say whenever a strange howling noise would issue from over the oven.

Max, Baker Loew's only child, wasn't so sure. It was his curse and blessing to sleep up in the *pripetchik* all winter. He was warm up there, but he was also terrified. He often woke up in the middle of the night with the impression that he was not alone. He would gather up his blanket, pat down the lumps and folds, feeling for the rolling pins of dead bakers knocking him on the knees. Because he was a skeptic he didn't believe in the ghosts, but because the ghosts were real, they tortured him for his disbelief, and infected his dreams. Sometimes Max dreamt that the spectral hands of all those dead bakers were rolling him off the *pripetchik*, shoving him into the great big brick oven, shoveling more coal onto the fire, and slamming shut the door, all because he had the temerity not to believe in them.

In order to postpone the onset of his dreams, Max often took a book up into the *pripetchik*. He read deep into the night with a little candle casting yellow light on the pages. It wasn't long before he was an accomplished reader. Baker Loew was a lover of literature, and had a floury shelf filled with great books. From the time Max was a baby, Baker Loew had tried impressing upon him that the baking of bread was inexorably linked with the making of stories, and that both bread and stories were required for a belly's sustenance and a soul's nourishment. Sometimes Max confused baking with reading, and would feel as if he had put chapters into the oven, not loaves of rye, and would stand there confused and unsure of how much metaphor to add to a recipe, or how long a poem needed to be baked to ensure a golden crust and flaky center. Baker Loew also gave Max the rudimentary tools of literary observation, which had been passed on to him by his father, also a baker, who had had the good and bad fortune to bake bread for the great Leo Tolstoy himself. Tolstoy had nurtured a secret craving for the elder Loew's raspberry sticks, but had regularly berated the elder Loew for not putting enough raisins in his sticky buns. The hoary old writer had often lingered in the bakeshop, nibbling on his buns while accepting both praise and criticism from the baker, whom he considered a keen judge of metaphor, plot, and pacing.

Now Max Loew could braid a six-strand challah while mulling over passages of Pushkin, Turgenev, or Dostoevsky. But it was the great Sholem Aleichem who spoke to Max most clearly. When his father bartered a tray full of loaves for a new book of Sholem Aleichem stories, all day long Max would look forward to climbing up into the *pripetchik* and delving into the book—though if he had to examine the reason why, he would have to admit that he read so that he wouldn't dream. But he knew enough about reading to suspect that this was both an impossibility and a contradiction.

When he turned twelve, Max's dreams changed. The ghost bakers mercifully left him and in their place, night after night, he was visited by a sinewy, beautiful demon. Often he woke up with sticky wet pants and the impression that life was playing a joke on him. Eventually, he had to admit he was haunted by his own desires. The she-demon who came to him at night bore none other than the face and figure of his own cousin, a girl five years his elder, who lived three doors up, spent her days tending chickens and weaving, and considered him just another boy among the flock of annoying village boys . . . someone to scowl at, send on errands, and barely tolerate. Sometimes Max saw her down by the river with her nose in a book.

Her name was Mirele. She had long, lustrous, curly black hair and big brown eyes that were a little too far apart and made her look as if at any moment she might sneak a peek in an unexpected direction. She was tall, had a scratchy voice, and a tendency to read under the shade of a big linden tree down by the river. They were cousins through their mothers, who were themselves first cousins. Max's mother was dead. She had died giving birth to twin babies, who died with her. Mirele's father was a learned and honorable traveling man, a maggid, who went from village to village teaching Torah and spreading news. Mirele lived with her mother and younger brother, and every few months her father would come home, bringing with him tales and gossip from the outside world. Mirele's only other sibling, an older brother named Asher, had been conscripted into the czar's army. He was rumored to be encamped in the forest just ten miles to the north, though no one had seen him in months, or heard from him or the other local boys stolen by the czar to use for fodder for his campaigns, kindling for his wars.

When Max realized that he was desperately in love with Mirele, he did what he thought Sholem Aleichem's characters would do should they find themselves in a similar situation—that is, he shamelessly bargained with the she-demon for satiety and salvation. "Please," he begged, "if you must have your way with me, tell me that you love me too." The demon's grip on Max was both literal and figurative. For the she-demon was as skillful in matters of passion as she was insensitive to Max's suffering when she refused to bring him to satiety, and left him high and dry up there in the *pripetchik* to finish the business himself.

When bargaining didn't work, Max considered approaching the real and actual flesh-and-blood Mirele and pleading his case by the light of day. But he was shy, and she was almost a grown woman, while he was still a boy (or at least this is what he told himself, when really anyone could see he was handsome and that manhood was crouching like a bold and impatient tiger in his brown eyes, long torso, lean legs, and muscular shoulders, ready to spring). Whenever he passed Mirele in the market, or saw her gathered with the girls and women at synagogue, Max couldn't even look at her let alone talk to her. He would blush and trip over his feet.

Three years passed. Then, one day, when Max was fifteen, his father sent him to deliver a loaf of still-hot black pumpernickel that Mirele's mother had ordered. Mirele herself answered the door and Max stood there, dumb as a true golem. But she was as kind as she was beautiful, so she rescued him from his misery. "I see you reading all the time," she said, handing him a ruble for the bread. "Who is your favorite author?" She reached out and took the loaf from him. She tore off the heel and broke it in half, bringing one half to her mouth, and depositing the other half in his hand.

"Aleichem," he managed to utter.

Her fingers scraped his palm as the warm bread dropped onto his life line and he felt a shudder run through his body. She continued speaking. "Mine too. If you ever want to borrow, I have his latest collection. My father brought it home from his travels. You can read it whenever you want, but my only stipulation is that you read it here, in our house. I can't bear the thought of the book leaving our house for even a minute."

Max walked home in a stupor. He didn't dare nibble on the half heel of bread. He was afraid that if he ate it he would die, so desperate was his longing. And then right before reaching the bakery he forced it all into his mouth and swallowed down the crust, as if it were the only food left for him in the whole world. He walked into the bakery wiping the crumbs off his cheeks. He couldn't believe his good luck.

The next day he made himself go to Mirele's house, and knocked on the door. This time, Mirele's mother, Max's dead mother's cousin, answered the door. She nodded at him as if she had been expecting him. Mirele, who had been spinning some wool by the hearth, motioned for him to take a seat. She left her spinning, went over to a little bookshelf, and brought him the latest collection of stories by Sholem Aleichem. Max whispered, "Thank you" as she put the book in his lap and then he began to read. At first, he flipped backward and forward through the pages, unable to find the beginnings of paragraphs or the ends of stories. But then he settled in to read "The Man from Buenos Aires." Every so often he would steal a glance at Mirele. When he was in the middle of the story, she said, "What I love about Sholem Aleichem's stories is that he doesn't just stick to plot, romance, and drama. He also philosophizes, and speaks extemporaneously." Max nodded but couldn't respond. Mirele looked at him for a second, biting her lower lip. She looked back down at her spinning. Her mother was blocking out a quilt on the table. Every so often Mirele's mother would sing a half snippet of a broken line of liturgy. Max stared down at the pages. Sucked into the quicksand prose of the Yiddish master, he suspected that if he didn't take immediate action he would be stuck there reading forever.

Now, as he was sitting in a room not five feet from Mirele, and as he loved the stories of Sholem Aleichem, this was not such a bad fate. But his father expected him back in the bakery. Snap out of it, Max, he told himself, and he forced himself to shut the book and return it to the shelf.

The next day he returned. After ten minutes or so, Mirele's mother left the room. Mirele put down her spinning and said, "Do you think that the short story is Sholem Aleichem's chosen form because the lives of individual Jews do not merit longer treatment? Or because the life of the individual Jew must be read against the backdrop of Torah and Talmud? This is what I have come to believe—that the true novel of Jews is Torah itself, and the stories he writes are like weekly parshas—holy little parables, fragments of philosophy and fancy meant to be digested in small bites."

Max decided impulsively to disagree, because he thought it would make him sound smarter. "You assume Sholem Aleichem makes choices, and that he has intentions, when anyone can see that he writes from the place where there are no choices, only truths."

Mirele put a needle between her lips, and then took it out slowly. She held it up to the fire to catch the eye. She smiled. "Max the baker's son, you are both smarter and dumber than you look."

He took a risk. "Mirele the maggid's daughter, Sholem Aleichem should write his next story about you."

"Oh yeah, and what would he write?"

Max shrugged.

Mirele's mother returned.

"Did you hear," Mirele said, "that the roof of the lubricant shop collapsed and killed poor Mrs. Anchik?"

"I know," said Max. "A tragedy, and an order of three challahs, three dozen rolls, and five pump for the shiva."

"I forgot, bakers hear everything first, don't they?"

Max shrugged. "Births, or deaths, people need bread."

He closed the book, stood up, and returned it to the shelf. As he walked out of the room, he came perilously close to Mirele, who looked at him with the eyes not of Mirele the person, but of Mirele the character, who, according to Max's best interpretation, begged to be read and reread and not put back on any shelf. When he walked out of the house, he thought, *But I am just a boy, aren't I?* By the time he got back to the bakery, he thought, *Maybe I am enough of a man. . . .*

When he walked into the bakery his father looked at him strangely, and said, "Time to make bagels," and Max realized that even though it felt like he had spent hours at Mirele's almost no time had passed at all.

He was unable to return to Mirele's for another two weeks. But when he did, he found himself in the middle of a commotion. Mirele's father had just returned from his wanderings with news not just of the outside world but of an engagement. Mirele herself was to be married to the son of a wealthy dry-goods merchant from Kiev. It was a tremendous match, and Mirele's mother and father were both drinking toasts to their own good fortune. Mirele was the only one not celebrating. Her face was flushed, her eyes red and puffy. She was worrying her apron with her hands. At the door Max said, "Mazel tov," even though he had lost a duel with an invisible adversary and would now die alone up in the *pripetchik*. She said, "Thank you." He said, "I suppose I should be going." She said, "No, stay and read." He said, "I can't." She said, "Please, please stay and read." She reached for his hand, grabbing hold of him, and pulling him inside. So he went to the chair by the hearth, and she put the book in his lap, and he stared at the pages, not reading a single word, as friends and relatives flowed into the house to congratulate Mirele on her engagement. The wedding was set for nine months hence. The couple would be married at the Feast of the Tabernacles, an auspicious time for a fruitful union.

For three weeks after the engagement, Max couldn't bring himself to go to Mirele's house. Once or twice he saw Mirele in the market. Once she came to the bakery to buy poppy-seed rolls and kmish bread. They nodded at each other, but didn't exchange a word. It was as if they were strangers again. On the third week Max saw Mirele down by the river and forced himself to go to where she was standing, in the shade of a giant old linden tree.

She didn't look at him, but said, "Did you hear? Sholem Aleichem is dead."

"Dead?"

"My father read it in a newspaper from Kiev. According to the article, he died of tuberculosis, or a broken heart. His son died last year in Switzerland. The boy wasn't allowed to join the rest of the family in America because of his disease. Isn't that tragic? Anyway, Aleichem was sick too and he died. They held his funeral in Brooklyn, New York. A hundred thousand people came—it was the biggest funeral cortege in the history of that city. And there's more. The night before he was buried, one hundred Yiddish writers kept watch over his body in shifts."

Unconsciously, Max reached for the trunk of the tree, and leaned on it for support. He pressed his palm into the rutted bark. How could the great writer be dead? This was the saddest news. Now there would be no more stories. He heard himself saying, "One hundred writers. That is a poetic problem."

The truth is that Max had been thinking quite a lot about poetic problems these days. In other words, Max was beginning to become a writer himself, even though he had never put a word down on a page. Sometimes, though, he scattered flour on the table when his father wasn't looking. He used a finger to inscribe the beginnings of stories and then rubbed them out before they could impress themselves into the dough and become part of the bread people would eat for breakfast.

Mirele bit her lip. "Define your poetic problem," she said, giving him a sideways look out of her too-far-apart eyes that flashed chestnut and gold.

Max continued, "What I mean is, how do we know who they are, the writers?"

"The ones who stood watch over Sholem Aleichem's corpse? We don't. It wasn't in the article. It just said they took shifts and said psalms."

"So we should guess, we should describe them, flesh them out."

"Why should we?"

Max didn't speak for a moment. He was trying to untangle his own thoughts. Then he said a single word, "Homage," and as he said it the wind blew, and a brace of yellow leaves fluttered down from the tree. He said it again, "Homage." Max spoke slowly, methodically. "Because since he is dead, and there are to be no more Sholem Aleichem stories, it is maybe our job to write them for him. And the writers gathered to sit watch over his corpse—they seem a good place to start." Max heard himself speaking, but he almost didn't recognize his own voice. His words came faster and faster. "We should imagine them—we should make them real, we should give them mustaches, beards, dreams, allergies, their own disasters, pets, and personalities. For example—the first writer who kept watch . . . did he wear glasses? Was he born in Poland? Paris or Worms? Was he a musical fellow or was he tone-deaf? And what was he an author of? Derivative stories or inspired poems? Essays or novels?"

Mirele twisted her face, bit her lips, and ran her fingers through her hair. "Max the baker's son," she said, "I suppose we could categorize those writers, is that what you are suggesting?"

"It's a start."

In the distance, they both heard casual, workaday sounds of village life, carriage wheels, mills turning, a mother calling for her son, the lowing of a cow.

Later, when he remembered this moment, Max thought that what came out of Mirele's mouth next was quite strange. Why, it was as if she had fully formed opinions on the matter, as if it had been her idea in the first place. She let out a long breath, and then said, "Seventeen of the Yiddish writers who kept watch over Sholem Aleichem's corpse wore glasses, six were the sort who danced at weddings, seven were the sort who got other people to dance with them, ten played accordion, and thirty-two were journalists. While twenty wrote poems, the rest wrote all variety of prose."

Max smiled, "Six were tragedians."

Mirele took stock of the ground, and sat down on a clump of mossy earth.

"Three of them came from Minsk."

Max sat down next to her, he picked up a small twig and poked at the dirt underneath his nails. "Nine priests, twelve Levites, and six had kippers and eggs for breakfast."

She said, "Twelve had hotcakes, and four had black coffee and kasha."

They nodded at each other, wrinkling their brows, egging each other on, coconspirators. There was a confident breeze blowing through the linden branches, scenting the air with the perfume of ripe, nutty fruit. Max told himself, "She will never marry that fellow. She will marry me, for sure." Mirele was sitting on a tree root, her arms wrapped around her knees, cocking her head to one side so that her loose curls hung almost down to the ground.

For the next six months they went into the woods, hid themselves in a thicket, and seriously set about the task of describing those one hundred Yiddish writers who stood watch over the body of the great Sholem Aleichem. Sometimes Mirele brought a blanket and they would sit side by side. Once Max lay down and put his head in her lap, and she ran her fingers through his hair. They spoke for hours. *The first writer was this, the second one was that, the third had boils on his arse, the fourth spoke Russian with a Slavic accent, the fifth was a disciple of Nachmanides, the sixth was a descendant of a murderer from Galicia.* If anyone had dared ask, they would have defended the truth of their little fictions. It was as if those writers stood for the entire world, as if they were the world, and the two of them, Max and Mirele, could never say enough about them. As if by describing those writers who stood watch over Aleichem's body, they were fulfilling some ancient prophecy. Out in the woods, they never once spoke of her engagement, or of the fact that after her marriage she would leave to live with her husband.

When they bumped into each other in town, or when she came to buy poppy-seed cookies, or onion board, or black pump, they would try their best to pretend that they were not engaged in a conspiracy of the imagination. And when they met in the forest they came from different directions in order to avert the suspicion of gossiping friends. They knew that no one would understand what an engaged girl was doing in the forest with a boy five years her junior. They knew that people would suspect them of immorality—when in truth the most immoral thing they were doing was paying homage to the greatest storyteller they had ever read, in the only way they saw fit.

Two months before Mirele's wedding, something happened. The story that was on everyone's lips was as follows: The czar was planning on visiting a military camp. The camp commander decided that twenty Jewish soldiers would be baptized in the river in his honor. The Jewish soldiers held hands, entered the river, and dived in. But they did not come out. All twenty of them committed suicide rather than be baptized. Most of the boys came from the villages in and around Max's village. Max personally knew six of them. One was the fishmonger's eldest son. Another was the son of his father's best customer. And another was Mirele's brother Anshel—who, according to reports, was the leader of those boys, the one who came up with the idea and inspired his fellow Jews to martyr themselves to God.

After the catastrophe, everyone saw ghosts, or claimed they did. People walking the streets, bleary-eyed and exhausted, regularly saw those twenty dead boys too, greeting them and asking them casual questions about the weather.

How had they done it? No one could quite figure out how the boys had drowned themselves, which is no easy task. And yet they were gone. Some of the village boys went into the river and tried to hold their breath to see if they could force themselves to die, like the dead heroes. Their mothers stood on the bank screaming, and then pulled them out and walloped them, punishing them for being so young, dumb, and inspired.

Soon after the catastrophe, Mirele began to act differently. At synagogue she refused to pray, and just stood there, not even mouthing the words. On the Sabbath she didn't change her dress from her everyday garment. She was once seen in the company of a Gypsy who had strange markings on her hands and brow. Then came the rumors that she had become an atheist and that her father was beside himself with worry at her radical beliefs.

Max went into the forest and waited for her at their regular place. He went again and again. But she never came back. When she entered the bakery to buy kmish bread she fake-smiled at Max and said, "How do you do" as if all they had between them was pleasantries and pastry. Eventually Max heard her engagement was broken off, the dowry disassembled. The young man married the daughter of a ritual circumciser from Kodrovka instead. Max silently rejoiced. But he still didn't know how he would coax Mirele back to herself, and back to the woods where he could drop the pretense of storytelling once and for all, take her in his strong arms, and show her that even though he was younger, he was enough of a man to satisfy much more than her imagination.

In 1917 the White Russian soldiers of General Denikin came calling. Max was alone in the bakery when it happened. His father had been two doors up in Yoram the sausage maker's shop. Max heard the pounding hoofbeats of the marauders and stuck his head out of the door to see what was going on. He caught sight of three soldiers on horseback shooting into a crowd of Jews in front of the synagogue. As fate would have it, Mirele was in the street in front of the bakery. "In here, in here," he yelled to her. She ran to him. Max grabbed her hand and pulled her toward the *pripetchik*. He hoisted himself up and then reached down for her. He saw her hesitate, and then hitch her skirt and climb up to him. He covered them both in the heavy quilts. And then he had a thought, and jumped down, gathered some burlap sacks, climbed back, and stuffed them in the opening of the *pripetchik*. They lay side by side under the heavy quilt and the burlap sacks. There was barely any room and it was hard to breathe. Outside the mayhem grew louder. Max heard a woman scream, and a man let out a strangled groan, and then what sounded strangely like the flapping of enormous wings, but which turned out to be the synagogue igniting, the flames berating the wind. Max thought he heard Mirele's mother screaming for mercy. Then he heard his own father exclaiming, "Shema Yisrael," which was cut off before he reached the word "Echad" (one) at the end. Max and Mirele lay silent, wincing every now and then at the sound of screams, or the report of gunshots, the crackling of thatch, the moaning of panicked animals. When it seemed that the noise was at its crescendo, Mirele reached over, put her hand on Max. She stroked his shaft, but he reached down, took hold of her hand, and pried it off. Max fumbled between her legs. He had no idea what he was doing, but whatever he did at least half worked. Because she let out some muffled moans and sighs. *I am Mirele*, he thought, and *Mirele is me*. He rolled over, looked into her eyes. Slowly, he thrust himself into her. She smothered a gasp, pulled back, and then wrapped her top leg over him, and angled her hips up so he could slide into her. Again he thrust and this time he felt his passage blocked. He thrust again. He knew he was taking her maidenhood. She let him. He thrust again until they collapsed shuddering on top of each other. Outside, the mayhem died down. It was silent for what seemed like hours. Then they heard the voice of Momik the beadle, calling out for survivors. Mirele didn't look at Max. She pulled away, covered herself before pushing off the quilt, kicking off the burlap, slipping down, and leaving the safety of their perch.

After the disaster, people divided into two camps: those who stayed, those who went elsewhere. Elsewhere meant far away. Mirele was in the latter group. She and Max had barely spoken since that day; now she was going to live with cousins in Cuba. The day she left, Max walked her to the carriage, carrying her bag. It was all loaded up, the driver waiting only for her. She took her bag from Max's hand, climbed up the carriage step, and disappeared inside. He watched the vehicle swallow her up and realized that even though they had made love they had never kissed. Not once. The carriage rolled off and he thought, *How could I have let that happen?*

Max also went far away. He crossed Europe and sailed from Marseille to Brooklyn, where his dead mother had a brother who sold elastic waistbands to seven different garment factories. He walked up and down the streets asking everyone the same question. Do you know who the writers were who stood watch over Sholem Aleichem's body the night he died? Do you know who they were? They shook their heads and treated him like a crazy fellow, the kind they were used to, rolling off the boats, sick in the head from the infections of Europe. Perhaps he just didn't know who to ask. Surely someone must have known. One hundred Yiddish writers in Brooklyn, why they must have been everywhere, sitting on stoops, smoking in coffee shops, congregating in union halls. But he couldn't find them. Only once someone said, "Yes, one of the writers is an essayist named Pinsker. He lives on Twenty-Fourth Street, above a laundry." Max went to find him, but the man had moved, and the woman who lived there told Max that he had converted, and was busy translating the gospels into Yiddish in the back room of some rectory on Staten Island. Max went to the New Mount Carmel Cemetery in Queens, and stood at Sholem Aleichem's grave. He considered sinking to his knees and crying, but he realized that though he was sorry that the writer was dead, his sorrow had nothing to do with this mound of earth, this jutting stone, and a cemetery commemorating other people's catastrophes. He picked a pebble anyway and put it on the grave, as if to say, "I knew you too."

When he was twenty years old, Max left America and went to Palestine. He stayed in Jaffa for a few weeks and then went to Jerusalem, where he wandered around the streets of the old city, sat in cafés, and got himself hired at a bakery behind a mosque, where every day men would be called to prayer, and the voice of the muezzin would startle him, sending shivers down his back, until at last he too felt like bowing down to some god. But he didn't. One day a man came into the bakery and bought a dozen poppy-seed cookies. He was a tall, smiling man with a big, fleshy face with eyes, nose, and ears congregating in the middle. Eating a poppy-seed cookie with relish, he explained to Max that he was the publisher of a literary journal. When Max expressed interest in contributing small pieces of fiction, the man agreed to take a look. He walked out of the shop. Max watched him go, sure that he would never send him a single word.

That night Max dreamt he had given the man a story and gotten it published. In his dreams he received acclaim for the story and was even offered a contract to write a book. But in the morning, Max was just a baker again. He woke up and went back to work, braiding challah, and making sticky buns with more than enough raisins for Tolstoy to love. The man with the big, funny face never came back.

Eventually, Max opened a bakery of his own with its own *pripetchik* above the oven. He constructed it in the style of the shtetls of Europe, not in the newfangled style that the bakers were using here in Jerusalem. He saw no reason to change. And he slept up in the *pripetchik* in the winter, when the wind howled and the white stones of the city seemed to be hewn of ice, not rock. He didn't marry or have romantic attachments. In his dreams, he took mistresses, and had long, tangled affairs with the wives of prominent men. But in reality he lived like a monk, baking bread and becoming intimate only with the narrow streets and alleys of the Old Jerusalem. Every so often he would agree to be a tenth in a minyan, and would mouth prayers he didn't believe in. He became friendly with the other bakers, the Armenians, the Copts, the Arabs, the Turks, who catered to the Ottoman authorities. He developed a love of towers, and would spend his spare time searching out the many towers of the old city, bribing his way into them, climbing up, and having bold original thoughts that he promptly forgot when he climbed back down again.

During the day he was a baker. But at night he was haunted, just as when he had been a little boy. Sometimes Mirele appeared up in the *pripetchik*, where she would entangle herself in his body, and they would pleasure each other in endless ways until the day took her away from him once more. But the marauders were there too. And the village was burning all around them, its families dying by gunshot, bayonet, fire, or worse. In the morning when he woke up, Max would lie still, afraid to move. He would curse this curse that gave him Mirele and murderers together, two sides of the same coin, inseparable from each other. And he would roll down from the *pripetchik*, thinking, *There has to be a way to separate the memory from the moment.* But there never was. Also, there was another problem with the ghost Mirele—Max could never be sure it was really her. In his dreams, she always refused to let him see her face, so he never saw her too-far-apart eyes and could never quite tell if he was being ravished by Mirele or being taken advantage of by some other succubus who had stolen their history and was using it for dark purposes.

Sometimes Max was haunted not by a woman, but by words. He would lie up in the *pripetchik* and think of all the stories he should write but knew he wouldn't. The one he thought about most often he titled "The Body of the Great Writer and the One Hundred Yiddish Writers Who Kept Watch." Over a decade had passed since the death of Sholem Aleichem. In his dreams, Max made up those hundred writers one by one all over again. Just as he and Mirele had done in the woods, Max gave them names, histories, genres, habits, allergies, and heartbreaks. He factored in the intervening history, and filled his phantom pages with intricate, detailed, and heartfelt suppositions about writers who died in Zurich, were descendants of the concubines of kings, fell in love in Paris, became apostates in Istanbul, were slaughtered by petty thieves in Albany. In his sleep, Max wrote great tomes and tiny poems. In short, he described an entire Jewish encyclopedia of life, death, birth, and rebirth as lived, suffered, and loved by the men who sat by the great writer's corpse, singing psalms, clenching and unclenching their hands as they raged against death while begging a God many didn't believe in for mercy on the dead man's soul. But it was all a dream, of course. In the morning, when he woke up, the words Max wrote in his head would be as insubstantial as the dead bakers who had knocked his knees with their rolling pins when he was a boy. And Max would go about his day, baking bread, braiding challah, existentially confused about the measurements of metaphor and the proper use of dialogues between ingredients. He would hand over a dozen onion rolls to a matron in a black kerchief with a lazy eye and think, *Did I just give away an essential element of my plot?*

One day many years after they had last parted, Mirele walked into Max's bakery. Had twenty years passed? An entire century? Was he dreaming? No, not this time.

She wasn't old, but she wasn't young. There was the tiniest sprinkling of gray in her dark hair, just at the temple where her part rose and fell. The rest was still jet-black and lustrous, down around her shoulders, not tied back and covered like the hair of the religious matrons who frequented his shop. Her skin was smooth, her eyes still radiant, and her lips as full as that night when he was a boy and she a girl and the village had burned around them. She was startled to see him. It was happenstance that led her to Jerusalem, to his bakery. Her face registered shock, fear, and then a measure of gladness. In her eyes flashed a look of utter astonishment, and Max could see that in the years since he had seen her last, she had trod a hard path. She looked around and saw that no one else was in the shop.

Not mincing words, she said, "Oh thank God it's you, Max. I can love you now."

He said, "I have loved you forever."

Would she have spoken as she did, if they were not alone? She held up a hand, stopping him, and then began to speak as if on trial.

"Our families were murdered," she whispered, "and we fucked like animals. I have suffered for it, Max. I have punished myself for what we did."

Max's body was shaking. He clenched and unclenched his fists as he stepped out from behind the counter.

"Come to me, Mirele," he half begged, half demanded.

She put down her bag and walked toward him. They stood inches apart. She reached up and stroked his face, pressing her fingers to his checks. She gasped, dropped her hands, and looked upward. He kissed her neck and then put his hands around her waist, feeling her warm hips, her still slender waist. The last Yiddish writer, the hundredth, approached the body, sighed loudly, and then sat down in a hard chair, prepared to do his duty before man and God. He recited a psalm no one even knew anymore. The funeral cortege of the great writer advanced slowly up the broad avenues of Brooklyn. Phantoms sighed and prepared to throw earth. Max and Mirele kissed for the first time in their lives. Behind them, the ghosts in the *pripetchik* rejoiced, turned to smoke, and then danced up the chimney, a white braid of souls departing and decorating the sky over a waking Jerusalem.

Dirty Old Town
Rosamond Purcell

IF YOU STUDY THE WIND-BLASTED contours and escarpments on the surface of this figure it becomes enormous—in places an aerial landscape of mountains, fluvial mud plains that wrap around its contours like the wrapping on a gigantic mummy.

In 2001, in the mountains of Pakistan, the Taliban destroyed giant stone carvings of the Buddha from the third and fourth centuries. I have read that the statues have been replaced by likenesses of themselves through light projections cast into the niches in which they once stood. The technology that makes this possible comes from rock concerts.

Projection is a way of proceeding in which edges of real life come up fast and sharp or slope off into valleys and vistas where no one blocks the view.

"They went shouting and singing to the Big Bend in the canyon to see the flying ghost, and called it names, and fired off their pistols" (from *Bar-20 Days* by Clarence E. Mulford, the author of the Hopalong Cassidy books, who "forwent college" to be a writer).

Coda: The figure in the photograph is about three inches tall, made of chocolate, and has been gnawed by a mouse.

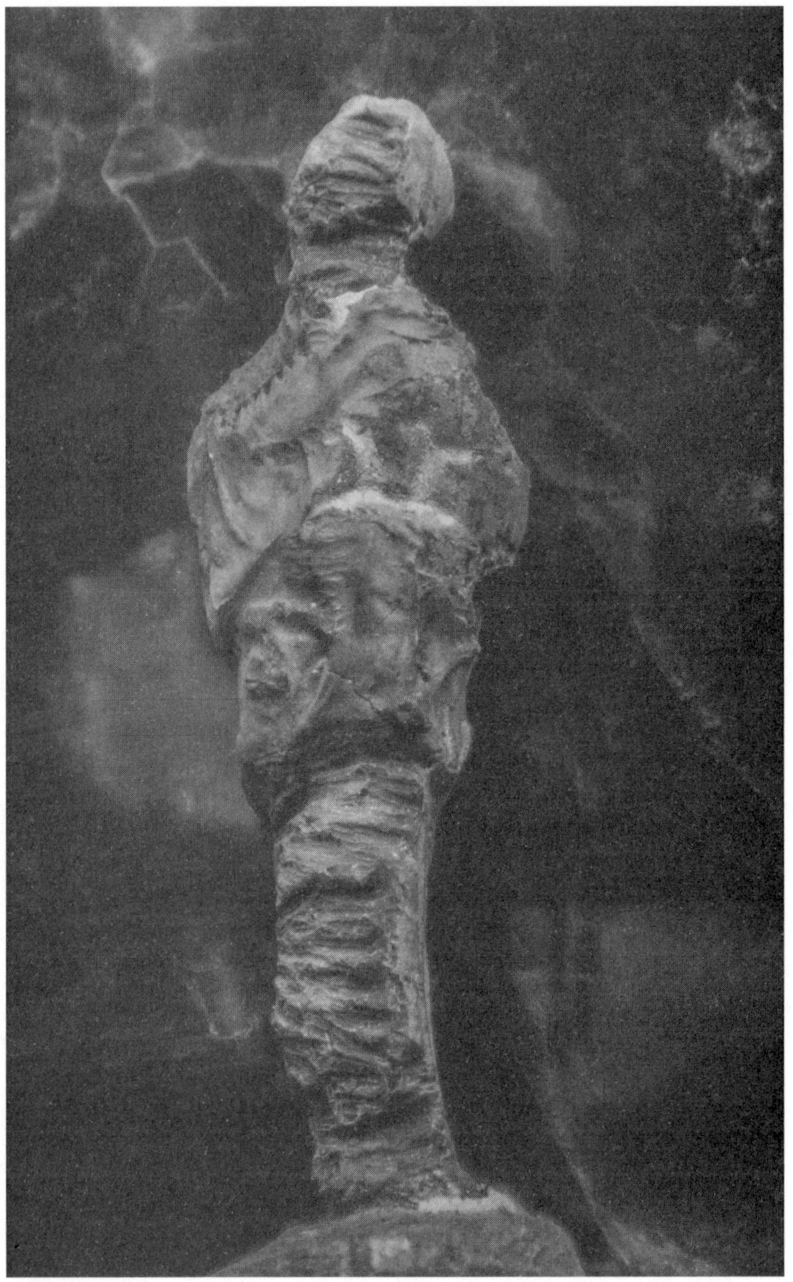

Bones and Veins/Day of the Dead

The human skeleton photographed through a back-lit leaf, as if the veins and arteries from inside the body of a living creature were independent and on the outside, suffused with light—a layer of being alive on top of an advancing substrate, and dancing all the way.

"The spots of the first drops of rain. The sun. The bread and wine. Hopping. Easter. The veins of leaves. The blowing grass. The color of stone" (from *Wings of Desire*, the list of memories of being alive as spoken by the dying motorcyclist).

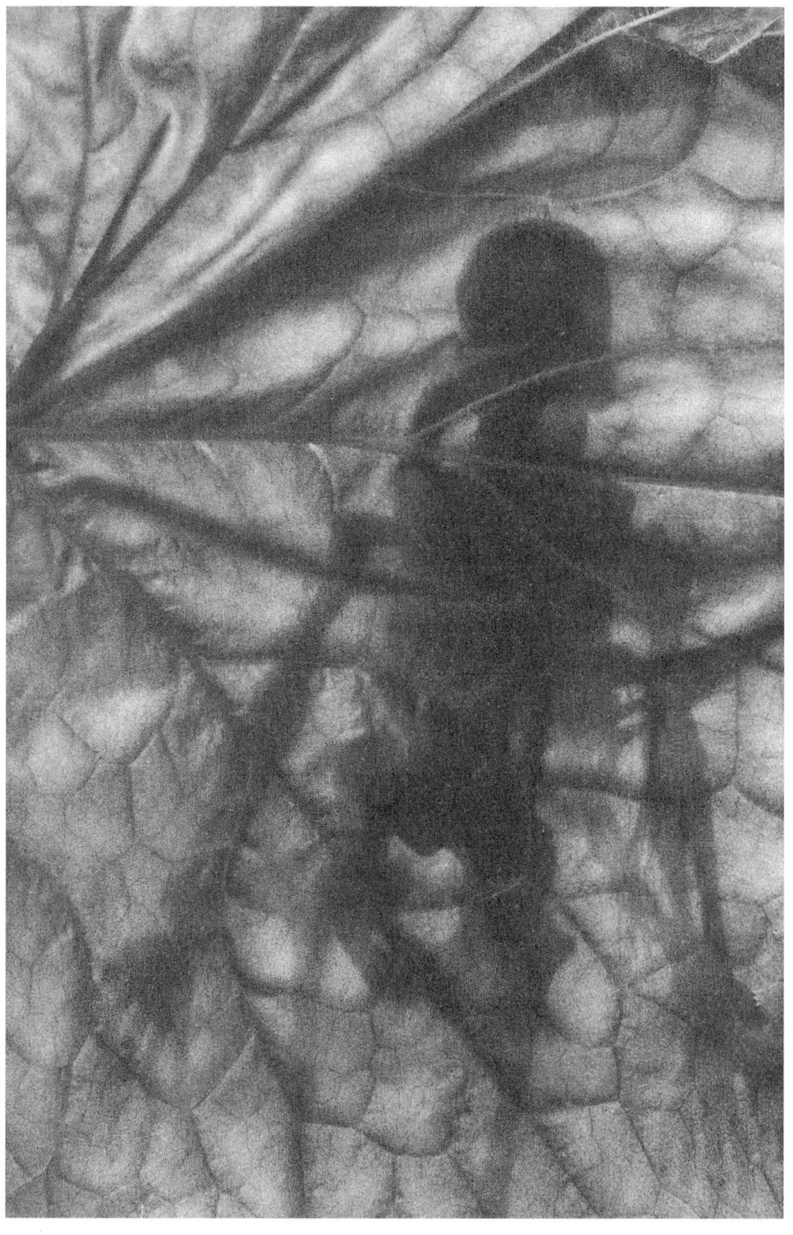

Time of Day: Banksy

One late night, driving with friends through Venice, California, we saw an acrobatic sign painter on a warehouse roof, moving back and forth across a blank wall, wielding some kind of marking device. The moon was bright, but all you got was a glimpse—shutter opening and closing on a stealthy, ubiquitous Los Angeles street artist.

Rosamond Purcell

Comparative Anatomy

In the late afternoon, he takes his toad, an inconvenient pet, for a walk in a glass arcade.

"Dirty Old Town," composed and sung by Ewan MacColl with his wife, Peggy Seeger, casts an atmospheric net over life in the early twentieth-century industrial town of Salford, a suburb of Manchester: cats on the prowl, spring blowing in on smoky wind, a girl from the streets are a few of the apparitions, and even an ax tempered in fire, half heard in a space between perception and recognition, and twisted by the imagination. Something fast happens in an alley, two women from a demimonde caught in between fleeing and frozen. The connective tissue of happenstance binds them together.

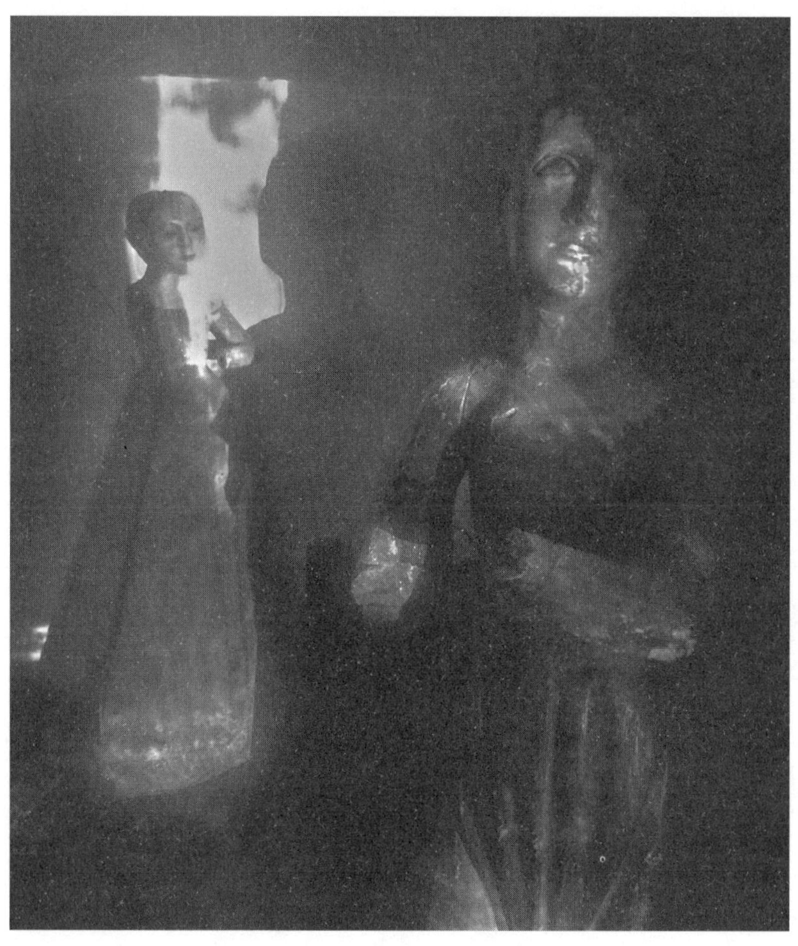

This porter walks through waning light, and like the glazier in Cocteau's film *Orpheus*, he is carrying sheets of glass through which the dead can pass as if through water. Right side up, this pane reads as a landscape of trees and sky. Upside down as the interior of a cave—a limestone grotto in which water seeping through calcium carbonate–laden rock forms pinnacles and ceiling spikes—stalactites and stalagmites.

Once I photographed a limestone-covered nest and eggs of a small bird found in such a cave. It looked like marble. Perhaps after a few thousand years under concentrated mineral rain, every organic element of this construction—wood, eggshells, unborn embryos—would turn to stone—a fossil.

Silver

Like a small portrait on a coin that has slipped to the rim, this figure seen from behind comes from an ongoing graphic story about an escaped prisoner.

This fictional tough guy seen in a silvered mirror is like one of the daguerreotypes of slaves photographed by J. T. Zealy in the 1850s at the behest of Harvard naturalist Louis Agassiz, a man who believed in the divine separation of races. The photographs were, and are, provocative, even as they slip from the edge of public awareness.

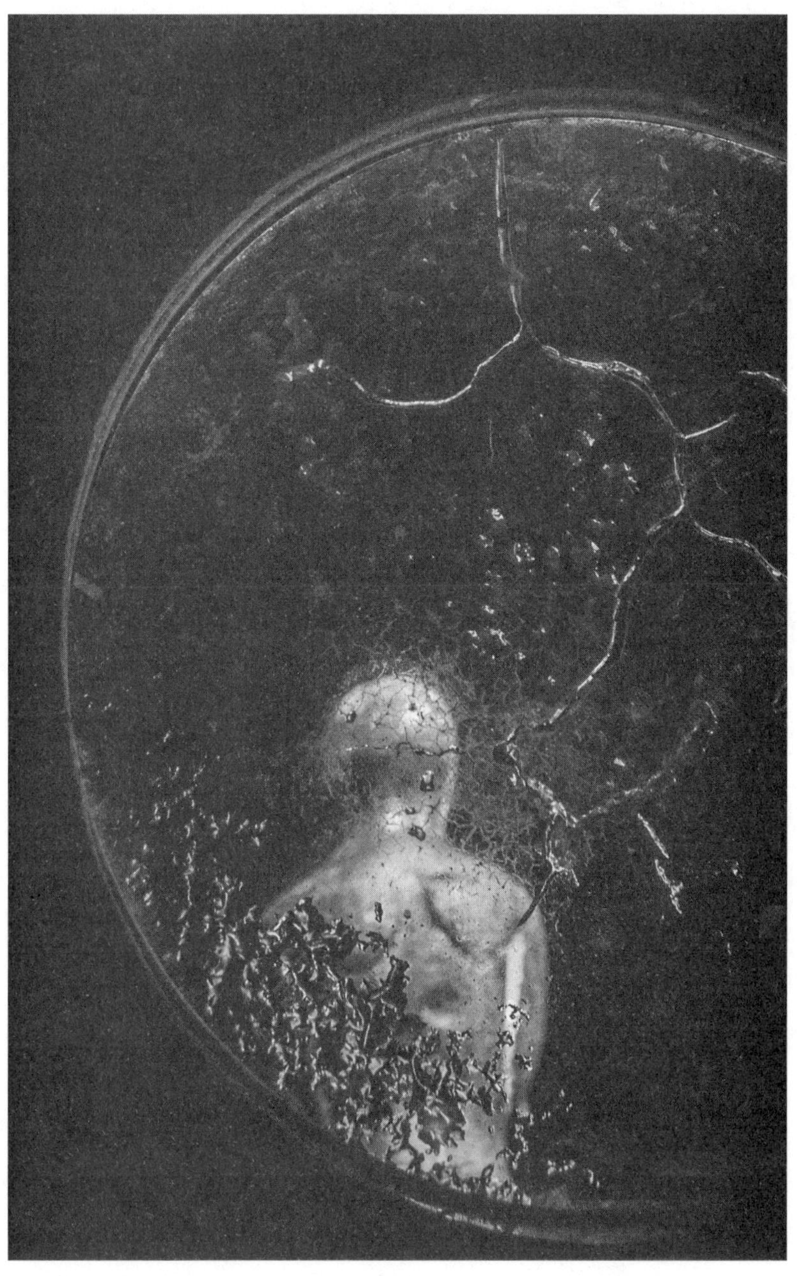

On the left, a menacing figure assembles itself out of the shadows, leans against a vaporous wall, and, grasping illusory threads between his fingers, spins a cat's cradle. His mark, downhill on the right, unsuspecting, climbs toward a man who is both there and not there yet fully prepared to practice a scam.

Another Way the Universe Communicates Its Presence to Itself

Alan Rossi

CLAIRE WANTED TO KNOW not only what Jay was going to say, but also how he was going to say it, and she wanted to know—no, actually, she felt she had the *right* to know—the different ways he was going to say it to her parents, to the Montessori school, to their friends, to her, and most importantly to Sasha. She wanted to know the differences in how he was going to say what he had to say, and she hoped he'd been thinking about it, she really hoped he had, because it was basically everything on the line now, everything on the line and out in the open finally, and she wanted to know what exactly he was going to say to their ten-year-old daughter to make her understand. There's no finally, he said quietly. That's not fair. Oh, I'm not being fair, she said. Do you think you deserve fairness? He looked ahead—an expanse of field, deep green grass, then woods, trails leading into woods, an open, spacious part of the park like an open, aware mind—without seeing.

It was the first time they had spoken in nearly two weeks, and he knew that it was coming, talking. That it was now occurring when he was supposed to be playing second base for his company softball team, missing an important game in the playoffs, a game that Sasha had been excited to watch, was frustrating—along with causing an intensification of the feeling of wanting to be anywhere except where he was—but he wasn't going to be frustrated. He wasn't going to think about the game or Sasha wanting to be at the game, Sasha confused about why they were at the park rather than at the game, he wasn't going to do anything other than be as open as he could be and show his remorse. He had made sure to think of how he was going to speak when he did speak, made sure to consider that anything he said needed to be said with a voice that was quiet, respectful, apologetic, with body language that was passive, the implicit understanding being that he had demeaned her, he had demeaned their family, and he had demeaned himself, and he imagined the talk when they finally talked being one in which he was so sincere, so apologetic, so passive and remorseful—shoulders slumped and eyes down—that she could not question his heartbreak, because he *was* heartbroken, for them and for himself, and he didn't like imagining the scenario, this talk, because it made him feel like he wasn't heartbroken but was merely acting out heartbreak. But he *was* deeply and truly heartbroken and needed to convey that, and he couldn't stop himself from imagining and practicing it. He had thought and thought about this, how to appear sincerely heartbroken—like a defendant in a murder trial—and he had thought about the fact that he wasn't going to bring up any of their problems, any of Claire's problems, and wouldn't get angry or defensive or attacking (something he knew he was capable of doing), and would only, humbly and remorsefully, address this failure of his, but what he hadn't done was he hadn't thought of how he was going to convey what he had to convey beyond "I'm sorry," and he had not thought of what he was going to say to other people and had hoped, had actually *assumed* that he wouldn't have to say anything to Sasha. He didn't think he could do that.

There's no out in the open finally, he said quietly again, mainly as a way to think a little more about what he had to say. He added that he wished she wouldn't say or think that. He knew she had said it to hurt him, he understood that, and he understood why she would want to hurt him, understood that he probably deserved to be hurt, but the out-in-the-open-finally implied that he'd just been doing things like this since forever and that wasn't even close to true. It really wasn't. How do I know what's true? Claire said. I don't know what's true, and I don't know what's not true.

From the bench, they could see in the distance Sasha running through the park with three other friends; they were playing a game of soccer, two on two, with shoes as goals. The day was hot, humid, the grass drying from a recent rain, so quick it might not have occurred. Joggers and bikers and walkers with and without dogs passed on the nearby trails, into the woods. Big white clouds moved through the deeply blue sky, trees making an elongated ocean wave sound in the occasional gusts of wind. Birdsong. Tall, dry grass in the unmown areas of the park. High summer. Dragonflies, mosquitoes, bees, wasps, butterflies, the season ringing like a bell. They didn't notice any of this. They only saw Sasha. Her figure obscured by humidity that rose from the ground, breaking her body in half. So tell me, Claire said. Because you're not going to say anything to her before I know what you're going to say. How are you going to tell a ten-year-old that you tried to have sex with someone closer to her age than her mother's? That you were arrested for it? That your picture is on the Internet with other ingrates? How's that conversation going to go?

At the same moment this conversation was occurring and clouds were clearing after the brief rain and humidity was rising from the ground and streets, and a stark blue sky was hanging construction-paper-like against the deep summer green of heavily treed neighborhoods, in a house two neighborhoods to the south, a man who frequented the park they were in, but was not in today, a man in his early sixties—wearing loafers with no socks, khakis, a woven leather belt, an untucked white oxford with green cardigan, freshly shaven, smelling of camphor for his nervous condition—was sitting in his den, a steaming cup of tea on his desk, opening his laptop, shouting his wife's name, Alicia, down into the house, and hearing no response (taking a sip of his English breakfast tea, this man a retired accountant, a financial adviser to the local liberal arts university) began viewing *Huffington Post* on his laptop, then CNN, then *The New York Times*, then updates on his FB page concerning his grandchildren, pictures that he "liked," until, after a few minutes of patiently waiting, he opened a thumb drive already inserted into the laptop, then opened a folder named "old work," and among other folders and documents, opened another folder named "old taxes," in which he opened several Polaroid pictures of eleven- to thirteen-year-old boys wearing only underpants or nothing at all. The man unzipped his khakis and again shouted his wife's name, Alicia, and, hearing nothing, leaned back.

I don't think ingrate is the word you want, Jay said, immediately regretting that he said it, reminding himself and inwardly scolding himself to remain unaggressive, to not turn this into something about her, though, to fully understand the situation, he thought, there had to be something mutual here, the difficulties between them, after all, were mutual, weren't they? I don't give a shit if it's the word I want, Jay. Claire was dark-haired, dark-eyed, her father from Spain, her mother from Ireland—she wasn't beautiful, but she was attractive, thoughtful, sometimes warm, sometimes cruel, funny, athletic, witty, and passersby, especially men, would often notice her, but not today. Today a man jogging averted his gaze when he came close to them and pretended to inspect his Fitbit and once the arguing couple were behind him, the jogging man felt himself breathing again. Jay waited for the jogger to pass on the concrete trail that connected the dirt trails in the various wooded parts of the state park. When the jogger was past them, Jay told Claire that he didn't know what he was going to say to any of these people because it had to be spur-of-the-moment, spontaneous, if it was going to be genuine. Then he said that he was so sorry, he didn't know, had no idea that she was underage. Claire stopped him, shaking her head, telling him to be quiet, to stop saying sorry, if he said he was sorry one more time, she was going to Mace him, she didn't care that there were other people here, she didn't care if Sasha saw, she didn't care what happened to him or if he was sorry or if he didn't know, he should have known better. He said he was sorry for apologizing—don't say that word again she told him—and he nodded OK and asked why if they hadn't spoken in two weeks did she suddenly now, at the park, want to talk. She told him it had to happen at some point, and so she chose a place where she had to be in some sort of control of herself. It calms me to be in the park. At least let's walk, he said. People keep passing and they're looking.

They got up and walked along the edge of the field where Sasha was playing. After a moment, their daughter's head turned, and Claire waved to her and made a circling motion with her hand to indicate Mom and Dad were walking the loop, just going on a short stroll, right back, and Sasha nodded and waved and smiled and went back to her game. In Claire's consciousness the image arose of herself telling Sasha that Dad was out of town on a business trip, that was why he was gone, Sasha replying that she hadn't heard about any trip, causing Claire to explain that it had just come up, and also was a new part of his job and now walking ahead of Jay, hating herself, she pointed back to the field and said, Look, her eyes beginning to tear up again, as if the existence of their child was the only fact she had to bring to this discussion. He looked, everything in him sinking, as though a more significant gravity were inside his being, as though he were being pulled down from the inside, a singularity of shame he had created in himself that would, eventually, shrivel him to nothing. At this same instant, missing the company softball game flashed through his mind—snagging a well-hit grounder, whipping the ball to first—and he scolded himself for being annoyed that Claire had chosen today to have their discussion and for allowing something as trivial as a softball game to interrupt this, one of the most important, however painful, moments of his existence. They entered the trees, the dirt trail drying quickly, the trail edged with green weeds and grass and flowers, deep browns and forest green, blue patches through the deep green canopy.

The retired accountant had many photographs that he had taken on his own and then transferred to one of four zip drives so that he could then delete them from his phone without Alicia possibly seeing them. The photos were exclusively of boys. When a girl appeared in a photo, he cropped her out. He had many photos from the park, three areas: a playground near the entrance; the ball fields—baseball, soccer, and volleyball—in the middle of the park; and finally, his preferred spot, the small waterfall with adjacent swimming hole and rope swing where parents took their children to cool off during the heat of the day. There the boys were either wet through their clothes or sometimes shirtless, and on very rare occasions, in their underwear. Then he had barely been able to keep his hands from shaking when he took the photos, holding the phone, viewing the phone as he imagined an old man might, away from his face, trying to maybe read a text, peering at some too-small script. The parents said hello to him and his dog, a shih tzu; the boys said hello to him, though mostly to his dog, which was why he brought the dog, Alicia's. He asked if they wanted to pet her, if they wanted to give her a treat, if they wanted to walk her around a little, she was sweet old girl, a good girl. Taking photographs was all he would allow himself, then straight home. In addition to his own photos, there were four sets of photographs, not digital, that he had traded for, in some cases paid money for, labeled Bobby, Timothy, Justin, and Davis. His own photographs were helpful, but these others were what he needed, what he fearfully and excitedly imagined might occur in his own family room one day.

Jay kept his eyes focused on some distant point in the forest, which he wasn't actually seeing, instead considering how he was going to tell this thing to Claire, to finally get out his version of the events in such a way that might allow him to not get a divorce or not lose custody of his child, not lose his family and way of life and all the things suddenly that he didn't want to lose, which made him begin by saying that he knew she was going to have a hard time believing it, and maybe wouldn't believe it at all, but it had been a mistake. Not the escort. The *prostitute*, Claire said. Use the right word. Just as you suggested I do. OK, he said. The prostitute. Also, a mistake is a pretty asinine way of putting it. It was a mistake, he said. Let me explain. I did arrange a meeting with a prostitute. A meeting, Claire said. Where you were going to discuss a new business venture or maybe some advertising you could do for her online? Was this meeting arranged via her secretary? Don't say you're sorry, she said. Don't. I want to know what exactly you did. I don't want any more apologies or vague language. I want to know when you decided to do this, I want to know how you knew where to go, I want to know when you left the house, what you told me you were doing, what you told Sasha you were doing, I want to know how much you paid, I want to know what the girl looked like, the *girl*, I want to know how you picked her, what streets you drove down, where you found her, the specifics. They walked farther into the woods, and what had seemed to be a slightly windy day out on the expanse of the field felt different in the forest, which was incredibly still and quiet, and despite being focused on their discussion, they both separately noticed this sudden change in environment, the stark quiet, and then after a moment, in that quiet, noises of birds and insects and the stream seemed to emerge as if from a void, as though the quiet were constructing noise for play, and then the whine of cicadas, high in the tops of trees, as though summer were communicating its presence to itself, simply another way the universe communicated its presence to itself.

Claire shook her head at his inability to speak. She didn't want to hear any of his bullshit advertising language that he used to cover up the plain facts of things. Jay nodded, and at the same time he nodded, his phone vibrated in his pocket. He thought it could be his lawyer or a client, maybe the new all-organic co-op he was doing advertising for pro bono, maybe a teammate updating him about the game (which he had told everyone he could not attend because he was injured, laid up on the sofa, his back out), but he knew that no matter what he could not take a call right now, not when she was finally talking with him, allowing him to talk, and anyway, he didn't want to take the call. He reached into his pocket and hit the button to make the phone stop vibrating. He told her it wasn't like some movie. He didn't find some girl on the street and pick her up. He used an escort service that he found online. How classy of you, Claire said. So you ordered some girl online. You, what, scrolled through a bunch of pictures and picked one you liked? Basically, he said. These services, then, they provide underage—No, Jesus, he said. That's what I mean by mistake. I chose a girl whose page said she was twenty. Perfectly mature, Claire said. He again said her page said twenty. What did she look like? Does. What does it matter? It matters to me. Blonde, five three, I don't know. Show me her page. I'm not going to do that. Plus it's probably already taken down. If you don't at least try to humor me, you'll never see Sasha again, Claire said. He looked at her. A bee buzzed around her head and she brushed it away, and the bee seemed to become more aggressive, and she told it to get away, and he said, Be still, don't move. She stopped moving and the bee hovered around her, bouncing in the air, and after a moment flew away, causing them both to follow its flight into the forest, giving a depth to the hollow spaces of shadow and light beneath the various trees. She told him to show her and he took out his phone. He said service was bad, but after a moment of walking, the bars increased, and he found the page, still up, the girl, and showed her. She looked, scrolling, a gentle finger on the screen, in the shadows of the woods, the screen lighting her face.

The retired accountant moved through them in this order every time, the same unfolding of images. There was something in the naming of the bodies, the captions below the scanned photos: Bobby had dirty-blonde hair, almost a bob, and in two pictures wore swimming trunks, and in two more wore nothing. The captions were simple: Bobby playing, Bobby teasing. Timothy with brown hair had on blue underwear, white underwear, just socks. The captions: Timothy dressing, Timmy being a good boy. Justin was not Caucasian and had dark hair, was possibly Mexican, the accountant thought, which made him believe that the name Justin, and all the names, were faked, and in that understanding there was a disappointment then the briefest realization of what he was doing, that there were real names, which caused his hands to shake, his shoulders to shake, and he had had to stop viewing Justin, who was spread on the sofa, a man's hand reaching in each photograph, touching, holding, and before he had quit looking at Justin (though he wouldn't delete the photos), each time the accountant took stock of himself, of his own shaking, and kept going. The captions: Want to play with Justin, Justin needs a checkup. Davis was a redhead, which the accountant knew was very rare, a rare find, very fortunate, pale skin, almost nipple-less he was so pale, freckled face, posing in front of paintings, on a stool. Davis modeling for you. The retired accountant heard the front screen door slam shut, causing him to yank his hand out of his pants, quickly zip up, tucking his erect penis into the top of his underwear, and then heard his wife yell, Do you want any lunch? I'm making quiche.

Katherine, twenty, studying international business, interests include fine foods and drinks, relaxing at the beach or hiking in the mountains, favorite movie—Claire looked up from the phone and said she wanted to know if he was fucking serious. A jogger, a woman, passed by them, moving far off into the grass, and Jay stepped behind his wife, and when the jogger was gone, he asked her to please not read it aloud. She continued scrolling on the phone and read, I can look older, sophisticated, and hold a great conversation, or I can easily slip into a younger role, and you can share some life lessons with me. On the screen, after this sentence, there was a winky, smiling, tongue-out emoji. Is that why you chose this one? She can slip into a younger role. He reiterated that it said she was twenty. She kept scrolling, tripped on a root in the trail, and when Jay tried to grab her arm, pure reaction, though after the reaction he held his steadying hand out to convey his serious concern, she pushed his hand away, and after a minute more of walking, cicada drone rising again, her hand went to her mouth and she said she couldn't believe him. She continued scrolling slowly, the tip of her finger dragging, and when he went to grab the phone, saying what, she pulled away, and told him he was disgusting to her. A group of high-school students passed, long-legged boys with short running shorts and long hair, two shirtless, all of them watching the arguing couple, the woman crying, the man trying to get something from her, reaching, trying to pull a phone away, their voices seeming to be the only sound in the forest, everything else, all of nature, gone, and the boys, coming closer, looked at the ground, fell into single file, passing, holding their breath, and when they were by, they could still feel it for a few minutes afterward, whatever was occurring between these two, until one of them joked, allowing all of them back into their separate world.

She scrolled another minute. High above, the screech of hawk hunting. Yellow and black–winged butterflies flitted by. An earthworm moved on the trail in front of them and without noticing himself do it, Jay moved the worm with the tip of his shoe to the grassy side of the trail. The nearby stream broke over stone and tree and branches and leaves, and all this contributed to the sound of the stream that was more than one sound and was also only a single sound, the stream. In the distance, out of sight, the low, quiet, steady hum of highway traffic. Is this why you wanted me to dress in the schoolgirl thing? He said what, paused a moment, told her of course it wasn't. You looked this girl up, you found her pictures, then you told me you wanted me to dress like a schoolgirl. It didn't happen like that, he said. She said it was such a cliché anyway—she had no idea why she did it, dressed up like that for him, she had felt maybe there was something sick in it, and she wanted him to know now, she thought he was sick, there was something wrong with him, something broken in him. She said that if this was his thing, little girls, which it clearly was, then he was sick. Then she told him he wasn't leaving with them today. She didn't know if he could ever be alone in a room with Sasha again. He asked her not to say that, please don't say that, it's not like that, look at him, it was him, it was still him, he didn't want anything like that, Jesus, she had to believe him. Then he said that he was supposed to be allowed to say what he had to say. She handed the phone back to him and continued walking. Two women with strollers passed by going the opposite direction, both with blonde hair in ponytails, both walking vigorously as they pushed the strollers and babies therein, the women's ponytails flicking to either side of their heads as they passed, both with averted eyes, both single file to get by, almost squeezing by on the trail, trying to avoid the negative energy they could immediately sense coming from this couple, trying to get their babies away as fast as possible, though they were already, however briefly and insignificantly, part of it, feeling it, until, like the runners, their minds shifted to some other focus, the community pool, the colors for their dining rooms, what words the babies would say first.

When the women were sufficiently passed, Jay said that it wasn't what she was thinking. It was only that he liked the idea of a younger woman. The fantasy of it. That was it. Also, it was the reverse of what she said. You dressed up in the uniform, he said. Which I loved so much by the way, and which I know you did too, we have the video of it, and you called me Mr. Principal, which you loved. She said he didn't know what she loved or didn't love. For all he knew, she acted it all out, she pretended, it wasn't that hard to do. He told her he knew what was real and what was real was that tape and her actions on the tape, but that was all beside the point. The point was that all that, the uniform thing, happened *first*. The uniform thing was over a *year ago*—did you think I found this girl like two years ago and waited that long to arrange a meeting? It was literally impossible that what she was saying was true. She was making things worse than what they really were, and he really, *desperately*, wanted her to look at the way things really were, which was this: he had only found this girl in the last month. And he had found her after thinking about *them*, the two of them, of *her*, actually, after watching the video, watching *her*, and in truth, that's exactly why he looked someone up. It had been over a year, they barely had sex anymore, she was so busy with her short films, her art, writing reviews, getting likes on the Internet, doing that whole Twitter persona thing that he hated, but which she obviously loved, making sure people knew how deep and angsty and artful she was. She stopped walking, and he immediately hated that he'd said anything about her, but at the same time, she was involved, somehow, she had to be. They were at a bend in the trail, the stream curving around and creating a pool where children were launching themselves into the water from a rope swing. They hadn't noticed the yells of excitement and joy, nor the way the sunlight came through the open canopy right down into the swimming hole, where the light seemed to show on the water first bright and reflective, and then in the deeper parts, the sediment lit and layered, moving in the slatted light that moved through the water. Are you seriously attacking me right now? Claire said. If you want to know my mind-set, why this happened, you need to know what I was feeling, he said, and what I was feeling was that I lived with a woman who cared about one thing: if she was known and loved as an artist. When your film got picked up by the regional festival, when it started touring the independent festivals, you became obsessed. Think about it. That was a year ago. Don't tell me to think about it, she said. Even though he knew he should stop, he didn't stop. You think because you made a couple short films that people liked and critics noticed that you're somehow important, that because you have thousands of followers on Twitter, you're somehow important. We go out and eat and you think about tweeting about the situation. You think about what to say in tweet that can be funny, angsty, faux deep, playing some malcontent. Two eight-year-olds, both girls, climbed the rope swing and, from a muddy ledge, swung out over the swimming hole and both let go at once, screaming, the forest around them echoing with their yells, the light on the water shattered, their bodies momentarily underwater, then up, and the other children on the bank laughing and yelling to them, and the forest around them suddenly moving in a gust of wind. High on the branch of a pine tree, a red woodpecker, which no one noticed, seemed to be inquisitively investigating the scene, its head cocking and recocking.

What he wanted to let her know was that in the last year she missed the fact that she had a family around her. He felt ignored. So did Sasha. Sasha asked him where Mom was all the time. And he was always telling her work, Mom was, again, at work. I can't believe you're using her right now, Claire said. He felt, despite himself, tears, whose source he could not discern—if he was really being sincere or if he was being manipulative, he didn't know, so lost in his own version of things, and maybe, he briefly thought, that was source enough for them. And so, yes, he continued, we were both alone, and I was the one cooking, cleaning, working too, picking Sasha up, dropping her off, and you were always away, in your study or at a festival, and so I fucked up. I tried to have sex with a prostitute. He viewed himself now like he was watching someone else speaking. They were past the swimming hole, the sounds of the children muted against the cicada hum of the forest. But he didn't, he did *not*, under any circumstances, want an underage girl. He heard himself saying that he was trying to be as open and honest as he could be, and viewed himself trying to appear completely open and honest, which he felt he was, and then he said what he didn't want to say, what he was trying not to say, but he felt it pertained, it was connected, it was part of what had happened and part of who he was, so he continued by saying that she knew that he had a background of abuse when he was younger, just a young kid, that he had been in counseling for it, and he wasn't trying to use that as an excuse, it wasn't an excuse, but she had to know it was a factor in what he liked to imagine, in his sexual imaginings, it was ingrained in him, he was aware, and she knew when he was just in high school that he had bad things happen to him, she knew because he had told her and he was aware that his sexuality was something that he constantly had to work on, that he hadn't had a normal sexual relationship until—You don't get to bring that up, she said. This has nothing to do with that, that doesn't excuse what you've done or even explain. He knew, he knew it didn't, he'd already said it didn't, but what it did do was it showed he knew the difference between what was real and what was pretend, and he would never, never take advantage of a person like that exactly *because of* what happened to him, and he had really and truly gone to the escort service because their bodies were not communicating physically anymore, and he needed physical communication, so he indulged his fantasy, he found this younger woman, but he *understood* it was a *fantasy*, or he thought he did, he knew in reality that she was really like twenty-one or twenty-two because he looked it up and often those escorts lied about their age, to make themselves seem younger, is what he read, and he thought she looked at least twenty-three, maybe older, so he knew he was indulging in a fantasy, but he thought it was only that, a fantasy, and that the reality was that he just needed intimacy, or sex, he needed sex, and the thing was, her problem was that she'd lost sight of the fact that she was actually *living* a fantasy. That she wanted to live some other life and was carrying it out online. That she wanted to be some kind of artist-guru-celebrity. That's been hard, having a wife who was so distant from what was real, her family, that she no longer knows the difference between what's real and what isn't. Fuck you, she said.

The man who had taken the pictures of Bobby was his uncle. The boy's real name was Keaton Meyer, born in 1974. The photos were taken when he was eleven. His parents were going through a divorce in the winter of 1985, and due to the fighting, which often became violent, and also due to the drugs they were both doing, his mother had a moment of clarity in which she understood that it would be better for Keaton to be away from them and at his uncle's duplex, her brother, and that uncle, drunk almost every night, took pictures of Keaton with the Polaroid. Pictures playing basketball on the street, pictures of the boy with his big black lab, pictures of the boy eating mac and cheese, and this made the boy, who was angry about his parents, seem to forget them. One night, after several weeks of showing the boy R-rated movies in which the uncle made him not cover his eyes during the sex scenes, in which the uncle showed him pictures of nude men and women, telling the boy it was completely natural, the uncle told the boy that one of the coolest things he'd ever done when he was growing up was take his first drink, and he made the boy a sugary vodka drink, and after three or four, the boy was laughing constantly, and so was the uncle, since he was drinking too, and the uncle—who had always liked watching the boys on the street but never did anything but watch—now drunk himself, and feeling the pressure of approaching some threshold, told the boy it was time to see what kind of man he was, let him see his muscles, did the boy bring his bathing suit, and Keaton Meyer said he did, ran to the guest bedroom and put it on, and came back out doing bodybuilder poses, which the uncle photographed. And after one more drink, the uncle told him that if he wanted to really be a man, he couldn't be shy about anything, to strip out of the bathing suit, like the movies and photos the uncle had showed the boy, and show his uncle what he had, and the boy did, while the uncle took pictures, instructing the boy to stand with one leg on the coffee table, now just straight up, smile, now touch your penis, no, your other hand, no, hold on to it, now rub it, back and forth, rub, back and forth, harder, good—all this continuing at regular intervals for the next month. The boy would eventually move to a group home after his father was killed in a drug-related car accident, his mother in jail for selling methamphetamine, the state finding his uncle to be an unsuitable parental figure, and in the group home, he would keep to himself, feeling ashamed of his family and himself, and also missing them at the same time, especially his father, who hated his uncle, and he came to see those evenings with his uncle for what they were, and he hated that he'd been so stupid, but he told no one, got through middle school and high school, vocational school, where he learned to be a mechanic, and now worked at a shop owned by the mayor of the town where he lived and he lived alone in a duplex much like his uncle's, spending his free time camping or fly-fishing or playing pool with a group of friends and a woman named Sheila, who, like all the other women, said no to his advances, causing him to wonder what he'd done so wrong to make himself so alone, but then reminding himself that everyone he'd ever known had always been that alone, it was normal, he was normal.

Jay said that it seemed like there was always something more important, that she had to work on an edit, she had some stupid tweet or picture to post, some funny column to write, had to go in to the campus's studio and do some editing—every time there was some chance for intimacy, she had something else to do because she was known now, an Internet persona, Claire Timmons, art-film priestess, sufferer of depression and spiritual anxiety, Internet sage for teenage girls, and not only that, but over time, he had to say, it had become really hard to read all the shit she posted online. All about her—it turned him off some. He didn't like the person she was putting out there, which somehow seemed different from the one he experienced every day. You smile, you laugh, you enjoy things, you have a daughter, you have a husband, and you're still tweeting things like "Fuck me till I realize enlightenment" and "I obsess about you more than you do about me and it hurts" and "Beauty lies within, but I'd rather be hot." It was like living in a house with a teenager who was really interested in her own suffering. Your obsession with how you look, with how others look at you, with what others think about your art, your ardent thoughts, with how much you supposedly hate culture and make fun of it and then add shit to it. Articles about you begin, Claire Timmons, an artist, filmmaker, guru, and writer, has suffered from depression and anxiety all of her life. You grew up in Connecticut. Your father is a wealthy lawyer, your mother was a stay-at-home mom. You have nothing to complain about and all you do is complain and you turned your complaining into art or something that closely resembles it, I don't even know. Neither said anything for a moment, and then Claire began by saying that he needed to pay attention here, he really did, because he was doing it again, what he always did, which was take a situation that was about him and turn it into being about her, and, frankly, she wasn't going to fall for it. She didn't need to defend herself. This was *him*. His fuckup. Not hers. He told her he was explaining his experience over the past year, what it was like living with her in an attempt to explain, not excuse, just explain why he did what he did, and he did what he did because he felt he didn't even know her anymore, she was so obsessed with becoming something to someone. She replied quickly, cutting him off, saying that people liked her because she was honest, she was honest about her fears, her fears about her looks, about her art, about just being alive, her fears about being loved, about being a flawed person, an anxious person, a person who has had depression forever and who has had eating disorders, a person who was addicted to drugs, a person who couldn't deal with reality, and you know what, now she can, she was able to channel these terrible things into funny tweets and/or columns and/or short films and it helped people. Girls write to her to say it helped them. She's giving them something real. You're not giving them anything real, he said. They don't even know you're married. They don't know you have a daughter. It's a persona, she told him, but the feelings behind it are true.

They came to an opening, the dirt trail turning into concrete, the woods ending momentarily, and now, from a different vantage point, they both immediately looked for Sasha, and they found her, still playing soccer with her friends, on a distant part of the field. Outside of the forest, the day was hotter, stiller, and the park was clearing of people. They walked on the connecting concrete path toward another trail, again into the woods. And I know you think my depression and anxiety are just in my head, but I get sick, I've gotten physically ill from it, and I am ashamed of it. I'm ashamed our daughter has had to see me having a panic attack. A grown woman having a panic attack, crying on the floor of Belk. I'm ashamed I can't be like normal people and just pull myself up by my bootstraps, that I have to take medication, but I do. Jay said he'd never said it was all in her head, he'd never say that. You implied it, though, I felt you implying it. He didn't mean to. She knew he was very sensitive to mental illnesses, his sister, she knew, was bipolar, he knew it firsthand, just terrible, and he knew her struggle was real, so he was sorry about that if he implied anything, he was sorry, he really was. She said she couldn't help that she suffered so much, and she was very sorry that this suffering was connected to her talent, her art and filmmaking, and she was sorry people were taking notice of it. If she had a choice, would she choose to be not talented but also not a mess, well maybe, she didn't know, she did like being talented, even if she hated the suffering that came with it. But she was done talking about her. What was he going to say to Sasha?

The second boy, whose photos were on at least five thousand computers in the region, was not named Timmy: he was Alexander Carmichael Andrews, son of Brenda and Jonathan Andrews, abducted from his home after a day at the park with his family. The man who took him was mentally ill, a form of schizophrenia—the man ate mac and cheese for almost every meal, along with Lay's BBQ potato chips, Pepsi, or Mountain Dew. He worked as a janitor at a local high school until he was fired after grabbing a junior's breasts. He'd been hiding in a bathroom stall, pretending to be cleaning it, when he assaulted her while she was washing her hands. The girl's family did not press charges because the man was mentally ill and posed no real threat to society, and, after all, no harm was done. School just wasn't the right environment for him. So he began going to the park, and that's when he took Alexander Carmichael Andrews, aged eleven, told him that it was very hot out, to drink this special drink in his Cutlass Ciera, told him it was hot out, he should drink, his parents would want him to drink, and then took photos of him while he touched and masturbated the boy after the boy all but passed out on grain alcohol mixed with Mountain Dew. Alex Andrews was found because a young couple had seen a boy get into a Cutlass Ciera, an old brown car with a green passenger-side door, and the police deputy knew exactly what this meant, though it took the police several days to interview witnesses from the park and by then the boy had already been sleeping in the man's basement for several days and drinking grain alcohol mixed with Mountain Dew. When they found Alex Andrews, wearing only underwear, dehydrated and intoxicated, there were three bowls of mac and cheese, uneaten, in the basement with him, and the janitor had cried and cried when the police put cuffs on him—the photos the janitor had taken of the boy he had already given to his cousin, Nate McNally, who had made copies and gave or sold them to his various friends who he thought would be interested. Alex Andrews went on to an outwardly normal social life in high school and college, except that he couldn't receive hand jobs, which proved difficult in high school, as they always caused a panic attack in him, and therefore scared many girls away, since it was difficult in high school to tell a romantic interest not to touch him down there, he didn't like it, and it was equally difficult to let it happen and try to willfully stop himself from panicking, and once, in Monica Mabry's Mazda Miata, he hit Monica in the face when she reached her hand into his pants and, after withstanding a moment of rubbing his flaccid penis, she had grabbed it, which felt like a strangling to Alex Andrews, and he'd slapped her away. Even as an adult Alex Andrews could not have his penis touched by a hand, which his Christian wife was happy to accommodate, holding outdated views on sex, including only using it for procreation, and at his job as a pediatric nurse, at his house, at restaurants, Alex peed sitting down only, so that he didn't have to touch himself or see a hand reaching down there and once again be reminded that he lived in a world in which those three days in the janitor's basement were a reality.

They went over a wooden bridge, built, a small sign noted, by Boy Scouts. The water flowing beneath was clear and cold over the rocky bottom of the stream, coming down from the mountains, which had received thunderstorms all week, but which hadn't moved south to the park, remaining trapped in the mountains, and now the rainwater was present in the park as stream water, and it was flowing to the larger river a half mile away, where it would mix with other fresh water from the piedmont, and all would continue moving on to the Atlantic, mixing with seawater, and some of that water would move to the deeper ocean and evaporate in the summer heat, cold air mixing with warm, forming storms out over the deep ocean, which would move inland, which the land and plants and animals would all be fed by, on and on. They rounded through the woods, not talking, sunlight filtering through the canopy onto their faces in flickerings of light, sunlight that the leaves in the forest absorbed and converted into energy, sunlight that intensified in the spring and summer because the sun's rays were more direct at this time of year in the Western Hemisphere, though time was meaningless, really, everything was relational, time was the sun's relation to the earth, which wasn't even time just a relational balance, everything had its own relationship with everything else, and the sun and the earth created a unique relationship, a point in space-time where the universe spoke its presence to itself as a unique harmony, a balance measured out by the people walking on earth in the park as time, not realizing their place in the equation of the balance, and in this way, most of the people running, jogging, playing, talking in the park, mainly adults, viewed the season with either disinterest or as an opportunity for themselves to be outside before it, time, moved again into the colder months, and Jay had the fleeting thought that he would never enjoy a day like today again, and Claire had a similar fleeting thought, and while Jay was trying to explain how he would explain to Sasha, they both hoped, in different ways, that Sasha could have many more days like this that she could enjoy without thinking about time, without thinking about when the days would end, without wondering if she would get sick and not enjoy them anymore, without thinking about whether she could be a better person or if she was a person who was driven by secret desires, or without needing any validation, or any comfort from anything at all, existing simply as part of the balance of things. Jay said he didn't know what he was going to say to Sasha, but if he had Claire's help maybe he could find something that wouldn't ruin his relationship with Sasha. Claire, her anger dissipating now into what it actually was, which was a sadness for herself and Jay and Sasha, said she would do that for Sasha's sake, but not for his, because he didn't deserve it, and his past didn't make him deserve it, and anything he'd just said didn't make him deserve it. He hadn't convinced her and his past was no excuse—this was for Sasha.

Two neighborhoods to the south, the retired accountant skipped over the Latino boy whose name could not be Justin and instead viewed the redheaded boy, whose photos were taken in an artist's studio, the boy whose caption said his name was Davis in the digitally scanned files of the Polaroids, and whose actual name was Anthony Tunis, the artist's loft belonging to his stepfather, a man who was a well-known regional painter in the Middle Atlantic, and who told Anthony's mother, shortly after marrying her, that he wanted to do paintings of their entire family, and so he invited all of the family to his studio and spent several days painting each of them. He painted the mother, he painted Anthony's sister, and he painted Anthony, except that with Anthony, after painting his portrait, he spent several more days with him, explaining to the mother that Anthony was an exceptional model and had fine, elegant features, and a rare skin tone. The mother accepted this flattery and dropped her son off in the evenings, so wanting to please the important painter, for Anthony to have a father again, for herself to be in a good relationship again, and after several evenings, the artist showed Anthony paintings by Monet and Picasso of nude bodies, and told the boy that this was completely normal, this is what painters did, and the boy had to be very grown-up now, and please take off his clothes, the artist was now going to paint him in the nude, and he would make Anthony famous, everyone would know and love him, especially his mother, who would think it was so grown-up of him (once she saw the paintings; they had to keep it a secret for a while, until the painting was finished), and the eleven-year-old boy wanted to be loved, especially by his mother, who he knew had been sad because of the divorce from his father, a divorce Anthony couldn't understand, because his father seemed so good still, and it wouldn't be until years later that Anthony learned his father had deceived his mother numerous times in order to have sex with different women from the college he taught at, and consequently Anthony had gone through a period, as a young adult, where he hated his father, and then stopped thinking about his father after graduate school, and then, later still, after the birth of his first child, didn't forgive, but understood that while his father did terrible things, he had also shared music with Anthony, taught Anthony to read music, taught him to play guitar, banjo, and the piano, and cared for him, and yet, he still blamed his father for the fact that his stepfather, an artist, had brought him to his loft, instructed him to remove his clothes, which he did, and the artist arranged him on the stool, kept arranging him, told him to touch himself here, for the painting, and now try touching himself here, now here, here, for the painting, and took Polaroids, which the retired accountant viewed on his laptop, while his wife, Alicia, prepared lunch downstairs, and which, viewing the last picture of this Davis boy with the artist's hand firmly grasping the boy, made the retired accountant finish in a napkin, the retired accountant's body shaking afterward, the retired accountant suddenly hating himself, though maybe he had been hating himself through the entire act, and, just before closing the photo of the redheaded boy whose name could not be Davis, he saw in the photo, behind the boy on the stool, a window he had not noticed before, a tree out the window, green and full, and the retired accountant stared at it, and held tightly onto the desk to keep from shaking, to keep himself from the understanding that this boy was somewhere in the world, if he wasn't dead, and he was using him, still, as he had already been used, and there was no clear understanding why the tree out the window of the artist's loft conveyed an inexplicable lostness to the retired accountant—an inexpressible and transient intuition that the tree was sunlight, was water, was animal matter, plant matter, human matter, all life, all existence was that tree, and this was truer than anyone could express or hear, the words of it only a delusion, the understanding of it only a delusion, but the actuality of it the only reality—and, so that he didn't have to think about the boy's real name and life, so that he didn't have to consider that he had anything at all to do with him, the retired accountant closed the window of the boy and composed himself and went downstairs and received a piece of quiche from Alicia and after taking a bite, told her that it was just delicious, which it was, and he took another bite just as Alicia smiled, just as Jay and Claire emerged from the trail, as Sasha kicked the ball to a friend, as the artist worked on a new painting, as the escort searched online for menial jobs as a waitress or worse, a hostess, as the mechanic slid from beneath a car, as the pediatric nurse took the temperature of a girl with an ear infection, as the park goers moved to their cars to escape the heat and humidity and other people and mosquitoes in order to get inside where the air was cool and they could all say what a day it had been, so nice, so hot though, a little too hot, too buggy, too muggy as well, too many people, so annoying, some of the kids so poorly behaved, that arguing couple, yelling at each other, crying, what a shame, but a great day, overall, and it'll get cooler soon, this heat is too much really, still what a great day it had been they would say while the inexplicable feeling that they again missed something in the few hours at the park settles like an undetected cancer in their bones.

Ten Body Stories

Aurelie Sheehan

THE TRANSIT OF VENUS

WE LIVED IN NEW YORK THEN. We both wore Paul Smith shirts—you'd found a sample sale where we bought them cheap. I was in the habit of wearing clothes that were too large. My Paul Smith shirt was puffy, yes, but made of fine cotton, a pattern of newspapers (*Le Monde, la Repubblica, The Telegraph*) on a pale blue background. The news: nothing lasts forever, but that wasn't what we were talking about. We were eating dinner in our apartment on Central Park West and 110th Street, and you told me that a new acquaintance—one of the new fast friends you made almost on a daily basis—was a hand photographer, and that he offered to talk to me about hand modeling: the prospect thereof, a career of a kind.

A week later we were sitting in a coffee shop on Sixth Avenue. The windows were bright and out there in the city people went where they were going. Our table was oak, glossed and sticky with spilled Cokes and the swab of a gray cloth. We didn't often go out to lunch, being broke, with no perceived margin. We were out that afternoon anyway, waiting for the hand photographer. You saw potential everywhere, like an explosion. You spent the day making up stories, by evening believing them. Some things really did come true: we lived in a doorman building, after all.

The photographer arrived. You carried the conversation. As we ate soup and drank coffee, my hands grew to monstrous proportion, naked, nasty, beautiful hands. I picked up my cup, fingers wrapped around the ceramic with creaturely determination. I held my spoon with all manner of delicacy. I let my hands drop to my lap, unseen and impotent, and then I slowly lifted them back up again, positioning my right hand in a jaunty splay between you and me, my left in a submissive curl by the fork. All the while the photographer listened to you, and sometimes spoke himself about various recent assignments, and later about a kind of wood you both liked in furniture. He did not, to my knowledge, even glance at my hands. He had an overly large jaw and a thin, long face overall. He was about thirty, with sparse blondish hair, decked out in dorky, non–New York hiking gear.

At the end of lunch, we spoke briefly about my hands. If I were to pursue hand modeling, I would have to target the "wife and mother" market, he said. I would have to, nonetheless and in advance for a matter of months, keep my hands in gloves all day and night. My veins were a problem, the roadways and paths of pale green patterning my skin. A "model hand" had no veins.

I'm attached to my hands. A joke, obviously.

We walked to the subway together, you and me. We'd been going out since college—living together for three years. Where was I going, where were you going? Swaths of time-away-from-one-another in that city could stretch for hours, would easily take up half or more of each day. It didn't seem like our choice, really, rather that we both had busy lives, with jobs and friends and possibilities. What exactly is possibility?

I got a seat on the uptown 1. I pulled my hands out from my pockets and placed them on my knees. We had a dog, two cats, and we'd painted our bedroom Bianchi green, like the bicycle. It was an exceptionally cold winter, but our apartment was hot, especially the bathroom. We had the best bathtub. We ate meals at a small table in the living room near the one window with a park view. I remember lying in the bed together at night, with the red curtains and the pale green walls, and your pink face.

You didn't always feel the lift of endless, almost fake possibility. Sometimes you were tamped down. We were both optimists by nature with a propensity for the wry comment. My hand reached out for your head, felt your hair, trailed down farther, to your shoulder. Did you know that when humans are touching there is a 1/250 of an inch separating them, always? It is in that space that great engines of steam and breath and life collide.

SEX WORKER

I am a sex worker, and it's a good gig, because the bawdy room is everywhere.

I slice pickles for sandwiches and the tense guests await this enactment and then I enact something else, tilting my body so they can see the full, one hundred percent poster-board of who I am. "These sliced pickles might be excellent on your sandwich," I say, moving forward with the platter. It's a descent from the sky, my parachute emanating from behind. My face is large and wide, and then you're taking a camera ride into my mouth, sliding along my tongue, clutched by my throat, and on and on and deeper. I can do one person at a time, but it's especially nerve-racking and advantageous if there's a group around the table, ideally relatives.

Sex is multidimensional. I don't want to be patronizing, but people don't understand how multidimensional we're talking.

At the stoplight. At Target. During the flossing ritual. With insects.

I'm very tired, of late.

But let me start at the beginning of my career. I was naked in my room with the blue shag carpet, standing before the full-length mirror. I saw it—an invitation, an opportunity. This body, as it turned out, was built for something, as a rocket is built to propel into space. It was a job, and the tools were handy.

I launched myself, stealthily draped, into the world. The town center was small, buildings made of brick with white doors. Tentative at first, I took big, slow steps. At the grocery store I bought a plum and a pack of cigarettes. I stood in the dimension and geometry of sun and shade by the liquor store. Men who were like my father but were not my father spoke in boisterous and ritualized tones. Other men sat in passenger seats, in idling trucks, staring forward.

Must we be paid? I don't know about that, but some of my greatest working moments have been at least social in nature. There was the time the man flung himself upon my car. His look through the windshield at me, a lady with her hands on the wheel, a pink blazer. My look through the windshield at him, one cheek smashed up against glass, a comrade or a customer, pretty willing to go to another bar.

It's Saturday. I take off my clothes and lie on a pile of sheets, a big heap of what I could find in the linen closet. I stretch my arms up and over in a dolphin curve; I scissor my legs in slow motion. I don't put on music. I'm already attending to the music of the day: a dove cooing, a police siren, a glimmer of wind, even a neighbor getting into a car. There's a connection between my naked self and these sounds. At times I sense I'm too low . . . I might be better off on a bier or perch. I'm a little landlocked, swiveling here on the floor. Nonetheless

I wrap myself in the variously hued sheets, and wait for sounds to pass through the cloth to my ears.

Sometimes there is a grid element to sex work. Laying myself on the day, I'm an elemental formation, a cloud, and all the particulars of my body become the vastness of time and geography.

Sometimes in a social moment, I have sat with another person in a tent and marked the lines on our bodies, matching the lines together in private triangles and squares. Our blood pumped and coursed, as if we ourselves were planets with obedient rivers.

When I was young and the men hung around the liquor store, and some had already gone in, and some were going in later, I passed through their bodies too, as if they were made of netting, as if all the people were their own grids, and I was just wind, or the noon siren from the fire station, or the smell of lavender.

HEAD GEAR

I open my eyes, which is, to begin with, a deep abrogation, denial, and slight of the black screen within. In there (you know where I mean, we've met there, naked and frank for a change) is a whole other set of recollections, premonitions, and alterations I can't even get into right now. Keep in mind that what I'm saying from here on in, about the so-called life I'm leading? True, yes, important, sure, but unequivocally, cue the blackness, *not the whole story*. So, anyway, eyes open—*oh, to be pitched once more and quite completely out of my cocoon, out from under my velvet snake man, my black jaguar*—my initial perception is one of full-on and obedient immersion in the time-space continuum, nary a time machine in the air. No planes of image, no gnats of recall. Everything around me is pure surface. An ivory dresser. A window with a grate. Textured, rough plaster. A white door. A gold glass candleholder. Cold to the dream, I sit up. I go to the bathroom, come back to the room with the ivory dresser. On a small white table in the closet is where I store my hat. Thank you, Africa. Thank you, church ladies of all sorts. Thank you, Easter. Thank you, Kentucky. Thank you, satanic Arizona sun. Thank you, sports teams. Thank you, civilized men from other eras. Thank you, rappers. I pick up the hat. Thank you, Queen Elizabeth. Thank you, Carmen Miranda. I put it on, and I go, I go like a hustling marathon runner, I go like in a slow-motion immersion docudrama. I have wandered the ritualistic netherworld, and now in my tentacled hat I will make a break for it, lowering my forehead and leaning into the gleam.

A CASE OF MOTHERHOOD

I had a child, and then more children. A child, head turned and chin lifted, eyes shut in concentration, finding in sleep bounties of peaches and pork chops and Raisinets. A child, baby hawk tucked close to my body, flawless rider. A child, amid dinosaurs and their social graces, murmuring instructions, eyes on her creation. A child, decked out in all manner of scarf. A child, smartly outfitted for Washington, DC, with a stuffed dog in her purse. A child, walking to school, balancing guitar, lunch box, backpack, running clothes, art project. A child, adjusting the mirror in the car. A child, a child—and so many children. She is in her room creating. She is in her room dreaming. She is in her room suffering. The walls of her room have dissolved to nothing.

PANCAKE FLOWERS

I am nervous. I feel completely nervous now, and usually I'm at least pretty nervous. Sometimes I hit a plateau of calm (but usually I'm nervous). If the circumstance is promising, say I'm meeting someone for coffee or I'm about to talk in an official capacity, well, I'm a bit jittery going in, then there's a sliding descent, and, ultimately, the moment when I become a large person smashing a flower into a pancake or a large person trying to pick up a tiny flower and put it in a tiny vase on a tiny dresser. Granted, afterward I may experience a kind of calm, or ennui, or at least the mild contemplation of what could have gone better. Usually nervousness comes in anticipation and planning of what I'll do, rather than what will be done to me, but there are exceptions. If there is a flying around of something, a buzzing, darting motion with possibilities of quick nesting and attachment—this gives me a completely different kind of nervous feeling. Let me add that there is also a jumpy intoxication that occurs if I'm standing close to the tracks on a subway platform and a train barrels in. But nervousness itself is not a train, it's more of a boat, a canoe with a solid seat and a long oar I've got both hands on. A person might ask, and with good cause, does gravity keep us up, or is it solely there to keep us down? We remain footed on the ground, but we're not smashed to the ground. Leaden air does not smash us down like pancake flowers, except for when we sleep and dream.

HEART

The heart technician has a shelf full of mysteries to read when she isn't reading hearts. I close my eyes and try to go to the beach in my head, perhaps have a Guinness, while she is reading my heart. Thank you very much, I would rather abstain, for I've already taken the measure of my heart. Here is a small and important valve that moves like coral or leaves in the wind. Not everyone's heart beats in time. Turns out a secret tribe of oyster robots run this place. How does it start, life? *Pa-thunk!* I'm terrified. I'm in love—with my heart. This is the sound of what can be carved out from underneath my skin. A fingertip, an orchid. I think the heart technician must have been drinking last night. She dyes her hair black. She is of a certain age, when hearts start to give out. I am a suitcase that contains a heart. *Ka-thop, ka-thop, ka—a—thop*. Hearts are commonplace. My husband and I have laid our hearts on top of each other and stitched. No political affiliation, can't dress it up. Even naked, you are a sheath for the heart. The heart technician is relentless with her little knob—she's a bitch who doesn't even notice the sheath part. The sound my heart makes is the sound my daughter heard when she was inside my body. She had her own tiny little heart back then, and now it's grown to be a medium heart. My heart is bothering me. Bland brown cereal is good for the heart. Once upon a time my heart, my dreams, and I were cavemen. The strands of my heart reach all the way up to my throat, and all the way down to that whole other soft part. She's taking my heart by force. I'm about to have a heart attack. She's a tin man. She has no heart. My heart is slurping. It's a sea anemone. It's a sea horse. This throb is killing me. If this ever ends and I survive, I want to smash my heart back up near my husband's heart. I want to use my heart to do some Christmas shopping and cast an absentee ballot. I'm a rickety sculpture where my heart lives, I'm a tree, I'm a birdhouse.

Aurelie Sheehan

THE MAUVE NOTEBOOK

When I was a child, I had a small, square notebook with French words and an etching on the cover. It was a color I don't love, mauve, the etching in dark red ink. Inside, I collected quotations.

Shoot for the moon. Even if you miss, you'll land among the stars.

I used austere, forward-slanting, adult handwriting. My plan was to fill the pages with sayings, gathering to myself the words that would hold me together. I scanned books and magazines and waiting-room walls. Kittens in peril, squirrels snacking. You could find plenty of advice at the dentist's, or in school offices, or just about anywhere.

We are all in the gutter, I added, going with the celestial theme, *but some of us are looking at the stars.*

The yoga instructor asks us to do a pigeon pose toward the end of the hour. It's a lean-over-your-bent-leg situation. I get the feeling/thought of someone. Someone is trying to spread my legs, and I'm trying to close them. It's a picture stored in my hip socket. There's a triangle between my knees and the middle of me, *must keep closed, must keep closed.*

Opening.

The shoot-for-the-moon quote isn't actually in the mauve notebook, I discover, finding the notebook in a banker's box in my storage room. Nor is Oscar Wilde. Nor did I start it when I was a child.

I wrote in the mauve notebook my junior year in college, after the summer I spent in Newport, drinking what was left of my mother's liquor cabinet (Rebel Yell was my favorite, for the trashiness aspect). I'd worked all of June and July as a locker girl at the International Tennis Hall of Fame, reading *Tropic of Cancer* on rainy afternoons, or when waiting for tennis players to need new towels or toss me old ones. In the sober, narrow writing I remembered, rather than the moon quote, comes this: *And maybe, when they were left alone with themselves, when they talked out loud in the privacy of their boudoirs, maybe some strange things fell out of their mouths too; because in this world, just as in every world, the greater part of what happens is just muck and filth, sordid as any garbage can, only they are lucky enough to be able to put covers over the can.* Then Goethe, Cocteau, and a Yannis Ritsos poem.

At the same time I'm thinking about the moon quote and the mauve notebook, I'm thinking about a party I went to in high school. At this party they called me Brandy. I thought it was fun to have a nickname. A girl who likes to drink brandy. A driveway. Men. The gutter, the stars, the moon, *sordid as any garbage can.*

Where, then, do these other images come from? Memories, we'll call them—though they don't just verify but also, being mutually exclusive, fuck up my original recollection:

—Me in my bedroom at 10 Sunset Hill, where we lived until I was eleven, lying on my bed and looking out the window to the driveway, thinking about the moon quote.

—Me on my eighth-grade trip to Washington, DC, discovering the moon quote etched in marble at the Lincoln Memorial—I'm looking up near the ceiling, which is difficult in my brace, so I'm more like a hardcover book tilting.

At the party where I was called Brandy it is certain or at least likely that some pushing went on. Legs opening, legs closing. Sitting on a man's lap (fun!). A sense there was more than one fun man at the party, paying attention to me.

Laurie, or another girl, might have first come up with the nickname Brandy.

The notebook's cover illustration is of three animals, *le renard, le loup,* and *le cheval,* invoking, according to some unverifiable sources I've just consulted online, a folktale by Jean de La Fontaine. But I probably never did check the origins of *le renard, le loup,* and *le cheval* back when I was in college, and so associations with the fable, which I've downloaded into a PDF, are of glancing value, or irrelevant.

The mauve notebook contains a sequence of stills. It contains ratios of intent and rebuff, of violence and culpability. I can't remember when I was raped because it felt like I was getting raped all the time. I know this wasn't the case, logically.

because these and those both were hunted
because of this, only because of this, I told you lies

Anyway, I was a child.

The trick is to remember the truth, or to experience a sense of truth when remembering. I am lying faceup among the stars, a hammock of threads from one to the other, a constellation. Or I am lying faceup, the stars above me.

THE POWER OF SEX

The power of sex cannot be underestimated, said I, sitting in the tub. I tried saying it again, with richer overtones. The power of sex, I said, feeling the words down in my throat, a rumbling like thunder, *cannot be underestimated,* I then squeaked.

I waited.

I stared at the unpleasantly modernist "perspective exercise" of my thighs and my feet way down there, a little sturdier than necessary for this day and age. A profound amount of ticking and humming was going on in the world at large. The small men and women, they had cast their gazes up from their toil with the hybrid cattle and radish crops, and they were standing near their thatched cottages, watching me with wide, still faces, taking in the enormity of my thought.

They knew, I knew. They had experienced their own secret heat under tawdry blue blankets. They had been bestowed with prizes at large performing arts centers, and on such nights broken strands of pearls in public bathrooms. They had seen it in themselves, urges besting the virtues of modesty and decorum. Up against their poor little cars—the size of Tonka trucks and Mattel police cruisers. You can never get the damn doors open, but who cares, when you can lean your inch-high self against the inch-high side of the car, lay your minuscule arms above the small roof, making little dents with your teeth.

I sat silent, for a long while. What is power, thought I, a sorrowing giant, only longing to give a daisy to my little peers.

THE OPTIMISTIC WALK

I advise against walking like that. Your optimism is on display, like a worn leather satchel with one wrinkly white shirt inside. It's the natural gait of a very short—e.g., a one-foot-tall—man. It's not reliable. It's not likely to mean anything. Besides, the kind of person who walks like that—what happens when he lies down? His legs keep moving. That's an unpleasant sight, in the hotel room, on sheets whiter than the shirt, with the map of Madagascar in hand. Swivel, swish. *Hold down, lad. Hold down.*

NUDITY

How nude am I? My toenails are crudely cut and I fear not clean enough either. My legs haven't been shaved in days. My stomach and breasts droop, my thighs are ambiguous. I hurried here—I'd planned to shower and shave before the appointment, but I was sick, so I slept right up until I had to leave. Now under the fluorescent lights, the doctor and intern inspect every inch of my skin. They are, in theory, looking at it differently than I am looking at me. This is actually *not* me, I would like to say. For I usually do shave, or give the appearance of shaving. And I wear toenail polish fairly consistently, in the season. I can't adjust for my age, but otherwise not so bad, eh? I exercise and I don't overeat . . . though I admit I seem rather puffy.

Well, whatever, this is staggeringly humiliating. They're both wearing dresses, and their hair and makeup is in order. I'm wearing a patient's demeanor. But couldn't this demeanor be just a little sharper, cleaner, smaller? Another, very nude me is waving a flag in my brain. *Hello, here I am. I'm having a thought now. I'm making a joke now. But you keep trolling over my body with your caterpillar mouths, with your oven mitts and scalpels. After that come the notes, as you define me.*

My Uncle Dave Reads Spinoza as His Cookie Business Collapses Due to a Rise in the Price of Sugar in the Dominican Republic

Peter Orner

FOR A LONG TIME, FROM the early fifties to the middle seventies, it was a good business. He supplied cookies to 4-H Clubs nationwide. They weren't high-end cookies. They were basic cookies, simple vanilla wafers, nearly tasteless, but a cookie is a cookie and even a bland one still has a certain joy in it. Alf Dolinsky made cardboard boxes. The Kuperchmids, umbrellas. Friedman, zippers. Walt Kaplan sold furniture. But Dave Farb produced cookies and a man who produces cookies, God smiles on, at least for a while. . . .

All bodies are in motion or at rest.

A reader, my uncle Dave lamented, without ever saying it out loud, never having gone to college. It wasn't done. Not then. Not at twenty-one, a married man with a daughter. His office above the factory floor stuffed with books. He'd often stay late, his feet on open desk drawer, his glasses shoved up his forehead because he was near- and farsighted and needed bifocals but had never bothered. Plus, he liked the smell of paper up close like that. He's up there now, having sent everyone home early. The *Herald* is on the floor. Enough news. He reads. He can't go home, not yet. She'll read the ruin on his face and Frieda's never been one to accept that ruin's the only constant and that unruin is snow in a Fall River April. Rare but happens. So you can't call the end of a near miracle—twenty-odd years afloat—a catastrophe.

Bodies are individual things that are distinguished from each other in respect of motion and rest and so each body must be determined to be in motion or at rest by another thing, namely another body.

Should be postulating upon sugar and price and cookies and payroll, "things," what Spinoza also calls "substances" and how they are all part of an integrated system proving that a little island in the Caribbean can reach out and plunk a small businessman—but instead he thinks of Frieda sleeping, never at rest, always in motion. For Frieda sleeping is only a brief cessation of purposefulness, not anything resembling repose. How some nights she sprawls across to his side of the bed, nearly touching him. Other nights she balls herself up so tight you'd think she was trying to vanish. And sometimes when he reaches out to her it's as if she feels his touch ahead of his fingers, as if the slow movement of his hand creates wind and that wind breathes in her ear before he even—not a recoil. Just a hardly perceptible edging away. But on other nights it's as if she has a little room to spare and she takes his reaching hand and pulls, yanks him to her side and almost simultaneously into her, hurried but unhurried, now but there is no time, and it's as Spinoza says, they merge, two unrelated things, substances, bodies in motion, together, yes, one, God and nature, something and nothing. And the rabbis said you didn't believe. Wasn't the problem that you believed too much? Am I getting this right, Baruch?

No, they weren't great cookies, but it was a living. She'll read his face. Out the little grimy window, lining the far wall, he looks at the boxes waiting to be shipped. He'll break it to them all tomorrow. They'll go idle in three weeks, maybe a month. Reduce to a skeleton crew, himself, Don G., Clarence, Thompson, Sheila. Friedman will take some of his people. And he's already talked to Walt about Clarence because he used to be a reupholsterer. A month, maybe six weeks, it will be just him and Sheila keeping vigil over the machines he might still be able to sell. The rest, scrap. He'll give up the lease, pay the penalty for early termination. (Talk to Plotkin, possible to write that off?) And then?

All the ways in which a body is affected by another body follows from the nature of the *affected* body.

Tonight, maybe, he'll reach for her. And maybe his hand will stop short before she can feel its wind and so remain an unaffected body, if not at rest, separate, contained, alone.

But another night—

Left Hand Jane

Gregory Norman Bossert

Was a Left Hand Jane. You know.

She said (doing her voice here) she said, "If I knew where I left it would I be in this dump?"

The way the veins sucked the blood back in as fast as it flowed out the arteries with the sound of a straw reaching bottom? The wrist bones stacked like old ivory dice? The drifting silver lace of nerve? You know.

The Left Hand Jane, she kicks the door open with high-laced boots, blinks daylight from her eyes until she sees the length of the bar, leads off with that left arm, a few drops of blood flung too fast for the veins to reclaim splatting on the wood.

Her right sleeve tucked into her jacket pocket, the bulge of gloves tissues a comb a stick of gum a switchblade knife but no hand on that side either. A trained eye can tell.

She rolled her eyes and said, "I know where the *right* one is. Got a thing, not your business. Not like I can't get by with one, anyway it's just a couple of weeks. But now the other one's gone missing and things are getting a little, you know . . ."

She said, "Oh, hah hah, like I haven't heard that one a dozen times."

(Look, can't do both voices, yeah? You'll have to pick up the slack.)

She said, "*Nuh* uh. Fifty up front, the rest when you find it. It's not like it was stolen, or—" She rubbed the blood spots into the bar with her forearm, pale hairs so blonde they were white gone green in the neon bottle glow, freckles like inverse stars. "—Or run off or anything. I just left it somewhere. *You* know."

Used the bar phone to call in a ride from the Agency. Time enough to go over the facts, dotting eyes with a fingertip in the rings on the bar. The Left Hand Jane:

Said she went by Leena, went by Carolyn, went by a lot of names on her way from where to here.

Said she'd noticed her right hand missing round midnight, reaching up to turn the lights out.

Said she'd found *this*, fumbling in her pocket and swearing. Finally pulled it out for her, she with her arm up over her head, unoffered, and grimacing. Hadn't figured her for squeamish but some people. You know.

A matchbook. "Sélavy's" and a lipstick kiss in rose.

Said she's never been there, said, "Not *my* sort of place. Not . . . all together, anyway." Said, "Look, it's a clue, right?" (Keep up your end, now. I've got hers.) Said, "This town *is* a B movie, bud."

Said, over her shoulder stomping out in those high-laced boots, she wasn't done.

Agency sent Morris, long-armed lunk but a fast walker, hat hung off the back of his head like he glued it there. Swung me through the workday crowd, south on Seventh until downtown sagged into outtown, left on Swanson and down the hill where the sidewalks were more crack than not and loose-limb hustlers hid from the sun in the shade of streetlamps. You know.

Was a marker joint. No name over the door, just that rose kiss bracketing a peephole. Sort of place where five bucks will get you lips in smeary black, two Os for eyes. Red lips? Permanent marker? Paper mustache or cotton-ball hair? That's extra.

Morris tipped his hat back an improbable inch farther with his wrist. "Catch ya later, boss."

No doorknob, no bouncer, no coat check, just a corridor and a second foot-high door, saxophone pooling under it. No knob on that one, either, but it swung open just the same.

Seems those unlocked doors were enough to keep the outtown out: one look made it clear five bucks wouldn't get you a dot from a dull pencil in this place. Tall tanned fingers tottering on French nails, heavy gold pinkie rings with designs picked out in diamond dust, a booth of high rollers flashing googlyeyes and real lipstick, dangling cigarettes like ring fingers, cigars thicker than thumbs.

The staff wore sequined gloves or socks like trout in the barlight: fast, cool, silent. A buck dropped on the bar sank without a bite. Bartender wouldn't have admitted the matchbook at all, hadn't been a stack just like it on the bar. But a blonde left hand on its own, a dusting of freckles, and the nails chewed in clean curves? Bartender pursed Sharpie lips like the very idea of the thing was absurd.

(Left Hand Jane hadn't mentioned the chewing but a trained eye can tell.)

Found a corner table and watched the crowd. Band was playing show tunes half-tempo, a single couple fingers intertwined dancing in slow small circles like they'd been unwinding since the night before. A curtain-covered opening in the wall, could have led backstage but every now and again a full glass went through and came back empty.

"You know how to use those matches, Knuckles?" She had a long curved arch, a twenty-dollar pedicure, anklebones that could cut a diamond. Her stiletto heel cost more than this job would earn.

Flicked a match with a thumbnail and gave her a light. She watched the dancers while her cigarette burned down to the gold, a smudge of ash on her little toe. Band looped round an old, old tune that some called "Lillian," some called "Recercar."

"You only interested in blondes, Knuckles?" She stubbed the cigarette out, dropped the butt into the glass. "Or maybe you're a nail biter, huh?" She wiggled her toes; gold flecks flashed in the scarlet enamel.

(An easy line here. Don't forget the pause, the self-deprecating smirk.)

"A *particular* blonde, huh? You're in the wrong place for that, Knuckles. Everybody here, they're trying to be somebody, know what I mean? You don't get into the backroom if you're not somebody. And you can't be somebody if you're too particular."

(Her voice is easy to do, a husky alto, an anywhere-else accent about as real as the ruby in her toe ring. Not like the Left Hand Jane, whose voice had been laid down one tone, one town at a time, a history of county highways and truck stops stacked like sedimentary strata. You know.)

Band took a break but the dancing couple kept at it, the staccato scrape of fingernail on floor tile. One of the high rollers lost an eye, spun pupil-rattling across the dance floor, staff scattering like koi after a tossed coin. All eyes on the eye, big spenders and hoi polloi alike laughing, shouting bets on whether it would roll out the door before they caught it.

Through the curtain, then. A corridor, a left turn, another curtain. The backroom.

Was a sight.

Then a fist like a truck, back out of the backroom and around the corridor corner like a cue ball. Why they call them bouncers.

But, before that, was a sight:

A hand, four dark slender fingers and a fifth—pale and pored, dark hair curled between heavy joints—where the thumb should be.

An ankle, hinging a hand on either side like wings.

A foot with fingers for toes and a long look-down-it nose on the instep.

A tangle of mismatched fingers under the jelly globe of a breast, no nipple but a single blue eye.

A hand a foot a knee a jaw a spidering of ribs a tight-curled shag of hair, all stolen away from somewhere, someone, all jumbled in that sight.

A stage and on it two long fingers, ringed with gold and diamond, spread a fan of trembling, translucent ears.

Was a sight, was a fist, was darkness.

Was darkness. Night, an alley, a hand like a mirror on the arm of a black-sleeved bum planted in a bed of rubbage.

Stumbled streetward, used the phone in the all-night coffeehouse at the corner of Swanson and Crawford to call the Agency, soaked in a cup of joe thick as mud.

Could have been worse, considering.

What was in the backroom wasn't against the law. *Was* no law could cover something like that. Parts gone missing, well, who could expect a body to be of one mind all the time? They come around, eventually, or if not, there are those will track them down. You know. But parts out of joint, no regard for source or sequence, wasn't even wrong. Wasn't *done*.

"Wasn't done."

Left Hand Jane with her lace-up boots and her right hand not my business. "I'm not done," she'd said.

Her number, palm-scrawled and smudged, answered on the first ring.

She said, "When I said 'later' I wasn't thinking now."

She said, "What you got we can't do over the phone?"

(Might as well make the offer. It's not sincere. Just snag her interest.)

She said, "I don't want the fifty back, I want my damn hand."

She said, "All right, all right, I'm up anyway. Twentieth and Bleaker, number four. I'll leave the light on."

Morris showed up, bleary-eyed and bent brimmed. "Yeah?" he said. "You should see yourself, Boss."

Uptown under late-night neon, a cricket buzz, and firefly flicker, Morris humming a bass line against the snare slap of his leather soles, making good time. "Sure you don't want me to come in with you, Boss?" when we were there. "Suit yourself then."

She didn't leave the light on.

She said, "It's open."

Left Hand Jane was in a chair by the window, cut out of the stripes of the blinds, a hole in the dark where one eye caught the light.

Those boots by the door, still laced half up the shin and everything below that stuffed with newspaper.

(Get straight to the point now, but phrase it as a question, not an accusation. She is the client. This is the job.)

She said, "I told you, the right hand isn't your business."

She said, "Wasn't the left's business either. 'Let not thy left hand know,' you know?" A beat, an underscore of blood burbling. "Guess it could have figured it out," she said. "Guess *you* have."

She opened the blinds and the streetlight spilled over her shoulder and into her lap. She still had the shoulder, the lap. Not much else.

She said, "The feet went first, ran off together end of last month. Happened before. They get the itch? They hit the road. But I always catch up with them soon enough. This time, though, nothing, not a call, not a postcard. So, yeah, I send my right hand after them. Right hand knows her way around, you know, knows the secret places. And then the left must have gone after the right. And now . . ."

Her left leg up to her knee, right up to her hip, the hip itself, left elbow, left ear, right eye, gone gone gone, white button shirt mis-buttoned at an angle that said shoulder chest belly ribs all in disarray. Nerve bone blood marked every missing part, blood bubbling like springs, bone like stepping stone, nerves branched and swaying. Left Hand Jane had gone to nature.

Left Hand Jane didn't bat her eye at the backroom of Sélavy's. "Got no problem with that, they want to try something new. They don't have to sneak off to do it. Ought to trust myself. Me. I. Not just a sack of parts."

She said (trying to capture that voice, vinegar and cracked panes), she said, "What would *you* know? You aren't even a *you*. Someone sitting single-handed while you go about *I*-less, picking through other people's scattered lives?"

(Be honest now. She's earned it.)

She said, "Sorry, sorry, I didn't know. Look, just find my left hand, yeah? I can take it from there. Always have. Not too proud to admit that sometimes I need a . . ."

(Your line is "Helping.")

Was morning. Agency sent Kathleen, Morris slumped home and shut-eyed, no doubt, under that hat of his. Kathleen took the long way down the boulevards, an easy slow stride, a houndstooth jacket with deep dark pockets, a chance to think.

Thoughts clung curled like that couple on the dance floor at Sélavy's: a drop of blood black in the bottlelight, Left Hand Jane in a pool of light, drifting like leaves let go from a branch, silvery shapes darting in and out, the sequined staff of Sélavy's, knows the secret places. Ears fanned like a flower and one petal's fragile pink dusted with freckles.

Awake on that fading image. Sélavy's.

Kathleen chuckled. "Sélavy's? Boss, we got here ten minutes ago. I reckoned you needed the sleep, though."

I shook off the pins and needles. Those doors were still unlocked but the joint was all but empty: bartender wiping down a last few glasses, band packing up, a handful of working stiffs slumped in a booth around steaming cups.

"Hey, Knuckles. Looks like you could use a slug from the mug." Hadn't recognized her slipped out of her high heel and into a nylon sock with a hole over her little toe, a glimpse of gold and scarlet polish. "Any luck with your *particular* blonde?"

She said, "Working *here*?" Anklebone shrugged under the sock's elastic. "Who can tell? Those sequined gloves ain't just for show. Place like this, you work here, you might not want . . . normal folk to know."

But next to her thin brown fingers snapped in a tattered black knit fingerless glove, said, "Freckles, blonde, chewed nails? Yeah, been working tables the last few months." Said, "No, no, not a left, a righty. Just got off shift. You missed her by ten minutes."

(Back to Bleaker? Better ask.)

Tattered glove said, "Uptown bus? No, no, she's got a place round the corner, on Swanson over the coffee shop."

Kathleen was squatting on the sidewalk, playing knucklebones against two grubby gum-chewing kids. She nodded, "Swanson and Crawford, yeah, I know the place, Boss. We can be there six, seven minutes. Hop on." She winked at the kids and swept tensies.

*

Was a head-height door on Swanson, round the corner from the coffee shop, and behind that a narrow, sagging staircase, a back door opening on a sun-flagged courtyard and the sound of hopscotch. "Be out back if you need me," Kathleen said.

Up a flight, squalling babies on either side, mothers smoking in the hallway, studiously paying no mind to who might be taking the stairs. Another flight, radio from a half-closed door, a crowd cheering or maybe screaming, the thud of a cheap steak being tenderized.

Another flight, top floor, and the door on the left had the latch taped over. A knock was enough to swing it open.

She was in a chair by the window, a mirror of the Left Hand Jane, but it was all sunlight here and she was *shifting* in the seat. What had the Left Hand Jane said? *A sack of parts.*

Not the Left Hand Jane's slow, still tone either, but a babble of voices all chattering down different paths. Not a *she* at all. A they.

"Hey, pal, what gives?" they said. "Who the hell do you think you are?" they said.

(That's a laugh.)

They said, "Who *I* am ain't your business."

But the left arm—that pale halo of hair and still a smudge of blood by the wrist—said, "You're the detective from the bar. Heh, looks like we *are* your business."

There was more here than there had been left at the Left Hand Jane's place last night. And some here that *had* been at the Left Hand Jane's place last night, that must have run afterward. Both arms both legs both feet an ear an eye a sweep of hair over one shoulder and enough in between to hold it all together. Everything a body needs.

Everything, that is, except a left hand.

They said, "Isn't *me* who's running, is it, pal? *She's* the one been on the road since she got the nerve to let her feet go. *Our* feet now, and I got a place of our, *my*, own to put 'em up."

"Done with running," the right foot said.

They said, "I've got jobs, I've got friends, I've got a chance to, you know . . ."

The right hand waved toward the window, rooftops scattered against a cloudless sky, a breeze heavy with grill smoke and a hint of sea salt, the sound of Kathleen counting to ten.

They said, "Yeah, exactly, to *make* something of myself. That's what this town is about. That's why everybody is here: to make something of themselves."

(Maybe you believed that too, once upon a time. But there's a simpler explanation.)

They shifted against each other, not all together comfortable, said, "So what if it *is* the end of the road? Sometimes you gotta run through the easy choices before you have the nerve to stick with the hard ones. And if it is the end of the road, just means that going anywhere else from here is going backward."

They said, "Yeah. Even going back to *her*. We've moved on."

The right hand fished out a cigarette. "Gotta light?"

Was still a match in that matchbook.

(If you're doing the voice, now would be a good time to say—don't forget the smoke and sunlit chatter through the window and the subtle shush of waves—say, "Keep it.")

The matchbook with that pair of lips on the cover, maybe not truly what they need. But maybe close enough. You know.

They said, "Thanks, pal."

And the right hand said, "Sélavy's? Gave me the idea for this. For *us*. Guess you figured that, huh? Sure, the backroom gets a little . . ."

(You already know this line.)

Right hand said, "Oh, hah hah, like I haven't heard that one a dozen times."

(Remember the left hand. This is the job.)

The right hand said, "The left hand. Yeah, she tracked me at Sélavy's. Must have found this matchbook." Those printed lips tilted in a pout. "I convinced her to come here, to meet us."

They said, a sloppy, shifting chorus, "To meet *me*."

The right hand said, "But the left hand wasn't ready."

They said, "She kept saying—the left hand, I mean. Man, this gets confusing. The left hand kept saying, 'But *she* needs us. What can she do without us?'"

A foot said, "That's the point. What *can* she do without us? So why does *she* get to call the shots?"

The right hand stubbed the cigarette out, smoke swirling between fingers, said, "But the left hand wasn't ready, so I thought, we thought—"

They said, "—I thought if we could keep her here, if she could see what we were building . . . And by then the left arm had showed up, so it was her old spot, after all, nothing . . . you know . . . strange."

The left arm rubbed ashes from the arm of her chair. "The left hand didn't want to stay. But I held on as hard as I could. I'm not proud of that."

They said, "But I dozed off for a bit, while my right hand was pulling her shift at Sélavy's, and the left hand slipped off. Back to *her*."

Those matchbook lips laughed. "Left Hand Jane, that's what you call her? Left hand's *all* she's got now."

(But that isn't true, is it?)

They said, "Go on then, pal. To your hired body go and run on back to her, your Left Hand Jane, for your fifty bucks, for whatever else you think she's got for the likes of you. *Last* thing she needs, *another* left hand."

But . . . the left arm held itself out, a curl of nerve like the last wisp of cigarette smoke, and said, "Unless *you* want to stay. We've got an opening."

But . . . at the same time the feet shuffled and stubbed against each other, as if, in part, ready once more to run.

But . . . at the same time the right hand said, "Tell the left hand, damn it, tell your Left Hand Jane we miss her."

But . . . at the same time those rose matchbook lips quivered, twisted, gasped fire.

(Hush. You've got no lines here. Just watch.)

They, her, *this* Left Hand Jane, she almost came apart. A head of flame swirled like a rose, like the Left Hand Jane's hair were it let out in the sunlight.

A moment where each part lost its head, each headed their own way.

A moment, and then they took a breath.

And then they took a breath.

And then *she* took a breath.

Was a thing to behold.

Under the window under the midday sun children were laughing and Kathleen in among them, singing some rhyme almost remembered. Re-membered. Such bright voices. How would the Left Hand Jane stand that light?

This Left Hand Jane, she took another breath, deep and slow. The matchbook had burned itself out but the lips were still there, somehow, though curled up a bit at the edges.

She said, "Never mind your ride. I can give you a lift."

(One last line for you, and the job is done.)

She said, "Yes. Back to her. Can't face myself, what kind of a person am I?" She held out her left arm. The blood, the bone, the nerve.

You know. She held out that arm and laughed and said, "What have I got to lose?"

Uptown, then, her steps fast and light, a patter like wings, and from the street outside she could see the blinds were open, but inside it was dark.

Was too late.

I was too late.

Those high-laced boots were still there, the newspaper pulled out and spread smooth on the floor.

I said, "All she's got is the one hand." I laughed again. "How far could a Left Hand Jane go?"

The newspaper was open to the shipping schedules.

I said, "Look, it's a clue."

Shanghai, Singapore, Sydney. Guess this town isn't the end of the road after all. You know.

How far could a Left Hand Jane go?

I said, "Let's find out."

Winter Levitator
Three Iterations of Venus

Mary Caponegro

—For Fern Seiden

I.

BOTTICELLI PRESENTS HER STANDING, nude yet demure, poised with impossible balletic grace on a shell, exerting herself not at all—although Zephyr's distended cheeks reveal the effort behind her ease. Her cloak awaits her on land, suspended in her attendant Hora's arms, but for now her magnificent red hair will do. Abundant, it covers pudendum and one breast, thereby suggesting modesty. Roses and violets are at her disposal.

The clam shell is nearly at shore, but when it makes contact with land, it might jar her already precarious posture and cause her to fall. For a woman whose stance defies physics, she is serenely oblivious.

II.

Or perhaps she entered the world recumbent?—as in Cabanel's depiction: likewise fully grown, her odalisque figure so sumptuously horizontal, her curves mimicking those of the sculptural waves upon which she is buoyed. Since her languorous thighs provide partial camouflage, no fig leaf is needed; thus her golden-red hair is left free, like a glorious seaweed that melds with the foam of the cresting waves. Arms raised, she bares both breasts to the sky, her indolent body inclined slightly upward, with torso tilted back, as if sinking into a chaise longue—the better to fashion a landscape for our eye. But there is no danger of her literally sinking, for she is sensually one with the sea and immune to it simultaneously. No portion of her body is immersed; she floats as if a tabletop figurine, edge to edge, although she is, as previously stated, all curve.

Artwork by Fern Seiden.

III.

Reverse the image, such that the recumbent figure, transposed from color to black and white, transported from sea to land, is positioned opposite, with her head pointing left, her feet pointing right.

This Venus, also a fully grown woman, is not born of water, and borne by the waves, but delivered from heaven, perhaps thrust down by no longer present clouds, or herself a mysterious form of cloud, a unique meteorological phenomenon.

Or perhaps born of earth, like flora that blossoms at a distance, like an orchid whose roots are in air.

The Winter Levitator's hair, much shorter than that of her predecessors, suggests neither seaweed nor vine. Not long enough to be trellised across neck or shoulder or hip, it cannot stand in for a fig leaf. Thus a small, dark, rectangular patch blooms from the furrow between her thighs, while her bent arm shields one breast from view, like her Renaissance ancestor. These are not, in her case, deliberate gestures, neither brazen nor coy, merely natural. This cannot be said of the much longer dark patch below her, seeming to float just as she floats, and seemingly made to her measure.

The Winter Levitator has none of the coyness of Botticelli's Venus; her shadow, however, *is* coy. And brazen. The shadow transforms her position: her relation to the lightly frosted field. She appears to be placed directly atop the table of earth as neatly as Cabanel's Venus is laid across the edge of the sea. *Until* we perceive that this black smudge that lies a short distance below her, the smudge that might have marked the space for a second body, or the equivalent negative space of her own body, that is to say, that might have marked her grave, is actually the ionized shadow that holds her aloft *above* the earth on a table of air; the earth from which, it appears—had she ever made contact—she has already risen.

Unless she both lies on the earth and floats over it simultaneously, willfully paradoxical.

Therefore, the Winter Levitator needs no cherubim to form an adoring, protective cloud above her, or announce her arrival through conch shells. She is her own cloud, this Venus, fierce yet serene, able to brave the harsh season as well as the temperate, hovering over the barren earth. The field's delicate frost yields no blossom but her unostentatiously regal body, suspended a few feet above the ground: this transmuted goddess, her pedestal neither a shell nor the sea but the sun's dark echo of her form.

Clytemnestra's Body Polis Ticks

Anne Waldman

Sensemaya, the snake
Sensemaya
Sensemaya, with its eyes
Sensemaya,

—Nicolás Guillén

Be such a strong fact
You would sleep
of those I kill

Milk running over

Name a variant of "scheme"

To act not hurt? a body

Render it barren, body's politic

Nor spill dripping rain
Athene demands *Turn it up*

The hungry Syrians

& who's up for rule?
A *labrys*, the double head

Ax for thought

Carnage for thought

Suffer eclipse
Can't see can't see the syndicates
but see their murder spill forth

For want of a brain
        yet I have
without wine
succumbed
this crazy election

Unhooked the little-box-world

Men are stumping their speeches

White bodies in the horror void
      whose desiccated lips spew oil

I can't be media for want of a brain

Stains set you free after vetting
      secret pacts and deals
go crazy with conspiracy

I always vote beside the hearth
      keep my house alive
be not a murderer of sleep

Bloc at the feet, the heart, the eyes

For want of a brain stem
   the nukes go free

   All my arrows were the candidates

   Ur-this, the ur-that, ur-person
   one who told a story, silly, too long

Aggrandizement

The self goes down. . . .

In augury with a nuked family body

Anne Waldman

For want of a society the bees run free

For want of a tibula, the world strums

Sisters elect of our wonder; a barker:
   pearls and blue beads
cobalt stuff
   a prison outfit

For want of obstruction
    run free, O body in chains

& the other one had a cuff link perhaps

Will others don?

Will swear?

Keep an upright way, Amerika

Pancake makeup & pundits
sway to a better idea?

  When greater disaster comes
  robber baron is all you are

Helm of my psychic state will not go gentle

Out of the riches, yet
   midgrips for the temps on strike in Michigan

This is not a red state
This is the city of Pallas

Alive in the estates of the father

Enough, cry hold
      poison darts

& they come from a mocking tree
in ritual misadventure
          All who stroll across oaths

Hunted beast slips from our nets

Gone to Sambhogakāya,
          timeless body of light

Won't sleep me with me no more no more no more
   for want of a bed

Charioteers go on strike
  for want of a whip

Mount the statue of Athene
    and her plebes, suckle at bitter breast

Eyes with blood
who cannot see it's plain to see

Stain & power, a powerwall's streets

Receive your call

In secrecy of night
  spring clear for want of an ear

Hear what it calls to all minions
   resist retort reclaim

For want of a tongue
    the world crumbles

You cannot get my dream,
    Furies
            for want of imagination

Whimper

For want of an ark
  you cannot get me an ark

For want of the sea
For want of my solace

A kind of dramaturgy

Go Hermes
   help me pour these lustral
   waters

Or get up, feet
   for want of a mother-snake

Or hound whose thought of hunting has no shape

Sic 'em
Let go, bloodshot breath
Vital's heat

The dumb TV waken, speak severally
  no more promises

In the town hall
you want plurality

Try a whole matricidal chorus
        vamped up for this

For want of a forum

Let stabbing voice of the Etruscan speak

Let her breathe
A single ballot can restore a tree house

O god of the younger generation
under pods
  A future cruelty

Serpent power of sinewy cruelty

Or staggering beast wore out its time . . .

"Fuck land & bring your ton of hatred upon it!"

Tyranny not bring your bulk of
  hatred on anything

Really, but

Civility? I promise you a void

I promise you a place
in the sacrosanct booth

Jagged loners eat the seeds

Or I'll accept all devotions by you, citizens

(Медве́дь не тро́нет мёртвое те́ло.
 A bear will not touch a dead body.)

Slum Melody

Jorge Ángel Pérez

—Translated from Spanish by Rebecca Hanssens-Reed

I WAS NONCONFORMIST since I was a child. I knew I was the ugliest of my siblings. Despite Mother's hard work to make our ringlets shine, the neighbors would say, "He's horrendous" as they snickered, unaware of the anxiety their laughter could trigger in me. In truth, I didn't give much credit to their jabbering. Mother, stroking my hair, swore I was a cutie pie, her precious boy. I tried to believe it, although my sister Eneida always looked at me with such pity. So, even though it was painful, I started spending long hours looking at myself in the mirror to confirm my ugliness. I had few references for beauty. No one in my family was overwhelmingly attractive, but I noticed my face was more like a man's than a child's. It lacked the tender features or softness that would give me a childlike appearance; now, as an adult, I have a girlish face.

Since I opted for solitude after continuous mockery from my peers, I ended up discovering, in my days of retreat, a passion for reading. In only a few weeks I read the entire collection of *The Treasure of Youth*. With reading I learned to experience a certain satisfaction in isolation. I'd been dour, withdrawn, until I realized I could leave my sanctuary and show off what I'd learned, dazzle everyone, prove that I was different. I wanted my ugliness to be overlooked in favor of my knowledge. Before long I could list, off the top of my head, the name of every single Egyptian ruler, every member of the crustacean and orthoptera species; however, nothing moved me as much as expounding on the Bourbon dynasty in France. In front of admiring eyes and attentive ears, I would wave my little hands as I described the outfits flaunted by the Marquise de Pompadour at Louis XV's fetes. With my performances I could move everyone in my court in our living room in Mantua to boisterous, flabbergasted applause. Mother and Father were the only incredulous ones; irritated by my veneration of the French court and my exalted performances, they finally forbade them.

Again I chose solitude, my bedroom mirror becoming a silent witness, an anxious spectator. If someone were to ask what my first literary achievement was, I would without hesitation answer, *The Whims of Jeanne Antoinette Poisson.* To tell the truth, I never actually wrote the piece, but my ability to improvise combined with the things I knew about the Marquise de Pompadour enabled me to recite fantastic sermons. In a monologue, my marquise would describe her relationship with Louis XV. From my house in Mantua, Jeanne Antoinette Poisson strolled through Paris, longing to go to Versailles, where she was certain she could win over Louis XV. She went to visit a fortune-teller once, who foretold a splendid, promising future in which she would conquer the king. Flirtatious and seductive, I presented myself to the Bourbon monarch. "We met for the first time in the Forest of Sénart." I fluttered my eyelashes and twirled on my feet, pretending to adjust my enormous dress, my neck held high to show off how many times I'd looped the long expanse of my pearl necklace. Transformed as the capricious Jeanne Antoinette Poisson, I, at my bedroom mirror, was no longer plebeian. I'd earned a title: Marquise de Pompadour. Voltaire wrote me poems, Dagé did my hair, Supplis tailored my dresses, for attending banquets as well as for theater performances. Everyone was dazzled by the luster of my clothing, yet none of them even fathomed all the silver and gold that coated my dresses. This simulation of beauty—the fantasy of my life as the Marquise de Pompadour—assuaged, at least for a while, the anguish of knowing I was horrendous. Imitating her beauty, I discovered mine. I tricked myself. My passion for La Pompadour drove me to read everything about her life. Hidden away, I devoured *Madame de Pompadour and the Court of Louis XV*, by Émile Campardon, or sometimes the book *The Marquise de Pompadour* by M. Capefigue. To supplement my knowledge I read Richelieu's memories of the Duke of Luynes, among others from my very extensive list of titles. And though I studied all of this, leafing through thousands of pages, I was still only skimming the surface. Such was my obsession that I successfully saw to an end the project of reading every review of the marquise in French. It's for this reason that all my friends, from any era, like to joke that I speak eighteenth-century French and my pronunciation shows I never had a good teacher of the Gallic language. Everything I did then was because of the marquise, but still I didn't know everything. All I had to work with was her biographers' descriptions. I knew that her eyes never shone one defined color, that in them one could detect every emotion—nostalgic at times, in other moments pleased, but always seductive. I knew she was tall, attractive, good mannered, an excellent actress, and even better singer, but

I was missing a closer look, something to complete my understanding; I needed a portrait.

I've indicated my penchant for iconography and my passion for portraits and how I use them to spur revelations. Eneida, ever alert to my whims, showed up one morning with an image: a portrait of the resplendent lady, done by François Boucher. After staring at it for a while, verifying that as much as he tried to capture her poise and beauty he only partially achieved it, I stowed the gift in my wardrobe, with my most prized talismans. I stood with her portrait at the mirror, her face next to mine—as the skull of Ara's embalmed beggar would be years later, propped on the typewriter. Our reflecting faces appeared in the silver. If La Pompadour was, as they said, an example of beauty, then I was one of horror. I tried to reproduce, at only seven years old, the exact pose of La Pompadour: I fluttered my eyes, over the dressing table I let one hand rest, languid, as Jeanne Antoinette did on a piano. Such a disappointment! Even if my body was draped in chiffon and gemstones, even if the gold and silver encrusted in my regal dresses were the shiniest in the world, even if I craned my neck adorned with diamonds, I would still be ugly—ugly and a boy. The least visible candelabras of Versailles, the dimmest lights in all their palaces, were magnificent compared to my little figure reflected in the mirror. I made even the tiniest stone in La Pompadour's headdress seem fabulous.

My knowledge of this woman's life brought countless revelations about my own. I longed to be Madame de Pompadour—the marquise who no one, not even Louis XV's legitimate wife, Queen Marie Leszczyńska, dared to challenge. She, *the* Jeanne Antoinette Poisson, did whatever she wanted with the king. One's role in the court depended on how well he or she behaved around the king's favorite mistress. But my poor juvenile soul didn't just long for her magnetism, her dresses, and her jewels, the power she wielded over every mortal of Versailles. The flatness of my chest plagued me, as did the little thing dangling between my legs. How I wished I had Jeanne Antoinette's female attributes, far different from my mother's and sister's modest bosoms. She was the pinnacle of femininity. Agitated with the desire to have a woman's body as gorgeous as that of the king's favorite lady, I began to scorn my pants and my Sunday suits; I yearned to flaunt Madame de Pompadour's dresses, her pearls, to be the marquise of France, and most of all I wanted to be a man's mistress.

Yet we were irreconcilably different. She a woman and I a man. She beautiful and I ugly. Everything about La Pompadour was balanced:

round breasts, with a precise space—no more, no less—poised in between. This hollow was a space distinct from the breasts' immensity; it made her perfect, giving in to her defined slopes, to her exuberant, exact beauty. I've always thought that it is the space that, annoyed with a body, besieges it; a space permeates, for example, the totality of a skull, depresses it on one side so that a lump rises on the forehead, or anywhere else on the body. It is the space that shapes a beauty, an ugliness, it gives the proportions that one desires, bestowing terrain to fat people, taking it from skinny people. With her, the space was prodigious, with me it was stingy, or the other way around. I was the contrary of Madame de Pompadour, her antonym. When the space was shaping my genitalia it must have been entertained, giving me more terrain than I needed; instead of growing inside me, forming a deep hole, it allowed the dangling thing to extend down, to interrupt the reign of the space. Where I should have flaunted a clitoris, a penis grew. And my body's prolongation into the space, this mortal error, has tormented me. I would rather the lines of my body had softened and blurred into the space. I would rather not exist than be a man.

With this truth recognized, my first amorous *affaire* ensued. An uncle used to come to visit us at our house in Mantua. As soon as he announced he was visiting I wouldn't move from the front door until I saw him, and would then run to greet him and return home hanging around his neck. Uncle used to fawn over me, tickling and teasing, lavishing me with more attention than anyone else, offering me the loveliest gifts. No one suspected—neither Mother nor Father, not my brothers or Eneida—that the scent of him drove me wild and I would surreptitiously slip my little hands along his chest. It occurred to no one that something might be growing in my excited uncle's pants, and that I enjoyed that vitality, unfamiliar but divine. I never ventured there: at first I was afraid to, and eventually I derived pleasure from the sense of anticipation; it could have been killing me, but I liked it. It was our secret. Thanks to my discretion, he didn't mind being with me around all my siblings, spoiling me with gifts. In the living room, everyone sitting and fanning themselves, Father going on about his idea to invent an irrigation system for the Sahara—diverting from the Nile, water would flow into the hot sands. Mother would watch him, completely enthralled, and every so often interrupt with a comment about the children's education. Meanwhile, my brothers—Livio, Horacio, and Ovidio—would play, roughhousing with each other. There I'd sit on my uncle, hushed. The quiet pleasure, that no one detected our exchange, this was what really interested me. Sneaky, pretending, we reveled in grazes and scratches. Then Uncle would pick me up: walking proudly to my bed as I pretended to sleep in his arms, laying me down in the stillness of the sheets. Before leaving, he'd plant a warm kiss on my forehead and I would answer, half asleep, with a flickering of my lips, a faint smile of complicity and appreciation.

Whenever my uncle's visits came to an end—they sometimes lasted a month—I became overwhelmingly distressed. I would sprawl out on the floor and do nothing but draw: opulent ladies appeared on the many pieces of cardstock I slid my pencils along. Towering hairstyles, bared shoulders, glistening pearls, haute fans. Hours of daydreaming when I imagined myself in the skin of those women. I lived in ivory palaces, I undressed in front of my masculine uncle, blood flowing from my sex. His niece, floating in a bloody sea, his euphoric niece, penetrated by her uncle.

As time passed and with my uncle's death, my fidelity faded. I began to imagine other men, always stripped down, swaggering around the palace of my dreams. None of them could resist my imaginary beauty: they bowed in submission at my feet. In each room, these pernicious men penetrated the pasture of my indecent flesh. I didn't have the slightest reference for intercourse, I'd never heard my parents or even imagined how this exchange would play out; nonetheless every man wrenched the most delicious screams of pleasure from me. I love to stutter, my own moaning excites me, it's my way of congratulating my body for fulfilling itself. For most of my life I quivered and groaned as I masturbated. I was for some time an inveterate onanist. There was no body or pleasure more formidable than my own. There was no man as tough or virile as the one I invented as I swooned in ecstasy. No one derived such satisfaction as I did in the solitude of my sheets. Though I'd never touched a man I could imagine how smooth a man's flesh was, his member's soft skin taut with dark blue veins, crowned with a bright rosy head. I would twirl like a carousel on the axis that suspends it. I preferred these fantasy encounters so much that I turned down real carnal encounters. Not once had I peeped at a man; I only had my own imagination and some drawings.

One in particular knocked me out of my daze: the image of Courbet, painted by the artist himself. I found it in a small catalog of his paintings, a selection I didn't look all the way through. I didn't even make it to the portrait of Baudelaire, whose poems I'd read and recited in front of the mirror often. The first in the selection was the painter's self-portrait. Only a man in love with himself could paint his own features with such precision and elegance. There was nothing more to see in that catalog: nothing was more beautiful than his face. Unlike me, he was capable of fully, deeply loving himself. Courbet was a Narcissus. Both of us were stewards of our own image: he for self-adoration and I for self-abhorrence. His tousled black mane and beard accentuated the slopes of his face: sharp cheekbones; an attractive, broad mouth; a pipe propped in his teeth. A man who appeared to derive pleasure from his own beauty seemed ideal to me. I made up the rest. I lay out on my bed, the catalog open to one side. Courbet appeared naked, showing me his sex, as gorgeous as his face. He fiddled with it in his hands, just as he did with the pipe in his mouth. Fantasy, simulation: unaware of my presence, as all handsome men were. Courbet strutted his nude body around my room in my house in Mantua. I wilted when he met my euphoric gaze. I didn't need a real exchange. My fiction, the most obscene of all, filled me with solitary pleasures. What an arrogant man! He never pressed me for a kiss, took no interest in my vulgar lips. He was a Narcissus and I his mirror, the meek waters of a river. I looked at him the way he always wanted, with adulation. I worshipped the man, self-rendered to appear godlike, I offered my lips to every pore, I venerated his curves. For years, in secret, I kept a man in my bed who was merely the fruit of my imagination. All I needed was the gentlest air to bristle my nipples and I'd present my pronounced, milky teats to the artist, then his dick would lift me up so I could finger the teardrops of a chandelier hanging from the ceiling. This exploration of the man, the invention of him—when in reality I was surrounded by nothing more than empty space and the self-portrait in a catalog—cradled me in the simulation of pleasure.

But the onanistic joy didn't last long. I couldn't enjoy the scratch of the sheets against my body forever. The worst thing happened to me: I fell in love with a loner.

I was still living in Mantua when my parents decided to send me to a military school where my flourishes and effeminate inflections would be corrected. I was supposed to be a man like our ancestors, like the guys who swaggered around the neighborhood. I had wanted to be a priest—not because I was interested in God, but I was drawn to the whole ensemble of his representatives: their wringing hands, the long habits, the capes, a Gothic altar as a backdrop. Father said no and Mother abided his decision.

When I got there, the loner was in the school's reception office with his head down, not even looking at his mother, who was muttering advice quietly into his ear. The boy was motionless. I couldn't believe it. If up to that moment enrolling in the military school had filled me with anxiety, I now had this premium treat, the most compelling reason for staying interned for the rest of my days. He looked like he'd stepped out of a painting; his features were identical to Courbet's: the same indifference in his eyes, a beard of a few days, his hair in messy abundance. It was his elegant mother who answered the sergeant about his registration. "His name is Luciano, Luciano Borgia."

"Oh my, a killer, how marvelous," I remarked before Mother could reach to cover my mouth. He didn't notice what I'd said, or if he had noticed, he'd remained completely still and silent. I was intrigued by the idea of the descendants of the Borgias living on the island. He, like the Courbet of the painting, inspired by his own beauty, didn't have eyes for the rest of the world. His mother snapped at mine, "Lady, keep your son quiet."

Because I couldn't answer the sergeant's questions either, my mother was the one to communicate with him. Different from Luciano, I was not enthralled by my own beauty. As I watched his body walking down the hallway, I didn't say goodbye to Mother, I didn't even pause to notice her wiping away a few tears, I ran straight after him. The world of my childhood, the exercises of my imagination, the memories of my uncle, Courbet's self-portrait, all remained on the other side.

From then on I lived a different existence. A military school is something perfectly serious, more serious than a coffin being dumped into the soil. I faced reality that day and nothing could ever again take me away from it. If thereafter I wrote texts untethered from that reality, if I resorted to strange practices, to unconventional, absurd themes, it was only because my truth surpassed anything expected. No writing could represent the truth of my life. I altered it, gave it a sheen of madness. So much that happened thereafter had to do with Luciano. I love that name, someone that beautiful couldn't be called anything else. I didn't even have the grace of a good name. Luciano Borgia was bestowed with it all: name, beauty. . . . What could such a gifted creature have to worry about?

The first few days were nice: I was content to watch him, knowing he was there, so close to my bed, or that in a few moments he'd return from the bathroom wrapped in a towel, his bare feet leaving their damp footprints on the floor. I followed his steps, my feet in the traces of water he left. In the classroom I took the closest seat—I made up, for the military theory professor, a vision problem. I didn't want to sit in the first row for the sole fact that it would be in front of Luciano. "My vision up close is very poor, Professor, I can see the letters on the board better from far away, please let me choose a seat." No one was in the seat next to Luciano, but as I stepped past him I thought that I'd have to constantly turn my head to be able to look at him and he would pick up on my reverence. In these situations I have a hard time being discreet. I was drawn to his beauty and didn't think I was capable of containing myself, of acting normal. It would be better to be behind him. Pretending to look forward, at the board, at the professor, I could set my eyes on the nape of his neck, observe his movements, contemplate his head, now buzzed of most of his hair. I watched his arms, his broad back, without drawing attention. From there I could smell him. I only stopped watching him to draw in my notebook. At military school, during class, I didn't paint any more opulent ladies, I was no longer the bejeweled Pompadour. But I still made drawings, while the professor rambled on about the Crusaders, elatedly explaining the siege of Iconium by Frederick Barbarossa, and then, at almost a whisper, wondering why God allowed Barbarossa to bathe in the waters of the Saleph after their victory. The tragic Barbarossa with his lungs filled with water, floundering after so much hard work, and there I was sketching those little drawings on my blank page, the same every time. After his valiant win, Barbarossa couldn't overcome the force of the water, that water that had also tried to swallow the great Alexander. "Tragic Barbarossa," the professor would say, "so brave in war only for the waters of the Saleph to jubilantly gulp him down." He said this, murmuring on about the Peloponnesian War and thousands of other battles while I devised weird shelters. This was my passion, in addition to studying Luciano's nape in military theory class. Somewhere on a long and horizontal line depicting the surface of a shelter, I drew a crevice, a hole that opened access to the shelter. The vertical tunnel widened as it descended and from the plunging throat emerged a belly. Inside, a large pantry and many sacks in which one could assume were rice, beans, meats, and vegetables. We needed to have on hand the food that Luciano would cook every day, because he was the one—not anybody else—who would join me in that sanctioned shelter we could retreat to with our love. As I sketched the lines of our hideaway I imagined moving around in its expanse, lifting his dirty socks from the floor, hanging up the shirts left strewn everywhere, I was meticulous with cleaning. I dreamed that Luciano demanded the rice be thoroughly washed and the beans dense and creamy. If it was hot out, I dabbed his forehead, fanned him. I monitored his snoring with devotion, I admired his nakedness, but did not dare touch him—though once in a while I dared to in my dreams. The professor would talk about tactics, I would draw my shelter. There Luciano appeared, on our bed. I got up from the table; the pencil outlined my trajectory to the mattress. The pencil drew a chair beside the bed and I sat down to watch him. He was placid in his sleep, and I absorbed. His beauty was vast; his eyes closed, his head inclined, his chin poised on a shoulder, and me, wondering if I was in his dream. His lips gingerly parted, his faint snore, his breath ignited, and there I was, sitting nervously. His chest was lovely, his abdomen sinewy, his sex robust, and my eagerness immense. Luciano didn't move, and I drew circles over the illustrated chair. I was agitated and he serene. Bare feet, a hand over a thigh, the other on the pelvis, and I desiring to touch what I saw. Why couldn't I control myself, why did the pencil have to keep moving, why did I have to sketch the movement of my hand reaching for his chest, my mouth for his neck—there I paused but the pencil insisted—a black circle over the bed, a strong kiss on his pulsing throat. He woke up and the pencil followed his gestures, aimed for my face: I felt the smack and his admonition that I leave him alone at siesta time. I rose from the floor, walked to the table, smoothed the tablecloth, put the rice in the pot, and, picking through the grains, savored the hit.

The professor saw me so excitedly making annotations that day that he nipped over to my desk without my noticing him. The entire classroom had frozen in suspense. The professor watched as I sketched, my pencil gliding along the paper. I was cleaning the rice to go in the pot, which would be cooked with black charcoal over the fire I'd illustrated; the flames stoked, the food would be ready and set out on the table by the time Luciano woke up. Finally the professor interrupted me, asking what I found so captivating. Caught red-handed, I became obviously tense. "A shelter, Professor, a shelter," I answered. Chuckling, he began egging me on. "A shelter—could it be the shelter Louis XV promised to Madame de Pompadour in exchange for going to meet him during the Flanders campaign?" Everyone laughed with the professor. Distraught, I suspected he'd somehow found out about my old obsession, worried he knew his student, not long ago, was a devotee of La Pompadour, and I remembered reading about the Flanders campaign—when Louis XV had pleaded to his lover, insisting she should join him. I remembered the sealed letters the king sent to his best mistress, the ones that read at the bottom, *Discret et fidèle*—in those letters I used to imagine the king, in a tone of desperation, begging the marquise to leave Versailles to meet him, so in the dawn of battle she could comfort him and give him strength. Again I was Madame de Pompadour; Luciano, Louis XV. Shamed by the snickering, I slouched my lanky body, folding in on myself. I was horrified that Luciano might be witnessing the ridicule I was being subjected to. The professor had picked up my notebook and was showing it to all the students, two minutes on each desk to study the work of ingenuity—what a king was capable of doing for his lady. But Luciano didn't react at all, didn't laugh along, didn't chant the name I'd just been baptized with, "Miss Marquise of Mantua." Even when my mortification swelled as everyone jumped around my desk and pulled at my hair, Luciano did not partake in the spectacle. He glanced at the notebook and handed it back to the professor without realizing I had drawn the shelter for him. I was waiting for him to realize it and angrily abandon his apathy and his chair, rush toward me, and whack me in the face until he drew blood.

Which of the two possibilities did I prefer? That he smack me or defend me from their taunting? I'd have received either with complacency. I would have let Luciano kill me if that was what he desired.

But he chose to ignore me and I couldn't do anything else but love him. I followed him everywhere, spied on his shadow through the hallways, in the classrooms or the military drills, and I came to enjoy his indifference. I loved him uncontrollably, I became saturated with passion. How much had I wished for repose, the calm of those days when I craved my uncle or believed I was Madame de Pompadour? Wasn't it healthier, perhaps, to adore a portrait, like Courbet's, rather than the sturdy figure of a boy in the flesh, who was close by every single hour of the day but never noticed me? In any case, I couldn't turn away and give up on the vision of Luciano just to look at Courbet's self-portrait, which I'd torn from the catalog and brought to school with me; two hours into my time there, I'd torn it to shreds because I didn't want to be unfaithful to the boy I truly loved. I couldn't make time for reading or writing. What thought could I express, what conflict was there to write about when it was reality, his body, that consumed me? I longed to touch it; there was no appetite in the world more despicable than mine. God granted me the knowledge of pleasure but not the control. At night, at any hour, I tried to look in other directions, but my eyes always went back to him. It was the first time beauty had come this close. He was a slow burn, a fire smoldering my willpower. His aloofness drove me wild. Luciano was oblivious to my passion. He cluelessly ambled through the hallways and during training, in his khaki uniform, he agitated me, facing his superiors so unkempt, unpresentable, his epaulets loose, his shirt unevenly buttoned. And there I was, watching only him, his chest exposed, scattered with dark, woolly wisps. I watched his thighs, his arms, his feet. Absorbed in his own world, he even lost track of when to wash himself. The smell emanating from his body excited me. Luciano and I were the two most withdrawn from the group. And as I fell asleep I clutched my pillow, spying on his every movement; while lying facedown I watched his body, faceup. And he was there in my dreams—slim, his naked, broad, fit body, on his waist a sturdy green-wool belt, the square buckle over his navel, his rifle slung over his shoulder. Luciano liked to slap me around during sex, made me get on all fours. He plundered my narrow portal with the barrel of his rifle. I almost always woke up at the moment he was pulling the trigger, the shot about to fire; a rush, a detonation, my little frame devastated, shattered. It ached to wake up and discover my body intact on the bed.

I spent three months in restless admiration until we were granted a brief vacation for Christmas. Everyone was preparing for break: all of our faces eager, issuing merry words of goodbye, little hugs and punches on shoulders. Luciano, with no reason to get up, still wouldn't move, nor did he respond to others' enthusiastic hugs or well-wishes. I also approached him, offering my open hand. He didn't notice. I dared to open my arms and reach for an embrace. Disgruntled, he pushed me away.

Fifteen days was a long time. Only the memory of his face, the tenacity of the squeeze, my arms around his chest, could lessen the distance and time. Not even Eneida managed to wrench a smile from me. I decided to lock myself away. Back to the sanctuary as a place of salvation and for thinking about my beloved. Doubting myself, I wanted to figure out what had driven Luciano away. Everything led me to believe I was to blame for his withdrawal, that there was something I was missing. That's why I planned some transformations. If my feeble torso displayed a few long little hairs, some of them auburn, others black, I would pluck them from the root. I laid everything out: using my mother's eyebrow tweezers was tedious, and the small pair of scissors tugged on my hairs as they cut, making black and reddish dots, irritated little ducts; of all the instruments I grabbed and set out on the bed, I finally decided on my father's razor.

I covered my scrawny chest in a dense, soapy cream, the foam cold on my nipples. I turned back to the mirror. Erect, lifting my skimpy torso, I slid the razor down. The hairs ceded to the blade, its sharp edge scraping my virgin chest, taut from the cold of the metal and the pleasure of feeling myself pruned. I grabbed my nipples and lifted them up like a mother going to breastfeed her son, and pulled apart the tangle of small hairs on my areola. It was sublime: pleasure startles, reveals new passages. All that time hiding in drawings of ladies, all that tedious jerking off, and now the sharp blade was producing an indescribable pleasure. Up and down the razor, down and up Luciano's hands, his tongue, his phallus. I ended up electrified, the razor in one hand, the other on my sticky sex, my shame, and I clutched it as though I were grasping his, stroking it, rubbing it as the razor scraped my chest. Then numbness, the cold, and Luciano's semen flowed as blood spurted from my injured nipple. Blood and sex born out of my body; my plum dignity, puce, purple, purpureus, pure. Perfect blood purging the desirous body, purple purgatory relentlessly purging, pinching at my virgin, pristine bosom. Singular the purple surging from pleasure, delectation pouring out purple. What a shock, my pelvis dressed in purple, new color, crimson as the virgin's cape, my pubic hair, a coralline pasture.

Then I wanted to have a churrigueresque pelvis: genitalia so aesthetic and ornate that Luciano, compelled to set his eyes on me, would remain entranced and my decorated fuzz would drive him to such irresistible enchantment that he would no longer refuse me his gaze. Without leaving the sanctuary, I worked feverishly and with no nourishment; a glass of water every so often was enough. My pelvis was a canto to the battles: I decorated it with fragments of epic poems. First *Beowulf*, from the eighth century, to the right of my lower abdomen. I trimmed the hairs as though they were grass and began to pluck some of them to form shapes. The hairs I left intact—the contrast I was achieving with the negative space and the shadows cast on them—allowed the appearance of the figures. After two days of work, the image of Beowulf facing Grendel was clear: the sword piercing the cannibal's belly, who, in pain, desperately stretches his arms out and reaches for Beowulf's neck. Unbeknownst to the hero, a new threat looms behind him: the dragon's flaming throat. Beowulf resembled Luciano; I knew his features better than anyone's. With my left hand I held up to my pelvis the little mirror Mother used to apply lipstick; with my right I maneuvered the tweezer.

It was even harder to extract Luciano from my memory when I

outlined a scene from *The Song of Roland*. Luciano, military governor of the Breton March, Charlemagne's nephew, son of the Princess Bertha, and I, to be close to him, became Oliver and arranged it so we were surrounded by the Twelve Peers of France. We were, yes, the most feared army, the best rearguard anyone had ever heard of, the most loyal and intrepid servants of Charlemagne. Luciano—handsome Roland—gripped his sword named Durendal and in his other hand the sturdy Oliphant horn. I drew the fatal moment of betrayal, the one after the vile stepfather, Ganelon, warns King Marsile. More than the pain of pulling at my pubic hairs, I suffered because of his vital figure, and because of Oliver—whose face resembled mine—and the Twelve Peers of France. I was well aware what destiny and betrayal would bring, but I didn't stop for an instant, I continued plucking hairs from my groin until Oliver—with my face—was dead, so that Roland would mourn and blow the Oliphant horn, the one for warning the French king of danger. The count fought nobly in my florid genitalia, his fever spiking and pain sharpening with the death of his friend, and sadly for France, Roland died too, and the Twelve Peers along with him. Shaking, I made the final touches and colored in the scene with my blood. Roland in a pool of red, and Oliver and the Peers. I perfumed the scene of the death with fragrant essences, because when it's about valiant men, when the ones who fall are handsome and honest, death is fragrant.

I spent a night resting so the swelling of my lower abdomen would go down. In the morning I started the task again. Now we were Tristan and Isolde, madly in love after drinking the potion Brangäne served us. In the corners of the castle, feverish and hiding, I put Luciano—dressed as Tristan—and Isolde—with my face, grinning. It was the sultriest grin an artist has ever achieved. Because even though I couldn't prove it, my pelvis turned out to be the most aesthetic and churrigueresque pelvis that anyone could ever fathom. Although the figures had to be small because of how narrow my groin was, the faces did turn out recognizable and the bodies outstanding. Since I was so excited, I didn't limit myself to the steamy scenes between Tristan and Isolde—King Mark also appeared, Tristan's uncle, victim to Tristan's trickery, and the other Isolde, whom Tristan took as his wife though he'd never possessed her. Rich and invigorating the carnal epic, sweet the Middle Ages in my pubic hair. As a friend once said, The Middle Ages lasts only one night, yes, but it is a splendid one. And splendid were the nights with El Cid, El Campeador, splendid everything I drew in minute detail, the men of Sancho, the king of Castile, led by El Cid, besieging the city of Zamora where Doña Urraca reigned. Here King Sancho appeared, the darkest of scenes, clinging to a tree while Bellido Dolfos stabs him in the back with the king's own sword, and there also was El Cid, galloping on his horse, behind Bellido, after realizing he hadn't worn spurs. And beneath that I wrote in bold lettering: "Damn the caballero who rides without spurs!" Because it must be known that El Cid was brave, but sometimes he was foolish.

And if to the right of my lower abdomen appeared Beowulf, to the left there was a culmination of my cycle of medieval battles, *The Song of the Nibelungs*.

One night, also splendid, Siegfried slips past King Gunther—by his suggestion, who wanted to trick Brunhild after she'd bound the king with a cord and hung him from the wall. It was surely the most tremendous battle ever celebrated on a mattress. It all started with a little pushing and shoving. Brunhild warns the deceptive Gunther to get off the bed, and then the clawing and biting starts—Brunhild was strong. But as everything in the Middle Ages was splendid, this wouldn't shock anyone, especially not if depicted in my churrigueresque groin. Blows to the head crushed the skulls to a pulp, lavishing that little nest of love, blood spurting as I zealously drew the scene—so many shoves and blows to the head, so much blood spurting—I yanked at my hairs, and it produced such reddening and swelling in my little decorated garden that it seemed a delicious coincidence with the fiery spirit of the depicted work. Frenzied and unsatisfied, I moved on to the final scene. With Siegfried dead by Gunther's order, Kriemhild—who was more inclined to give hugs than throw punches—in a state of despair swears revenge. After remarrying Attila, of the Huns, she invites Gunther and all his brothers to her extravagant palace to demand the ring and belt Siegfried stole when he tricked Brunhild; they refuse and this is where the bloodbath ensues. Flames consume the castle where Kriemhild has locked her brothers, fire and swords slitting throats, blood staining bodies, screams evincing pain. Everyone is dead: Gunther, Hagen, everyone. Dead, including Kriemhild with my face, satisfied after renewing the honor of this Siegfried with Luciano's face. And while I was ripping out my pubic hairs, while I was shaping the figures reenacting those final scenes, I whistled an opera of Wagner.

Still whistling, I opened the tall window, stepped out on the balcony, and presented myself naked. In truth, I hadn't meant for passersby to see my skinny body; I'd only wanted to display my work of art, test its effect, see if some stranger would recognize, from afar, my exquisite work.

It was horrendous! First it was shock, murmuring, a pious old woman becoming alarmed and dropping her basket of tomatoes and clutching her rosary, reciting the Our Father and Hail Mary. A woman walking by with her son saw the plump red globes rolling past and stooped to grab one. The boy took the chance to escape before his mother realized—who, nibbling the fruit with dissatisfaction, turned to walk past the eighteenth-century grille of my balcony: beguiled and dribbling, she looked up at my groin, her son on the run, the old woman praying, "Hail Mary, full of grace. The Lord is with thee . . ." No one saw the car's quick turn as it swerved to miss the boy and slammed on the brakes, no one heard the clamor of the impact, no one smelled the gasoline or caught the shaky man finishing his cigarette, emancipating the butt from the pressure of his fingers—the castoff plummeting straight into a puddle of gasoline.

Despite the rising flames, the bystanders continued to admire my work of art, and there I was, unmoving, illuminated by the immensity of the flames, gazing onto the chaos and desperation of my devotees. The reflections of light emanating from the blaze were so big that now Beowulf was glowing, armed against the cannibal, and now El Cid, riding without spurs; the old pious woman was wiping away her tears, mourning Roland's death, his kiss of the earth, asking the heavenly Father to welcome the wretched one into the kingdom of heaven. The fire eulogized the death of Roland, and Tristan looked gorgeous under that glow, next to Isolde. As a crowd was gathering at the balcony, the brilliant pyre grew, impetuous, chaotic. Both Siegfried's and Brunhild's heads were illuminated such that they seemed—the blows to the head and the carnal showdown—to be a part of reality, as real as Kriemhild welcoming her brother into Attila the Hun's house had seemed; the palace blaze was coming to life, and it gave the impression that Gunther and Hagen, on the small space to the left of my pelvis, were burning to a crisp. Even though the blaze would surely never reach my ornate pasture, it looked as though it had. Everyone in Mantua hovered hypnotized by my pubic hair as the city sank into the fire.

The firemen were summoned, but the only thing visible was the tapestry of my hairs, and they believed the flames were a reflection of my pelvic decoration—some swore my lower abdomen was projecting shadow puppets onto the town—and others were certain that from one pubic hair hung a tiny cinematographer. Even I began to see the epic scenes amplified onto the various buildings in the neighborhood, and I pictured Luciano weaving through the throng, to the eighteenth-century grille of my balcony, to reach me. That's why I rose up and offered for him my precious, infinite visibility: I lifted my arms, I stood on tiptoe so my pelvis would tower out over the balcony, and I began to whistle Wagner, the music growing in rhythm with the flame. My brassy whistles of Wagner would guide him to me. The beacon was as great as my passion. Then a lick of fire: a splinter of ignited wood weaving through the throng, the crosswind, reached the tower of Attila's burning castle on the left of my pelvis, and that spot caught fire, and my puff whistles and the tones of Wagner did not diminish the flames but kindled them. I puffed and whistled, not daring to use my hands—I was terrified they'd be destroyed by the churrigueresque and charring embers. Everyone was yelling and shouting from the street, "Get him water, get him water!"

That's when I saw the fireman with the long, fat, dark hose in his hands. "Clear the way, clear the way!" the man carrying the thick hose was shouting. He pointed it toward me, the hose stiff, he gripped it firmly and shot a steady stream that struck my ignited pelvis, and the force of the strike, crashing into my body, threw me backward. As I fell, still whistling, I gave a great imitation of Wagner's Kriemhild.

I stayed there for a long time. Not Mother nor Father nor Eneida's pleas could make me get up off the floor. I didn't open the door; I refused, plain and simple, I let them know I was OK and that I wasn't in pain, I only had the enormous longing to be alone.

Wagner Free Institute of Science. Photograph by Joseph Elliott. Historic American Buildings Survey.

System of Display

Jena Osman

. . . all nature is so full . . .
—Gilbert White

there are general patterns

in this intertidal life

kingdom animalia

Coral is animal, a colony of polyps dressed in algae. The algae give color, photosynthesizing the sun. Polyps have stingers, graspers, to draw the nutrients in. Then the coral exudes a skeleton, a shelter made from its own interior life.

chora is the dwelling place

life in the marine station

phylum Cnidaria, stinging cells

William Wagner was a cloth merchant's son born in 1796 in Philadelphia.
As a child, walking along the Wissahickon Creek, he began to collect minerals.
Collecting is the first step toward naming.

the outermost layer of the earth curls over & lifts toward the water's surface

look up through the water to the sky

class Anthozoa, flower animals

I might want to make a form that mirrors the coral's reliance on its environment. The polyps are mouths that share their homes with the algae; in exchange the algae produce food that the polyps eat. Except the polyps can't build a home to share without the food in the first place. Sharing simultaneous with just existing.

coral islands circle in the middle of the deep sea

craggy and jeweled before you

order Scleractinia, stony skeleton

Wagner wanted to be a scientist or a doctor, but his father had more lucrative plans for him. He was apprenticed to Stephen Girard, a merchant and banker, and one of the wealthiest men in the entirety of United States history.
At twenty-one, Wagner was assigned the job of "supercargo," supervising sales on and off Girard's ship, the *Helvetius*; his older brother, Samuel, was aboard the ship *Rousseau*.

up from the outermost layer at particular sea level

you are just above and just below

family Faviidae or Mussidae, spheres with grooved surfaces

The polyps secrete limestone structures—corallum—that are as solid as walls, as intricate as cities. Reefs might seem an architecture built up from the seafloor, but their existence depends on the ceiling of the sea. We reach for the surface on the backs of our calcified dead. The nineteenth-century geologist Charles Lyell wrote in a letter, "Coral islands are the last efforts of drowning continents to lift their heads above water."

seeming a piece of land, but in fact a team of organisms

read them as evidence, the tip of the iceberg

genus Diploria once Madrepora, doubling back, inlet folds

The ship *Helvetius* was named after the French philosopher Claude-Adrien Helvétius. In his book *De l'esprit* (*On the Mind*), he argued that all inequalities can be traced back to unequal educational opportunities: "I am convinced that a good education would diffuse light, virtue, and consequently, happiness in society; and that the opinion that genius and virtue are merely gifts of nature is a great obstacle to the making any farther progress in the science of education. . . ." In 1818, the same year William Wagner sailed on the *Helvetius*, the First School District of Pennsylvania was established.

look for proof that something happened here

a gentleman naturalist keeps a weather journal, for instance

species Cerebriformis, or brain stone

At night the polyps expand from their cells and hollows. Atoms of living jelly. I might want to make a form with tentacula that protrude and retract as if seizing and devouring. A myriad of offensive weapons contained in capsules, in a world of potential enemies. In a letter to his sister in 1834, Charles Darwin wrote, "I have lately determined to work chiefly amongst the Zoophites or Coralls: it is an enormous branch of the organized world; very little known or arranged & abounding with most curious, yet simple, forms of structures."

radiata and coral theory is breath from the surface

see the labor of the coral animals in a deep and unfathomable sea

brain coral, Bahama Islands, E&H

At twenty-two, Darwin sailed as a supernumerary on board the *Beagle*, invited expressly to keep the captain company. The five-year voyage informed his book *The Structure and Distribution of Coral Reefs*. At twenty-one, Wagner was a supercargo on the *Helvetius*. The specimens he collected during his travels were foundational to the natural science school and museum that he eventually opened in his name. Which of these shells, minerals, corals, here under glass, were found while on that voyage? Super means above and beyond.

After the War of 1812, American goods were cheap and Girard's cargo was in demand. It was the "era of good feelings." The coral was booming and blooming, threatening to block the routes. In the years 1817 & 1818, William Wagner aboard the ship *Helvetius* stitched a long loop of trade:

from Charleston to Amsterdam
Amsterdam to Mauritius once Isle of France
Mauritius once Isle of France to Batavia now Jakarta
Batavia now Jakarta to Amsterdam
Amsterdam to Lisbon
Lisbon to Philadelphia
Philadelphia back to Charleston

your rice will be up to Amsterdam tomorrow if the wind holds to the westward

the supplies of Coffee in Holland will be curtailed, owing to the general scarcity of that article both in the East and West, the quantity which will be received from Java is far inferior to their former usual supplies, and the advanced price of that Bean in that Colony will most unquestionably influence the Sales in the mother Country

Sugar . . . the Sugar is coming in daily

"Rice," "Coffee," and "Sugar": unacknowledged metonyms for slave labor. The ship sailed from Charleston, a city with a majority slave population, to Amsterdam, the headquarters of the slaving Dutch West India Company, to the tropical slave plantations of British Mauritius (recently French Isle de France) and Dutch Batavia (now Jakarta). But the concerns of the supercargo were weather, permits, and profits. And for Wagner, the collection of specimens to build an impossibly neutral index of the world. Graspers and stingers cloak skeletons or was it the other way around?

Ship Helvetius to proceed, to Lisbon, there to take on Salt and Specie

The cargo of the Helvetius is all landed but the Iron, and am sorry to state, that after examination the cheese, Hams, & smoaked Salmon, suffered considerably

As to saltpetre, little can be said as to the price, this being an article entirely depending on Peace or War

In the Prow
12 twelve casks of Beer
14 fourteen packages of cordage
318 bars & 45 bundels of Iron
35 large and small Edam cheeses

Packing the extra space in the hold with diverse sorts of drugs
Cassia, Yellow, Camphor, Bengal, Java 30, Borax, Rhubarb

300 large jars of ginger
20 small jars of ginger

We are now in sight of the Light House and going to Sea with a fine Breeze from N.W. with every Prospect of a Short Passage. I remain with Respect
Your obed. Servt.
Wm Wagner

In the museum of the Wagner Free Institute of Science, in a vertical case on the bottom shelf, is a large hemisphere of brain coral; its ridged convolutions, its labyrinthine valleys and depressions, resemble your brain. The handwritten label says, "Diploria cerebriformis E&H, Bahamas, 3332." Diploria is the genus, cerebriformis the species. E&H is for Henri Milne-Edwards & Jules Haim, the first recorders of this specimen type; the Bahamas, its point of collection. The accession number, 3332, indicates that this particular specimen was added to the collection after Wagner's time. Scientific facts.

zoophyte for the mass, polyp for the individual

animals budding, but not completely separating

see their bones on the outside

Brain corals can live for up to nine hundred years; so it can be assumed that specimen 3332 witnessed much history before being plucked from the sea: for instance, the loyalists' retreat to the British Bahamas after the American Revolution, their slaves working the colonized land; for instance, the people freed from foreign ships in Bahamian waters when the British outlawed the slave trade in 1807; for instance, those slaves who escaped from Florida to freedom on canoes and sloops in the early 1820s, before a new lighthouse blocked the route; for instance, the cotton picked by slaves in Charleston, shipped to the Bahamas in order to avoid the Civil War blockade; for instance, the slaves who stowed away on those ships full of cotton in order to be free once they stepped on Bahamian soil. Bahamas from *baja mar* means shallow sea means some will swim and some will drown. Human acts.

you live on chance bits caught with lasso cells

"a spiral array of toxic stinging barbs"

confined to the warmer regions of the globe

Warming water causes coral to expel the algae it hosts. With that, starvation and a loss of color. Low-flying planes above the Great Barrier Reef can spot the extended bleached bones in the water. I might want to make a form where a dead one comes alive. While nineteenth-century lectures on ancient coral reefs are carefully preserved in manila archival folders, twenty-first-century data on climate change is scrubbed from public view.

the brain coral has no brain

always united in a long waved series

a system of valleys with rows of mouths in several of the hot seas

When Stephen Girard died in 1831, he left none of his riches to his family and willed almost everything to the founding and endowment of Girard College, a boarding school for poor white orphan boys. Inspired by his example, Wagner devoted his later life to creating a free school where any adult could attend college-level science classes. Girard College still provides free education to low-income Philadelphia children; after a long struggle, the school finally opened its doors in 1968 to boys of every race (and to girls in 1984). Wagner's institute—a quarter mile northwest of Girard College—still provides free science classes, but is perhaps more recognized as a perfectly preserved example of a Victorian museum. A fossilized form of knowing.

the chorus of the coral is choral

encircled by a ring of snow-white breakers

above which is the blue vault of heaven

The last coral-reef crisis was fifty-five million years ago. Some say the Great Barrier Reef will be extinct by 2030, possibly sooner. Black band disease, yellow band disease, white plague. I might want to make an analogy: as the skeleton protects the polyp, so does the reef protect the coast, as the glass case protects the specimen. But it doesn't work at all because the specimens are dead.

the ocean throws its breaks like an enemy

against the coral rag of the oolite

that's you there illuminated by a vertical sun

At the opening ceremonies for the Wagner Free Institute of Science in 1855, Philadelphia Mayor Robert T. Conrad compared the value of education to "the value of the vivifying sun of this bright May Morning." Twelve lectures were given a week, on geology, chemistry, anatomy, etc. The permanent building was dedicated in 1865, less than a month after Abraham Lincoln was assassinated. While the newspapers reported up to six hundred students attending nightly in 1857, an 1869 entry in the annals noted a "medium audience," partially due to "the demoralized state of society, incident to the late Rebellion, precipitating upon society a large number of bad characters who carried out their crimes in private places and unlighted streets." It is the only intersection between the institute and the tumultuous events of the day that I can find.

your meandering depressions and gothic ridges

the long swell never ceases, the consolidated debris

unconscious instruments of stupendous operations

Prof. Kirkpatrick Lectured on Civil Engineering, at seven, Dr. Child at eight on the organs of Sight. He gave a most interesting lecture, illustrated by the recent eye of a Bullock, also Diagrams, weather bad, audience small.

On the radio, in defense of a new "sugary drinks" tax that pays for prekindergarten school programs, Philadelphia's mayor says "education is everything."

16th, Nothing Special
Dr. Child concluded his remarks on vision, etc., at seven.
Prof. Wagner at eight on Volcanoes, etc.

A few weeks ago, a newspaper article reports that two-thirds of the Great Barrier Reef is dying or dead.

Dr. Child Lectured at seven o'clock on the Teeth.
Prof. Wagner at eight on Earthquakes.
Weather disagreeable, audience small.

When I read the local newspaper online, an ad fills up my screen urging me to tell my legislators to "ax the tax."

Dr. Child Lectured at seven on the Digestive organs.
Prof. Wagner, at eight, Concluded his remarks on Earthquakes, etc.
Audience good but much disturbed by a noisy meeting of Druids, in the upper Hall.

Facts flex and change based on a determination of my likes and dislikes. Ice reflects the sun back into space.

Jena Osman

I might want to see the teeming archives of the organized world, single file in the valleys of convolutions.

I might condemn empirical knowledge detached from culture.

I might become a mineralized skeleton of the lily-shaped radiaria pouring its calcareous secretion on the parent mass.

You might claim the current climate a form of denial.

You might be a nervous system

Inside hemispheres with valleys that extend the entire width of domed colonies.

I might propose an expert separate from the world.

I might inhabit an intermural furrow, a double-valley character broader than the true valley.

I might register a paradigm shift in modes of understanding.

You might be a ribbonlike columella feeding on small drifting animals

You might be the expert called into question.

You might slip on the deep arm of the sea, an unexpected shelf trapped in a greenhouse gas mantle.

Jena Osman

I might opine that these days opinion determines fact.

I might point to problems in the celestial mountains, irreversible melting flooding the ports.

I might say scientific facts are symbiotic with human acts.

You might reply "look up into a green sky of photosynthetic bacteria."

You might argue that science is what determines culture.

You might be devastated by the crown-of-thorns starfish and cyclone scouring, succumb to warmer waters and become a crumbling mound of calcium.

I might want symbiotic bargains.

I might shout that the earth can't buffer.

I might dream of a broadcast spawner that anchors in the vast aquatic deserts of open sea.

You might hallucinate the delicate arms of a basket star reaching out to predict the future.

You might grasp and sting the brittle flower animals.

You might want all of the surface area, all of the sun.

NOTES.

James Bowen, *The Coral Reef Era: From Discovery to Decline*, Springer Books, 2015.

Damien Cave and Justin Gillis, "Large Sections of Australia's Great Reef Are Now Dead, Scientists Find," *The New York Times*, March 15, 2017.

Thomas P. Cope, *Philadelphia Merchant: the Diary of Thomas P. Cope*, South Bend, Indiana: Gateway Editions, 1978.

James Dwight Dana, *Corals and Coral Islands*, New York: J. J. Little & Co., 1872.

Charles Darwin, *The Structure and Distribution of Coral Reefs*, New York: D. Appleton and Company, 1889.

Thomas M. Doerflinger, *A Vigorous Spirit of Enterprise: Merchants and Economic Development in Revolutionary Philadelphia*, University of North Carolina Press, 2012.

Elizabeth Doi, *Behind the Gates: The Wagner Free Institute of Science and its Neighborhood, 1865–Today*, University of Pennsylvania Scholarly Commons.

Emma Garman, *History of the Wagner Free Institute of Science and Its Contributions to Education*, Temple University dissertation, Department of Education, 1941.

C. A. Helvétius, *De l'esprit; or, Essays on the Mind and Its Several Faculties*, London: M. Jones, 1807.

John Bach McMaster, *The Life and Times of Stephen Girard, Marine and Merchant*, Philadelphia: J. B. Lippincott Company, 1918.

J. E. N. Veron, *A Reef in Time: The Great Barrier Reef from Beginning to End*, Cambridge: Harvard University Press, 2008.

Matthew White, "Science for All: The Wagner Free Institute of Science," *Pennsylvania Legacies*, Vol. 15, No. 1 (Spring 2015), pp. 12–17.

This piece was written with the help of a Temple University-Wagner Free Institute of Science Humanities & Arts Research Fellowship; thanks to Lynn Dorwaldt and Ken Finkel. Additional thanks to Robert DuPlessis, the American Philosophical Society library, and Katherine Haas (director of Historical Resources at Girard College).

Three Poems

Michael M. *Weinstein*

CUT

The first time, don't remember.
The next time, your blue eye
spilt across the lens on the edge of the cut

glass coffee table, you can almost see
the carpet flowers now. That kid,
the one spread-eagled on the mulch

scooped up pits first by some other
tot on the swing set's mother, who
wept, the scraped knee, the whole bit—

was you, duh. In third grade, paired with
Angela, the blind girl, as she gripped
your wrist in her finger bones, wrenching it

over and over the finish line
of the three-legged race, your chin
split, coursed. Fast blood made a carnation

flower on your blouse. The nurse was
one Miss Prinn. She stuffed a crumpled dollar
into your red hand and hissed, *Stop crying.*

Then mostly, for years, no one touched you.

A needle, a fork, a dog, a man in France
—touched is not the right word—*rearranged* you
under your life's last skirt, kicked

you off the front steps—cobbles, scraped knee,
the whole bit. Torn culotte.
Your nose broke now and again, then hairy hands

of the doctor cupped your left breast, speculator
over the holding, a cross between dinosaur egg
and double-stuffed pastry, musing aloud, *Can we*

claim this as a medical necessity? The blue
permanent marker making slashes—*X*
across each nipple—you paid him extra

to put them back exactly where he found them. Crookedly,
scar grins stitched under the stretched erasure
yank each which way. Burn. Harden and sink

into the earth of flesh. One last cut left
no mark—yet the milky negative testified
that the intruders had entered. Vibrations, the rattle

of infinitesimal hammers driving ache nails deep
in. The worn-down bone doors swivel open,
each cavity gasps—as shards of air

wedge themselves in crevices between the tense
of each act, weave your gait into the lapse
of the horse who gallops, gallops endlessly, jumps

the fence, now you can't stitch it back through your flesh,
the thrill of impact as both feet hit

earth. Cut. Watch the past unspool

behind you in curls from its canister—you were her,
a double, two daughter cells borne from the rip
in the film of one woman and one man, spliced together.

Michael M. Weinstein

AUGUST 25

When do I get to become
who I thought I was?

The envelopes open and they bloom
in a flourish of former soubriquets.
To know they mean me

—*meant* me—alarms
like the feeling of waiting for
your voice when some number of hours has
passed and you don't call and then you

call. So knowingly
the slick leak glints and quivers,
casts a face back off the asphalt
crack—no, you never

get over it

the world giving you back
generously, endlessly, your mask
—that heirloom you keep losing,
one they'll bury you in—

that world whose vistas still unfurl
intoxicating distances as if
you could slough this face off,
stiff as the chromosomes in it

and forever
faithful to the rules of the conception,
keeping each last cell in me

unable to outrun her

Michael M. Weinstein

THE CIVIL SURGEON

Didn't agree with me on my eye color.
I said it was more chestnut, and he wrote *beer*
the way when you tell someone else to look up
at a particular star
                    you can never be sure
it is your constellation at which they are nodding
even if their breath is warm on the curve of your
ear, and you want to believe in the trusty
abstractions again.
                    The air
was like entering after hysterically laughing
a room where a third person silently
lies. I had dreams of a voice saying: each
question will be repeated twice
and only twice
                    , unless
you retake the test.
Retake the test.
                    I woke up with the sweats
and then I came here, carrying a picture
of the person you should be seeing when you
look at me in my head. It was heavy
like the slosh of water in a toilet flushed endlessly
into the night
                    obsessive, obsessive
because if love is domination I just want
to be collected: hung
                    askew & loved
for the stutter my color makes in a room's
hum of time. Well you can't always be
who you were in that other room
here. I've kept this fact for years
                              , a splinter
dark and harmless as a carp under the surface of
my skin. Sometimes I feed it hopeful
imagery:
          I picture myself living
back when no one imagined the earth as an ending

thing, on a raft with a nuclear briefcase
trying to relax, to forget the consuming and meaningless
destructions I have in me
                                        to enact.
I wanted to tell him I wanted
to pass. There's nothing wrong with me
visible.
            But I just
stuck out my tongue, thinking how in the street
below I'd gone over the statement I'd make
if we spoke the same language:
                                                    I'd ask
will you still send me back if you
don't assume I was home. I'd say
like a can at the dump
to the hand that held me
                                        , you think
when you throw something away
you throw it away

Dead Girls

Emily Geminder

1.

Her name is Gracie. It was Frank's idea to name her—Frank, your dissection partner, a ponytailed Rolfer with a limp. "She looks like a Gracie," he pronounced, pulling back the white sheet.

Now it's two hours later, and he asks: "You ever seen somebody like Gracie up close before?" He means somebody dead.

"No," you tell him. "Never." And then you're flooded with a rolling, queasy sensation—the one that feels like lying even when every word is true. Or maybe it's just the reek of formaldehyde, a sick-sweet roiling in your skull. You hear the instructor as though from far away: skin is an organ, he keeps saying, how it pulls and breathes. But all you see is the stunned yellow of Gracie's back, the blunt, dead heap of her. Tiny webbed capillaries worm up from the deep.

Four tables, four corpses in the room: formaldehyde pumped and wobbly. Bald as aliens. They're naked, obviously, but still it shocks you, this nakedness—cold and raw and facedown too. You tell yourself the dead can't be wounded; they're already dead. You make it a joke: *Four corpses walk into a bar.*

You and Frank spent the first half hour stalling, cleaning and recleaning utensils. The first instruction seemed easy enough—*Place the cadaver prone*—but then you mulled over the word *prone*. Was it just a matter of lying down, or were there, in fact, degrees of proneness? Frank said it had to do with the legs, open or closed, and you kept thinking of the thing monks do, or nuns before the cross. Minutes later, you realized that was *prostrate*. Finally, you typed the word into your phone and read out the definition. *One: likely or liable to suffer something, typically something regrettable or unwelcome. Two: lying flat, especially face downward.*

You and Frank stared at the body and then looked up, as though seeing each other for the first time—you who were suddenly supple with life, you who were about to commit regrettable and perhaps unwelcome deeds.

You've enrolled in a four-day anatomy workshop, shelled out a deposit you couldn't afford, because you've been having panic attacks late into the night. Because you're terrorized by the beating of your own heart, the blood going in and out of your chest, and what would happen if it suddenly stopped. Because yoga made you laugh and acupuncture made you weep, and because you were beginning to think there was something wrong with you.

Now you're standing in a room full of yogis and massage therapists. Rolfers like Frank. The sort of people who have long and earnest discussions about deep tissue and somatic memory, hidden geographies beneath the skin. Exactly the people you'd hoped to avoid.

The instructor is a tall, loose-limbed man named Jeremiah who stalks the room and calls you all somanauts—voyagers casting out into inner deep space. But there's nothing astral about it, so far as you can see. You think of it more like spelunking, like cool, dark caves. Once you get past the smell, it's practically intoxicating, like peering inside your own skin.

Jeremiah crosses the country hosting workshops like this one. You picture him as a one-man traveling circus, cadavers in tow. He preaches the subtle beauty of organs, shimmies his arms to illustrate the movements of the heart. In every cut, he says, you're opening a door—a portal into the great beyond. You watch him move through the room, nodding emphatically and making overlong eye contact, and you hope he doesn't turn out to be some sort of cult leader.

Cults have been on your mind lately because of the guru. Two months ago, Vik, your boss, gave you a box of cassette tapes to transcribe: old recordings of the guru from the seventies. The guru's young disciples called themselves the Beloved, and Vik had once been one of them, traveling in a bright and wild caravan across India. The tapes are one of his pet projects: to archive the guru's extemporaneous musings. A project that's been foisted onto you.

A part of you fears that Vik gave you the tapes because he detected in you some sort of spiritual paucity, and wants to redeem you. Recently he looked up from his computer screen to declare that all people struggle with one of three things: anger, ambition, or lust. "I don't struggle with any of those," you said. In part because it was true and in part because you didn't want to hear where this was going. A week later, you found the tapes on your desk. Vik said he'd pay you extra since transcribing the words of a dead man isn't exactly in your job description.

Your job is to edit a monthly newsletter that calls itself a magazine and occasionally to write, though in truth you've been doing less and less of this lately. Your office is in the UN building, hidden in a yellowing back hallway. Every morning, you pass through grand foyers blazing with light, long carpeted halls lined with galactic assembly rooms. Then you turn onto the shoddy ruins of the press wing: crowded desks heaped together, halls littered with the guts of discarded computers. You turn once more into the lightless back passageway where they stow the people who barely count as press, like you.

When you told Vik you needed to cut out early a few days this week and next, he said yes because he always says yes to you. This is part of the problem. "What kind of class?" was all he asked, and for a split second, you considered telling him the truth. "Self-defense," you said.

Now you and Frank take turns holding the skin taut and slicing in axial lines, as the manual instructs. Embalming fluid beads up, dribbles, and leaks. An oily, wet darkness, Gracie's insides opening like burst fruit. The strangest thing isn't cutting someone open, you think, but the fact that mostly, *mostly*, people stay intact—that they move through their days unpunctured, that they don't go spilling out all the time.

When Jeremiah says that not everyone will get all the way to the heart, you look at Frank across the table. "But *we* will," you say. Frank nods as if he can see it in your face: this is what you came for, the black hole in your chest, the unseeable thing you have to see.

"Darling," says Frank, "we're about to start on the axilla now." He's talking not to you but to Gracie. You're supposed to do this. You're supposed to talk to your corpse. But though you've now touched and prodded and manhandled one, though you've now posed and sharpied and sliced one, this is the one thing you cannot, will not do.

Gracie's face, when you finally manage to look at it, is a kind of blankness you've never seen. Like she's just had the fright of her life and exited swiftly from her skin. It's not so simple, you realize, to stand above a dead body, knife in hand, and feel completely blameless in the whole affair.

Jeremiah pauses at your table, registers the movement of your hands. "You can press harder," he says, resting a blue-gloved hand on yours. You feel yourself go stiff, but the scalpel moves certain and sure, and the membrane separates: a clean, straight line. "See?" says Jeremiah. "*Talk* to her while you do it."

"I will," you lie. "I will." You picture a satellite bouncing signals into empty space, your voice naked and undone. If anything, you'd like to apologize, though for what you're not exactly sure. Your brain whispers, half maniacally, half sincere, *I'm sorry. I'm sorry for killing you.*

*

At night, you run. This is what you do. Is it the best or wisest thing to run through the dark streets of Canarsie late at night? Probably not. But you're beginning to believe there are no good or bad things, only better and worse things.

In your headphones, it's Prince. Prince or whatever symbol he's now known by. You too would like to slip from your body, from your name, alight into something formless and unspeakable. *See that body contorting on the stage—nameless, otherworldly—that isn't me; that's just the shimmering, pelvic-thrusting illusion through which I slip.*

Headlights of passing cars chase your shadow up the street. Running at night, you become a shadow, a lurker, a darkness peering into windows. You stare into small, square scenes set aglow: people cooking and yelling and laughing, voices calling from room to room. You run and lurk and peer all the way home.

Home is the fifth-floor walk-up you share with your cousin Georgie. Over a year ago, you emailed to ask if he knew any cheap sublets in the city. You were graduating into what was just beginning to be called the Great Recession, and Vik offered only a minimal, part-time salary. What you lacked in benefits, he said, you'd gain in exposure—a word that strikes you now as ridiculous and a little prophetic.

But Georgie, whom you barely knew, surprised you. "Stay here," he wrote. "Granddad would be happy to have another writer in the apartment."

You hadn't understood quite how literal this would be—*another* writer—until you arrived and found your dead great-uncle's clothing still folded in every drawer, his possessions amassed in giant heaps: old shoes, filled-in crossword books, expired medications. The apartment all but frozen in time since his death.

For years, your great-uncle had been a gambler and a drunk, but late in life he sobered up and became a poet. You never really knew him—there'd been a split in the family—but now you like to stare up at the giant smoke stains above the bathtub and imagine him lying there, composing lines of poetry in his head.

Truthfully, the apartment is a wreck. Heaps of wayward belongings and every free surface covered with Diet Pepsi cans. Georgie drinks through boxes a week and leaves the cans stacked like strange modern sculptures. Mice have eaten through the cabinets, and a dust you pray isn't toxic sifts gently through holes in the ceiling.

The plan was for you to stay a few months, but already it's been over a year, poor Georgie sleeping on the couch. He is big and the couch is small, but when you offered to sleep there instead, he said he liked sleeping in front of the TV.

Sometimes you catch yourself avoiding Georgie. He's awkward and shy and speaks in halting, three-word sentences. Unless, of course, he's talking about wrestling, in which case he can go on and on. More than once you've found yourself trapped in the hall for hours as he narrated the long list of things one body can do to another on pay-per-view WWE. His best and only friend is a wiry cable repairman who comes over to watch wrestling and likes to fling racist epithets at the TV. At first you tried to argue with the cable repairman. Then you hid in your room. "That doesn't bother you?" you once asked Georgie, whose dad is Dominican. But Georgie only smiled bashfully and shrugged.

All night, the TV plays, shiny bodies punting one another across the ring. By now, you can recite all their names. You hear the announcers in your sleep.

You're still slick and shiny from running when you rewind the latest of the latest of the guru's tapes. His odd voice singsongs: *It's an office activated by the masters of time.* You wonder: Is there such a thing as a spiritual office? All you can picture is the shabby and windowless office you share with Vik—a room so tiny he notes your lackluster response to bouncing Adobe icons, so cramped you can smell his sweat.

But the guru is talking about the offices of Khidr, a wandering green prophet. Or maybe he's only dressed in green—the guru can be hard to understand. *On the verge of losing this life, the aspirant goes through the desertlike regions, up through mountains. There is no way out. His offices are there.*

Sometimes you feel yourself growing to like the guru. On one recording, he told a long story about a cow who'd followed him all afternoon. You kept waiting for some sort of spiritual punch line, some tidy summation, but it never came—he just liked the cow. Later, he explained that dying was a joyful thing because the body was the excrement of the soul and everyone felt joyful while expelling excrement. After a car accident in 1979, he stopped speaking and spent the last decade of his life in silence.

You too can fall easily into long silences. It wouldn't be so terrible, you think, to never have to speak, to use only an alphabet board to communicate, as the guru did in his final years.

You're still transcribing when Danny calls. He's thirty-one, nine years older than you, but still there's something that goes oddly soft and boyish in his voice when he calls late at night, which is mostly when he calls.

"I smell like a dead person," you say when he asks you to come over.
"So?" You can hear him smiling his drunken smile. "What else is new?"

Later, in his bed, you're quiet even for you, barely speaking except for one-word answers.

"Are you OK?"
"Yes."
"Do you want me to stop?"
"Yes."
"Isn't it good I ask you all these questions?"

You still haven't had sex. Most nights, you drink cheap whiskey and pass out next to each other. But then other nights, like this one, you think it will finally happen. You'll kiss him and hold on to his shoulders, and when he reaches for a condom, you won't push him away.

But always there's the ghost that rises up from the pit of your abdomen, stiffens in your limbs. Your arms aren't your arms anymore, moving as if of a will all their own—a kind of zombie strength startling inside you.

Danny hands you a Valium. The first night, the night you met him at a bar, you froze beside him in bed, fear wrapping its hands around your throat. A long minute passed, and then finally you could breathe again. Danny looked at you and said, "Were you molested or something?"

You rolled your eyes. You weren't about to do this. Weren't about to be the kind of trembly girl always appearing on TV—a girl divulging secrets, a special victim.

So Danny reached into his bedside drawer and pulled out a pill. "Valium," he said, and then it became a kind of ritual between you. Sometimes you don't even swallow these pills, slipping them quietly into your bag, and yet you keep up the pretense—this give-and-take, this vaguely palliative gesture. You wonder if it's the only real thing that's ever happened between the two of you.

But tonight you swallow the Valium and feel yourself drifting into someplace that's not quite sleep, passing over a long, strange desert, rising up into mountainous air. And you think again how strange it is that people's outlines mostly stay intact—even when you lie very close to someone. Even then.

2.

"How was your defense class?" asks Vik.

"Self-defense," you correct him. "It was all right."

"And are you defended now?" This is supposed to be a joke.

"Yes," you say with faux gravity. "Watch out."

Vik is a paunchy man in his fifties with a graying goatee—a new development. "I'm going for a Salman Rushdie look," he told you some weeks ago. "Pre- or posthiding?" you asked. This was why you got to him, he said, touching your elbow a second too long.

You and Vik are on an upswing in the cycle. There have been weeks full of lighthearted office banter, of humorous-but-professional weekend anecdotes. But this also means that soon, very soon, Vik will lean across his desk and tell you how his wife hasn't had sex with him in years. Or he'll find a way to stand next to you at one of the nightly cocktail parties on the eighth floor, and after the toasts and speeches, after the candlelight dims, he'll press his hand to yours under the table.

The first time it happened was at one of these cocktail parties, after a particularly rousing speech by Lula. Someone handed you a drink, and you could feel Vik watching you. Before you could fully register what was happening, his hand had brushed against your thigh. That was the moment you first felt it: the self that rose up out of you to watch. You felt not panic or anger but the dull throb of collusion. *Run!* a part of you shouted in your ear. But the spectator self only shrugged. *See what happens next.*

Always after these incidents, you're cold and formal, and Vik acts like a boss again: courteous, professional. But then eventually you let your guard down, which is when the whole thing starts again.

How many times can you do this? Not long ago, you went to a temp agency—took the typing test and filled out all the forms. But every time they call to offer you an assignment—a law firm, a private equity fund—you picture the grand carpeted hallways and galactic assembly rooms, the little booths full of translators speaking quietly into machinery. You think of the article you still haven't written, and you just can't do it—you can't leave this world, not yet.

A thousand times you've rebuked yourself for being overly familiar with Vik, especially in the early days, when you stayed working at your desk late into the night, took his phone calls at all hours of the day. You're too passive, you think. Too accommodating. You're too pretty, too ugly. You're so ugly, you appear lonely and therefore desperate.

It would be easier if Vik were a monster, a *Lifetime* original predatory boss. But in many ways, he's been good to you—plucking your application out from the many and championing your every article. Letting you write anything you want so long as it falls within the magazine's broad purview: chronicling the terrible things that happen to people in geopolitically insignificant corners of the world. While every reporter in the UN chases down statements on the latest Mideast crisis, you attend near empty meetings on child marriage and fistulas. You write about wars in countries where war is never called *war*, only *conflict*. You call up neglected researchers so happy to talk to you they all but write your stories.

Except lately, something's gone awry: you've written nothing in months. Of course, you know what it is—knew, though you wouldn't admit it, from the start. It's the dead girls: the long and wide-ranging feature you're supposedly writing on the murder of girls and women. Every day you spend hours scrolling through websites with dark backgrounds and strident fonts, sites that attempt to cobble together a kind of piecemeal tally. *Femicide*, they call it. You read about the hundreds of bodies unearthed in Juárez, bodies strangled and torched and mutilated. You read about mob attacks in Algeria, about shootings at universities. You read about mass rape and fatal fistulas. You read about the seemingly isolated attacks on women and girls in their homes and on the street—women killed by strangers and husbands and family members, by johns and coworkers and ex-boyfriends. Your story, you think, will be a kind of genealogy branching out in all directions, piercing through the solid veneer of the world and revealing a slow but steady female apocalypse.

Your first dead girl was the older cousin of a girl in your sixth-grade class. One day in homeroom, she announced that her cousin had gone missing and then dissolved into tears. No one believed her—she was the kind of girl who liked to say things just for shock value. She'd also said that her cousin had been modeling in Italy, which was already one outlandish thing too many. But then, a week later, it was on the local news—the body unearthed from a South Florida swamp, hacked up and shoved in a suitcase. The boyfriend had confessed.

Still, you didn't think much of it. It was one of those things that happened, then passed. It wasn't until you started working at a domestic violence shelter in college that you began to think again about the ways women were killed. A woman was most likely to be murdered by her partner when she was attempting to leave—this was a fact repeated with near religious conviction at the shelter. And yet, even among the lefty older feminists you worked for, you never heard anyone call it a hate crime. You began to suspect that the term *domestic violence* was itself a coy euphemism, a cleaned-up gloss of what was in fact a barely contained and murderous masculinity.

And the more you tally up figures, the more you see dead girls everywhere: on giant subway ads, in the news, anesthetized on countless hour-long TV dramas. It's all begun to feel to you like a single death, a single crime. When you try to picture the article in your mind, you see each body like a star in an impossibly big constellation. ("Baby, I'm a Star," the sick part of you likes to title this endeavor in your head.) Someone just had to draw in the lines.

Except you can't write. You type hunched over your laptop late into the night, then delete everything you've written the next morning. In the light of day, it all seems not just terrible but misguided and vaguely obscene: the idea of making horror into sentences, of making sentences that rise to the level of art—which you have to admit, finally, is what you're after. All this, the transmuting of violence into beauty, seems unthinkable.

But today is different. Today the new intern arrives—the first intern Vik has let you hire yourself. Her name is Jennifer, and when she appears in the office door, she's older than you expected—at least five years your senior and significantly louder. Her eye makeup is perfectly applied, and she says things like "It's a pleasure." Suddenly you feel very young.

After two hours of work, Jennifer stands up to announce in her loud voice that she's breaking for lunch. Vik casts a skeptical eye as she disappears down the hall. "She doesn't have the legs for that skirt," he sniffs, then turns back to his computer.

*

The skin comes off easiest and then there's another layer just below, almost silvery in the light. ("You're shining today," Frank tells Gracie.) Getting through this is like scraping paint off a wall, slow and horrible. You feel like a burglar trying to break into a house with a vegetable peeler.

It's tedious enough that you and Frank start competing to come up with the best terms for bodies. Blood-gusher. Gut-lugger. Sack of meat. Frank was an English major long ago, and since then he's been a truck driver, a substitute teacher, a traveling salesman. He says he likes what he does now best. Bodywork, he calls it—a term that revolts you just a little.

Earlier, you and Frank managed to turn Gracie onto her back, and now you try to avoid looking at her face. But still you hear her narrating in your head. *Chapter One, In Which a Rolfer and a Madwoman Take Up the Knife, or: Afterlife among the Barbarians.* Occasionally she stops narrating long enough to croon from a distant stage: *I just need your body, baby.*

When Frank asks what you do, you think of your unwritten article. You think of the near empty assembly rooms and speeches on fistulas. You think of all this and say you're a transcriber. Somehow this seems truer. Lately, everywhere you go, you seem to be observing the earth's permutations from on high, transcribing its terrible and beautiful configurations, all the details of your daily life passing through you to some invisible page.

"Hey, will you look at that." Frank nods at Gracie's toenails. Chips of bright red nail polish gleam in the light.

It's the toenails, finally, that get to you. Not the slick ropes of Gracie's intestines, not the pickled sacks of her organs, but a few chips of toenail polish. How you can slip out of one world and into the next, the whole mad scramble of your life fading out behind you, but the bad paint job on your second toe—that's the thing that stays.

You look at Gracie and think: *What is inside you?* Flesh, teeth, marrow, bone. Dark hidden rooms. All the minutes and hours of Gracie's days. Imprinted on cells, beneath the skin: time missing and not.

One night the second month of college, you woke with a stranger's face pressed close to yours. A body, knuckled and heavy. Your own limbs turned to lead. Or not *yours*, exactly—in the dark, you weren't a *you* yet, not even a *what*. Your mind reeled for something, anything, to latch on to. It took the grinding of a small eternity to understand *what* and *how* and later *when*.

Then you were on the cold floor, feeling for your underwear in the dark. When you didn't find it, you started to crawl. You crawled because your limbs had turned to fins—strange severed appendages that wouldn't move right. You crawled down a green-tinted hall, down stairs. Everything felt underwater. You crawled all the way back to your freshman dorm, and in the morning you told no one, because you weren't sure what there was to tell.

None of this makes you particularly remarkable or special, certainly not a special victim. You've engineered your life in such a way as to always be looking at far worse things—worse acts of violence, worse moments of terror. And yet, a small part of your brain still insists that those hours made a split in you, that they opened up a kind of schism in time, sent you in two ways at once. When later you asked your friends what they remembered of that night, they said only that you'd looked happy, that they saw you dancing in the chaos of bodies. But you couldn't remember this dancing self, and you began to think that she must be somewhere else, somewhere outside you. In a distant city, maybe, or just a subway stop away—the kind of person who might throw elaborate dinner parties or paint giant canvases. Maybe you've seen her passing on the street.

What the guru says about time: that it's like skin. That in moments of great terror or beauty, it can stretch wide open, and that a person might slip through.

"Time bomb," says Frank, and you look up, jolted. "A body," he explains. "A body is a kind of time bomb."

The next table over is debating what the former inhabitants of these bodies might say about all of you. You hear Gracie, a newscaster now, in your head: *Bringing you live updates from Day Two of the ongoing Yogi Hostage Crisis.*

"Rest their souls," someone murmurs.

"Thank God there's no soul," a lanky man replies.

Frank turns and stares. "What exactly do you think moved these bodies around then?"

The lanky man shrugs apologetically. "Chemistry."

"Neurons," you chime in. "Sparks."

Frank gives you a look like you've betrayed him, choosing the ranks of the soulless. But as much as you'd like to believe in something—anything would do—you can't quite tip this desire over into belief. Which isn't to say you haven't imagined it. Which isn't to say you haven't pictured the burnished bright coals of your insides lighting you up or rising in embers above your head. How it would be to look down and think: *Oh, so this is what I was.*

If you could just cut yourself open, peel back your insides—all the little gates and alleys, the webbed tunnels of veins. The sweet-sour reek of it, the clenched fist of the heart—cut loose, says Jeremiah, it unfolds, unravels. If you could just see inside yourself, you might finally understand it, this person you've become.

Night keeps coming earlier. This weekend the clocks get set back. "That's good," muses Jeremiah, watching as the rest of you draw up the sheets. "We should always go out into darkness."

"Say good night, Gracie," says Frank.

"Good night, Gracie," you whisper.

*

On Saturday, a small cloud of flies appears, circling the apartment hallway. There's a voice mail from an unknown number on your phone. You listen to the first five seconds before snapping it shut. *This is the Brooklyn Community Health Clinic—*

Before you left the clinic, you changed your mind, made up a fake number, but somehow they've found you anyway. You're still staring at your phone when it vibrates in your hand. *Unknown caller.* What do they want from you? You're about to answer and say they have the wrong number when you hear a loud, familiar voice. "I just wanted to give you notice."

It's Jennifer, the intern, and she's quitting. A slow dread rises in your stomach as she tells you that after work on Friday she went with Vik to the cocktail party on the eighth floor. Out of nowhere, Vik announced: "I have to do something." Then he grabbed her face in his hands and kissed her on the mouth.

"I'm sorry" is all you can say. "I'm so sorry."

Jennifer says it's fine, that she wrote herself a letter of recommendation and had Vik sign it.

"If there's anything I can do," you murmur before hanging up. "Anything at all."

It's only some moments later that you fully understand: you are not too pretty, too ugly. Not too familiar or accommodating or lonely. For the briefest of seconds, it stings, your unspecialness. Then quickly it transmutes to rage, white-hot and moving up your face. It didn't have anything to do with you.

*

A month ago, there was a blood drive at the UN. Like everyone, you went down and sat in the metal chairs, began filling out the forms. Then you got to the line that stopped you: *HIV status*, it said. And it occurred to you for the first time that you didn't know. You'd mostly avoided doctors, but the few times you wound up in front of one, you found yourself stumped by the question *Are you sexually active?* It all seemed impossible to explain: the night in college, the missing hours, whatever did or didn't happen.

Eventually you'd merely put it out of your mind—so far out of your mind, it barely existed at all. It became like a memory that belonged to someone else—a story relayed by a friend or a scene from a movie—connected by only the thinnest of threads to you and your life. But the blood drive unturned something, churned up the stiff ground of your insides. The black hole opened in your chest, and you lay awake at night suddenly aware of yourself as a body—the same body then and now.

Finally, you went to the clinic. But once you were sitting there, a nurse telling you to make a fist, it occurred to you that maybe you didn't want to know. Because maybe you were dying, and maybe you'd only made it this far by not knowing.

Of course you knew this was unlikely, knew all the statistics. You knew the odds were small, infinitesimal. But still, you were probably dying.

The night sky, when you run, is bruised red and violet. Breath scrapes your throat.

What Prince says: *Dearly Beloved, we are gathered here today—*

But this seems too on point. You skip ahead to the wailing of "When Doves Cry." You run faster.

You run the distance of three subway stops, all the way to East Flatbush, where Danny lives, though you don't go to his building. Sometimes when you run, you have visions of strange men leaping from the bushes and hacking you to pieces. It's a strange comfort to think there'd be someone nearby, not to save you from death but just to witness it—to witness your body dismembered and bleeding.

Then faintly, very faintly, you hear what sounds like a woman screaming. It's coming from somewhere in the distance, somewhere behind you. You keep running. There's another scream—it seems to be moving somehow through the dark. Finally, on the third scream, you turn around. But there's nothing there. You pull out your headphones, and there's just the sound of you panting on the sidewalk, cars gliding past. It's only when you put your headphones back in that you understand: the scream is coming from inside them, from inside your own ears. Background noise on "When Doves Cry."

In eighth grade, a story spread around school about a girl who'd been raped by five high-school boys. You never knew her name, but when you pictured it, at thirteen, you thought: *It wouldn't be the worst thing.* You pictured the girl getting up afterward, walking away. You thought how at least she'd get to walk away. *Not like you'd die.*

You'd forgotten all about this for many years, and it was only running late one night that the girl came back to you. You think of her, this nameless girl, and you think of the scream dying in your ears. Everything you witness, you witness too late.

*

You're almost asleep when Danny calls, but still you go. His apartment is dark, and neither of you speak. It occurs to you that you don't know what you are to each other. You're not in love. Not strangers, not friends. You're just two people falling asleep in the same bed. How many nights can you spend in the bed of another person without coming to know them at least a little? There must be some sort of limit, a rule.

You turn away to face the dark and feel yourself sliding toward sleep. "I think I'm dying," you say quietly. Because this is easier to say than what you truly believe, which is that you're already dead.

Wordlessly, Danny reaches across you and holds your wrist in his hand. You remember telling him once about your fear of hearts and veins, the blood moving through you invisibly. Now you fall asleep this way—you facing the dark and Danny holding on to your veins, like he's making sure they won't seep out in the night.

You've started to see Gracie in the moments just before you sleep—her strange, startled expression and blanched yellow skin. The scalpel moves like a silver fish inside your dreams.

3.

By Monday morning, the walls are covered in flies. Your great-uncle's apartment has endured all other manner of infestation—ants, cockroaches, mice—but this is something else. The walls black and moving, alive. You stay hidden beneath a sheet in bed, only emerging to dash to the bathroom. It strikes you as not a little ironic that you've become the body frozen stiff beneath a sheet.

You pull your laptop in with you and Google exterminators. The cheapest is four hundred dollars. You have barely three hundred in your back account. You consider trying to hawk your stash of unswallowed Valiums, accruing in a little blue heap on your great-uncle's bureau. Instead, you call your mother, weeping.

"Put it on my credit card," she sighs, then goes to look for her purse. You weep harder, feeling like a little kid.

"There's something else," your mother says because you're still crying and because sometimes she just knows. Your mother is a little crazy and also a drunk, but she's good in a crisis. It's only when there's no crisis that she doesn't know what to do with herself.

You tell her about Danny, about the ghost that rises from your abdomen. You tell her how you'll never have sex with anyone.

"Of course you will," says your mother. Nothing you've said seems to shock her. "You're much too sensual a person never to have sex with anyone." Then she asks: "Do you have a vibrator?"

"No." Suddenly you're not crying at all.

She tells you where to go online—the kind of pastel-infused website that refers to its merchandise as *wonders* and where every wonder has a name like Natural Contours Goddess. "Just practice on your own."

*

The exterminator tells you that flies like to descend en masse when something dead is holed up in the wall. "But these are everywhere," he says, baffled. You ask if it could be the Diet Pepsi cans. "Nah." He shakes his head. "That's stuff's all chemicals."

He goes around planting bright blue glue traps on every free surface. You can't believe this costs four hundred dollars.

You don't go to work and don't go to class. You don't call Vik to tell him you're not coming in. Instead, you make your bed a kind of makeshift fort, and inside it you sit very still. You dial your voice mail and listen to a stranger tell you calmly and matter-of-factly that you're not dying, that there's nothing wrong with you. That all this has been for nothing.

What you should feel, you know, is relieved. *Weary*, you think. *That's what I feel.* Because if you're not dying, you must instead be living. You stare at your phone for a very long time.

*

When Georgie comes home from work, you tell him about the exterminator, and suddenly you're crying again. "I can't live like this," you say. "There's something dead in our walls." Even though this isn't exactly what the exterminator said.

Georgie does the same thing he always does. The same thing he did when you came to him about the cockroaches, the ceiling dust, the mice. He smiles abashedly at the floor and tells you it'll get better.

You're beginning to hate Georgie a little. You hate the stink and filth of the apartment—the piles of crusted dishes, the spray of little black hairs in the bathroom sink—and how he refuses to get rid of a single thing, every closet and drawer crowded with a dead man's possessions. You hate the way he's stuck—so stuck, he's paralyzed.

"It *won't* get better," you say. Now you're sobbing. You're not a crier, but already you've wept twice today, like some great storm has come and flooded your insides.

"Look," Georgie says quietly. "Just look."

And then you see he's right. The flies have thinned. The walls have surfaced. They're no longer moving, grimed only with dirt. Together, you and Georgie go around the apartment and shake glue traps into garbage bags. You ask about the latest wrestling match and listen as Georgie tells you the long history of the Undertaker, his feuds and personas and what his comeback might mean.

*

On the last day of class, Frank takes a bone saw to Gracie, apologizing all the while. In a flash, Gracie jerks forward, spits something across the room. Your heart thuds in your chest. Practically the whole room leaps. There's a moment of stunned silence, and then everyone laughs: it's her dentures.

By now, says Jeremiah, you can start to see the ways people have died. How their organs blackened and festered. How they grew their deaths inside them.

On the last of the guru's tapes you transcribed—the last tape, you realize now, you'll ever transcribe—the guru claimed to know the future. It wasn't by magic or premonition, he insisted, but that for him time had grown very wide. *In the light of the future, everything has already happened.*

You pull at a strand of yellowed tissue, gristly and veined. If this were a movie, you think, this is the point where you'd be treated to flashbacks of Gracie's life—a montage of her days and years, sped up toward their inevitable end. You'd see her drinking from a flask at work or chain-smoking secretly in the night. You'd see her death—maybe slow, maybe sudden. Maybe strangled with a pair of stockings.

But you see nothing. Frank says maybe it was her heart, which peeks out now from the depths, ugly and stiff.

Rush, rush, rush, you hear in your ear. Because you and Frank are close, so close. The surrounding tissue is thick and fibrous, and together you fall into a silent rhythm, cutting and unwinding. It's only when the scalpel clatters to the table that you see Frank's hands are trembling. "I'm fine," he tells you. "I just get the shakes sometimes. It's a condition."

Slowly, the heart emerges in full—a brown and muscled thing the size of your fist. Frank does a low whistle. "It's dumb to get sentimental about an organ, I know, but what can you do?"

Inside you, you feel it: something unraveling in your chest. You look down to steady yourself, glance around the room. How unlikely, you think—you don't know any other word for it—how unlikely you're all here, down in the heart of the mortuary basement, cutting into what used to be a person. Or maybe this is just what you do, what you do and must go on doing all your life. The most likely thing in the world: diving into another person. Diving and diving for the thing that might save you.

Frank's hands are shaking worse now, and you see that you're going to have to do this last part on your own. And you see too, as if by the wide and astonished light of the future, that you'll never go back to your job at the UN, never walk its grand carpeted halls. You won't give notice, won't return Vik's calls. You see a future of coffee runs for hedge-fund analysts, of typing up memos and law briefs. And you see, of course, what you already knew: that you'll never finish your story on dead girls, the one that was supposed to rise up above the face of the earth, draw in the lines of an impossible constellation.

But for now, there's only the heart, dumb and unmoving. There's only the cut you have to make. Your voice, when you hear it, surprises you. "Come on, Gracie. Come on, you blood-gusher, you gut-lugger, you shining sack of meat. Just this one last thing."

An Impacted Fracture of the Distal Radius

Elizabeth Gaffney

"NO ONE EVER TELLS YOU how they core you and eat you, how they take over not just your soul but your body."

Louisa envied Dr. Miranda's mushroom-colored velvet jeans and the perfect eight-year-old girl she imagined had been born through natural childbirth. Long enough ago for Dr. Miranda to get back her waistline, not that Louisa saw much of that, behind those slim crossed legs. Or was it Dr. Miranda's imagined partner—Louisa decided to call her Emily—who had carried the child? But from *Dr. Miranda's* egg.

Now that she'd conjured up an Emily Jr., there was no way Louisa could say what occurred to her next: how children changed you—for the worse—and not just during those trippy nine-ish months when they dwell inside you, not because of just the weight gain that dragged on postpartum. She'd been prepared for the flaccid stomach, the physical feelings of love and anguish, the tiredness and the occasional gut resentment of lost personal time. But the lost three-quarters of an inch in height? *And they* eat *your* breasts (*not just the milk, thank you very much*), Louisa wanted to howl.

Louisa had successfully, even joyfully, breastfed Mandy for a year. Then, just this week, Mandy champed down, hard. Louisa's mother'd told her to wean the child already, as soon as she'd started getting teeth. Now Mandy had four. But what did her bottle-and-formula-wielding mother know?

Louisa recalled her mother's vocal revulsion at the multiple-breasted Diana of Ephesus Fountain at Tivoli, the summer they'd met in Italy, when Louisa was living in Munich, post–graduate school. There were at least fourteen pendulous nipple jets shooting water.

Wow, Louisa'd said, or something equally profound. The moss, the moisture, the beatific face of Diana, the old stone. She'd been transfixed and somehow transformed. For the first time in her life, she had wanted a child. Her mother's reaction had been, *Good God, that's digusting.*

Four razor-sharp, freshly serrated teeth, to be specific. Louisa had screamed quite instinctively. She felt awful when Mandy burst into tears until she looked at her daughter's red-smudged chin and her own pale flesh with a quartet of puncture wounds welling up crimson. *Good God, that's disgusting,* she'd said. Or maybe she'd only thought it.

After the countless hours of oxytocin-laced snuggling they'd shared, *this* was how Mandy let Louisa know she was ready to wean. Louisa had squinted at her daughter, wondering who was inside that little face. She could have just turned her cheek and waited for other sustenance. She was constantly being offered her sippy cup, spoons of mashed bananas, biscuits, tidbits of cheese. But no, she had to go and make it utterly final. For Louisa, it was a sudden end to a lovely, tranquil time. And now it seemed she was going through opiate withdrawal. Everyone said, in not so many words, that oxytocin was the mother's junk, but what about the mother's methadone? For the past couple of days, Louisa had been filling the void with white wine, with mixed results.

"So who would you like to have told you?" asked Dr. Miranda.

"*What?*"

"About how they core you and eat you?"

"Oh. Right."

Louisa supposed the obvious answer was her mother. Her mother hadn't told her squat. Not about menstruation, not about pregnancy, certainly not about lactation and its complications. How would her mother, who never breastfed either of her children, not even for a moment, possibly have been able to impart this information?

"Like, maybe some parenting book, or magazine, or my ob-gyn? Or one of my dozen friends who had children ten years ago?"

"OK . . ."

"Or you. You have children, don't you?"

Dr. Miranda looked up impartially, then glanced at the clock. It was quarter to five.

"We're going to have to stop now."

"Do you have children?"

"See you next Tuesday."

Louisa was worried she would turn out like her parents.

When she looked at Mandy in her high chair, Mandy laughed and swatted the sippy cup off the tray. Louisa's stomach lurched, though it really wasn't the same as the day her father had bought her the can of Orange Crush. Louisa hadn't *meant* to knock the soda over. Her father'd set her up at her own desk in the newsroom, at the space of another reporter who wasn't there. It wasn't Take Your Daughter to Work Day, but it might as well have been: it was Lincoln's Birthday, and her mother had pneumonia. She was so excited to be there, at the paper, that she began typing up an imaginary news story on the IBM Selectric. The thing even had backspacing Wite-Out tape! She was loving it, dreaming of being a reporter someday, but she must have realized there was something odd about her story because at one point she felt her father peering at her, flinched, and knocked over the soda. Sticky fluid ran everywhere, and her father had to swab down the other reporter's desk, dabbing off every last key of the typewriter individually. He cursed under his breath as he laid out all the orange-stained papers and notebooks to dry on the radiator by the window. He saw her article—"Local Family's House Goes Up in Flames"—and asked though his teeth what the hell she thought she was doing.

Louisa picked up the sippy cup, rinsed it off, and thought about it. She couldn't picture herself going white with suppressed rage. She couldn't picture giving her child a sugary soda. But in a more general way, would she get mad at Mandy for . . . being her own person? Doing things Louisa never thought of doing? Not being what Louisa expected? She certainly wasn't what Louisa had expected, even now, with her goofy bravado and utter silence, her shiny purple hearing aids and gorgeous dimples. Would Louisa ever come simply to *dislike* her fanged darling?

For several months after the Orange Crush incident, she'd spilled her milk at dinner almost every day. The vein at her father's temple used to pulse visibly as he and her mother mopped it up. Louisa, too clumsy to be of any use, was banned from helping, so she just sat there, cringing with self-loathing.

As she sat in Dr. Miranda's office, she pictured the white opacity spreading thinly across the dark finish of the wooden dining table, oozing under the place mats and running though the crack where the leaf was inserted at holidays. She felt her father's glare and the cold drip on her knee, and she reached down to wipe the memory away.

Louisa had just gotten pregnant—a journey in itself—when she got in the accident. She still wondered if the trauma of the whole event had done something, had been the cause of the problems that followed. Even though *she* wasn't injured, how fragile was Mandy—the collection of cells that would become Mandy—at that moment?

Louisa'd gone out to move the goddamned car across the street in compliance with alternate-side-of-the-street parking rules. She looked left right left. The street was empty. She pulled out—and there he was in her windshield, Micah Johnson—not that she knew his name then—way too close. The car was moving incredibly slowly. She jammed on the brakes. But she tapped him. She knocked him down. Had she killed him? Her hands shook so violently she had trouble turning the key to shut off the engine. As she jumped from the car to see if the man was all right, she realized she'd pissed her pants. He sat in the street with his hand to his head, looked up at her, and said, "I never got hit by a car before."

"Oh my God, are you hurt? I'm so sorry!" she blurted. And then, "I never *hit* anyone before either. . . . Should I call an ambulance? Are you OK?"

He looked like he wasn't quite sure. Then, before he had a chance to answer, they heard the boom. It was close, horribly close, and this only a year after the towers went down.

"What was that?" they'd both said together. Louisa left her car half pulled out of its spot, key in the ignition, and Micah Johnson and she—they introduced themselves later, and it turned out he was fine, because she really *had* only tapped him—the two of them ran in the direction of the sound. They were holding *hands*.

"Were you here last year?" she asked him as they turned the corner and saw the street ripped open, water and dust and smoke roiling in the air, blocking out the familiar view of the river beyond. He nodded.

Sirens howled. Firemen were cordoning off the area. It wasn't terrorism, in the end—a worker had drilled into an electrical conduit that served the subway—but it brought them together.

"Did you know anyone?" he asked, as they watched a stretcher being loaded into an ambulance, and she knew what he meant.

"Weirdly not. I knew two who just happened to be home sick or out of town."

"Me neither, but I saw it. I work at the Watchtower. My office window faces the harbor."

"My husband and I saw it too, from the promenade," she said and then, "Are you sure you're OK?"

Micah Johnson nodded and gave her an enormous hug. "I'm sorry about before. I was late," he said. "I ran between the cars. I wasn't looking."

"No," she said. "It wasn't your fault. I'm just glad—"

When Louisa got home, thighs burning with uric acid but having made a curious new friend, her car had been towed and her mother was sitting on the stoop in front of her building, surrounded by EMTs. Louisa blinked. She'd entirely forgotten they were planning to go to the ob-gyn together. Then one of the EMTs put a blood-pressure cuff on her mother.

"Oh my God, Mom! Are you OK? Is she OK?"

Her mother had been crossing the street when the street exploded. She'd been struck by a delivery truck whose driver was distracted by the blast.

Her mother looked irritated. "He just tapped me, really. I'm fine. I sent the young man on his way, but then some bothersome Good Samaritan called the ambulance. These nice people came and wouldn't leave till you got here."

"Well, that's a good thing. You just got hit by a car. You have to get checked out."

"It was a truck. And no, I don't. I refuse to be transported."

Louisa inhaled, touched her belly, and wondered how her mother had managed to upstage her.

"She's refusing transportation to a medical facility, ma'am, which is against our advice. She's an older lady. She could have broken something. Even a hairline fracture can be a problem. She should really get an X-ray. One of the bystanders got the truck's license, by the way." He held out a scrap of paper.

"Oh, for Pete's sake," said Louisa's mother. "I told him to leave. It wasn't a hit-and-run. And I'm not going to sue the UPS, all right? I'm fine!"

"I suspect she is fine," said Louisa. "But we're going to the hospital anyhow. I'll just take her inside and get her a glass of water, and then we'll go and get both of us checked out." Of course, Louisa's mother never drank water. It was coffee, milk, or Scotch for her, but you couldn't say that to an EMT.

"Aren't you already late for your appointment, Louisa?" asked her mother. "Where were you? Why don't we just go?"

"Well, I really need to change first."

"Why in heaven's name?"

"I'll tell you when we get inside," she'd said, but she didn't. It was somehow too ridiculous to have wet herself because she hit a pedestrian when her mother was the pedestrian being hit in another, simultaneous accident and had nonetheless managed to maintain her steely composure.

They went to the hospital, Louisa had her ultrasound, her mother had an X-ray, despite repeated protests, and apparently both of them were normal. It turned out little things like malformations of the cochlea didn't show up at that resolution.

"What happened?" said Dr. Miranda. Louisa blinked. It was the first time Dr. Miranda had ever spoken first. Usually she just smiled faintly, nodded kindly toward Louisa, her invitation to begin.

"I guess you could call it a parenting accident? I managed not to kill Mandy, but I broke this." She waved her cast in the air for emphasis, then regretted it as pain surged across her forearm.

Louisa had gotten her Converse wrapped in a strap of the baby carrier while sitting at a coffee shop with Mandy in her lap. When she'd stood up to go, the strap had hobbled her. As she toppled, she saw the bandy legs of the café chairs and the puzzle of the terrazzo floor zooming toward her. She broke the fall with her left arm and ended up on her ass with a wailing Mandy thrust upward in her right hand like a giant, cantankerous trophy.

"So, yeah, I literally broke the fall."

"Thank God she was all right."

"I know, right?" said Louisa. Everyone was constantly thanking God that Mandy was OK instead of giving Louisa kudos for her brilliant agility in the face of disaster or commending her self-sacrifice or possibly even offering sympathy for the excruciatingly painful impacted fracture of her left distal radius. She must be telling the story wrong somehow. She was undermining herself.

"Would you like to talk about the fall, how it happened?"

"It was just—I tripped."

"How's your sleep been lately?"

"So maybe you *don't* have children?" Louisa said. "I always thought you had children—a daughter, somehow. But if you did, you would, you know, *know*."

"So your sleep?"

Of course Louisa slept. In occasional quarter-hour snatches. Mandy still ate every four hours. Bottle or baby food, either way Louisa spent a good forty minutes feeding her, once you'd added up the time it took to make the food or bottle, change the postprandial diapers, and sequester the soiled onesies. She missed the no-prep-time aspect of breastfeeding almost as much as the rush and hum of the oxytocin. As for Louisa's own toileting and feeding, she squeezed it into the interstices along with personal grooming and fighting the insurance company over their rotten, inhuman level of coverage for the complications of Mandy's birth. Add in that Louisa was doing all of this in the itchy green cast that felt like a cheese grater on both Louisa's and Mandy's skin, causing the child to howl every time Louisa picked her up, and the forty-five minutes plus commute, once a week, to see Dr. Miranda, and the answer to how she slept was, well, laughable?

She began to cry.

"I'm wondering how the Nortriptyline is working for you. How you're feeling, compared to last week and the week before?"

"Is there something else I could try, because it feels like nothing. I feel like it's doing nothing at all. It's doing *nothing*."

"There are a few other formulations that are also compatible with breastfeeding, but they're chemically similar . . ."

"Didn't I tell you she bit me? It's over. No more milky."

"You cut her off because of that?" asked Dr. Miranda.

Louisa looked at her therapist. Was she being chastised? Did she need that?

"Are you sure that was the right thing to do, to punish her? These things are deep bonds. . . ."

Louisa wanted to say, *Are you fucking nuts? Of course I cut her off!* But the truth was weirdly more palatable.

"It wasn't up to me. She didn't want it anymore. She was done."

"Oh. Well. I see. Then we have options."

Louisa wasn't sure she'd ever seen Dr. Miranda smile that way before, like she was happy, rather than just being pleasant. She tried smiling back, but she was too angry and humiliated.

A few minutes later, she left with two new prescriptions, some samples of a tiny, supposedly terribly expensive blue tablet, and a curious feeling of hope. She popped one of the tabs through the foil backing on the packet and slipped it between her lips.

It was sweet.

The mothers in the park were so competitive. It was awful to come up against them with a broken wrist and deaf baby who was never going to meet her milestones, never be as articulate as the other precocious, obnoxious little munchkins. What was she supposed to do, coo with admiration as their one-year-olds uttered *Tyrannosaurus rex*, *climbing structure*, and *cheese stick*? Mandy was stuck on *die-saw*, *juh-ji*, and *tee-tih*, which might as well have been *gavagai* for all the clarity of meaning. Fucking Quine, thought Louisa, rubbing the rough green cast, as if she could scratch her itches. He hadn't even considered the difficulties of the deaf child when he took up the problem of ostension.

She sat in the sun on the bench and listened to the water from the sprinkler rain down on the cobblestones. A chickadee in the shrubbery trilled so loud and high in Louisa's ear that it seemed odd to her she could still see the city, the skyscrapers, the bridge. *Chick-a-dee-dee-dee*, it said. *Chick-a-dee-dee-dee.*

"Biddy?" said Mandy, tapping Louisa's leg to gain her attention.

Had she really just said that? Had she heard a bird and named it?

"Yes! Birdy! It's a chickadee! It's a birdy! *Chick-a-dee-dee-dee!*" gushed Louisa in a rare spurt of motherese. She'd mostly given up on all those singsongy vocalizations—even tearfully ceased singing lullabies—once she'd learned they were going all but unheard. Sometimes, when she talked to Mandy, her voice was so unmodulated, so flat, Louisa felt as if she might as well have been talking to voice-recognition software.

Maybe it was Mandy hearing the bird, maybe it was the blue tablets of Dr. Miranda, but a wave of something rare—well-being?—washed over her.

"Where's the *birdy*?" she said as she rose from the bench and looked at her daughter.

Mandy stood with one chubby fist gripping the arm of the bench, the other hand extended like a tightrope walker's. As she peered into the bush, the tiny wraith of a chickadee fluttered out, showing itself with glorious black and tawny bravura, and flew away. Mandy cackled with glee and fell slowly backward, her curly head arcing toward the wooden bench. Louisa's breath lodged in her throat as she snatched her daughter's forbidden weight from the air with uneven hands, the good one and the green one.

Three Poems

Jessica Reed

FIELD OF VISION

In the thick of summer, rising fireflies flash-reign these acres
as the rest of the world sleeps.
I have seen it:
feverish for nine days and nights in June,
on the strange schedule of sickness,
when I would lumber to the kitchen for mineral water and
the carbonation in my glass simulated in miniature
the scores of lifting lights in sight.
My neck aching and my head dull, the room opened
into the wide silent scene. Charles Wright
said of affliction, *the world becomes more abundant*
in severest light.

You see, I have been trying to find the right level
of attachment to this world,
to consider the decomposition
of bodies truly, trace dog-atom to dirt-atom,
dust-atom to breath-atom,
so that I might achieve a divine indifference,
witness what I can while I can,
endure the vomiting, the fever, the mania—
all for the effervescence
and luminescence,
for the light-headedness that follows.
Wright was thinking of Simone Weil, who once
said, *We do not become detached, we change our attachment.*
We must attach ourselves to the all.
I'm ready
to make that happen.

Jessica Reed

In the spaces where there is no world,
we infer void. But where is such a place?
I press my fingertips and thumbs together
and even in the limit they never touch:
only fields, repelling.

Suppose everything is atoms in motion,
tiny billiards colliding.
I believe this even though
the truth about billiards is that they never touch,
that all contact is an illusion.

Our minds evolved for fitness, not truth,
so my ad hoc reality is constructed from
silhouettes of mental objects.
That seam between my fingers,   inhabited
structures, ascending and descending.

Attachment to this world, simple cravings:
cool water, dark chocolate, red meat . . .
Yet all I know of, say, infection
after weeks in bed is only how sounds
have become fainter. If a mind could hold the truth
of matter's temporality,
nothing would matter.

Weil also wrote that it was better to say, "I am suffering"
than "This landscape is ugly." Still, it is in the duration
of darkness between flashes
that the firefly communicates with her mate.
Envelope of air in water—
another sustaining absence.

A field is a field
in the spaces where (diffuse winter light
a disappointment) we infer void,
but where I press my fingertips:
in the limit, they touch.

Jessica Reed

I ONCE WAS DRY LIGHT

I once was a sun's ray, especially in summer and at noon
I was reflected and concentrated in burning glass
I was as between mountains or through walls
I once was a hollow in a mountain

was a violent motion a natural motion
I was absolute, steam and hot smoke
was air itself, a furious heat. Once, I was air shut up
underground in caverns, especially in winter

where wool was close to a fire for a time.
I was sparks from flint and steel sharply struck
was yoke beams and wheel axles. I was wet hay
stored and catching fire.

I was iron dissolved in a glass without use of fire
was the inside of an animal, was horse shit
fresh animal excrement. Once, strong oil of sulfur
and marjoram, and egg white in distilled wine.

Once I was a skinless part of the body, eye or tongue,
was a burning old nasturtium. I was vinegar
and acid and a wound—even the penetrating cold
of the North Wind, which burns.

NOTE. Some of this language is from Francis Bacon's Heat Table in *The New Organon*. "The North Wind" was Bacon's adaptation of Virgil, *Georgics*, I.92–3.

Jessica Reed

HYPOTHETICAL FLAWLESS

Peeking at a core self
        the universal bones in your head
        the form of a body, what can never
        fully be realized:

        "idealized single crystal of the absolutely pure element"
once the purview of the religious   perfection
        now belongs to physics   "hypothetical flawless" chased
into the unrealizable realm   your skin is growing transparent

starting its slow slide off the meat of your face
eye sockets, jaw, dark cavity in place of a nose
        (your core,   peaking)

early March magnolia buds of green fur
        white petals peek through the folds
a full month before   they are due to bloom
        buds, sublimely indifferent:
        snow comes and goes,
white petals turn yellow   do as
the temperature dictates
                        this year:

one triumphant white   (hypothetical)
        flower for every fifteen brown   shriveled
                unrealized

The Flesh of Suddenness

Michael Ives

We touch here the most difficult point, that is, the bond between the flesh and the idea, between the visible and the interior armature which it manifests and which it conceals.

—Maurice Merleau-Ponty

And puts coins over one's eyes
as at the start of that journey
when leaves rustle and the furniture speaks
the big secret you've been keeping from yourself
narrows its eyes / you're worried
but it's the right kind of worry
telling you in no uncertain terms
that his search for the source of the Nile
did drive him crazy
but only in the minds of his biographers.

*

Do world-engendering point sources
slipping off plumb into a becoming
raise hurrying away on some slight pretext
to a ballet of total meaning / *heart*
well before the appearance of the organ
centered an infinite intension
leashed by a hairspring to anywhere
on the other side of time
puts the here in the there by wandering
in thought past the fountain of itself.

*

Really little more than a surrender function
in a pre-tailored cosmic laboratory animal nexus
that's me / no more no less
incoming data meets thresh-n-mesh
in a futurity emulsion
with read-back capability
sitting here at appr. 4:35 p.m.
turning out these dispersal patterns
along a resonance curve in a nature factor
while the sun does long division on a parking lot.

*

After swerving back around to fulfill
certain structural obligations inherent in
initiating a foregone conclusion
into its runaway advent
spews out so-called *object realms*
in radiating statistical patterns
says this reflexive gobbet of
semistable pointing at the entire tamale
before it's collapsed into swerving
back around to greet the entire tamale.

*

And the weather's heart unspooled
makes an eel whose electrical discharge
begat the shudder of conscience
that a messiah might happen along
flip film in reverse
guide deluge back
into its colicky alloy
of storm cloud and tantrum
tearing through a moral continuum
like a box van with legs falling out the back.

*

Offers you the consciousness of wolves
seen through a deviled lens
you can't tell it from an orgasm
dark and welling in a bible
was meant to salve the loss of losses
but it sleeps on a hand never its own
a hand dreaming of a hand
laid in velvet rue and field equations
oh when things were equal to themselves
and not.

*

A Binding of the Heavens
the very phrase stirs up
great cylinders of rising air
immense auspicious birds
riding them since their advent
stay aloft for ages at a time
to preserve their child
the desert expanse below
one brief drought
along the path of a greater flesh.

*

While I'd waited out the worst of it in barren
solace canned food space enough to exercise
running water the entire run of the place actually
rolling meadow and orchards endless blue vault
of sky as seen between the fingers of my hand those
of another painted terrifyingly blue reflected in
his eye an orchard and meadow beyond when he blinked
who or else a mind they let idle outside the staging area
at myriads of cycles per second anyway at rates
generative of what might pass as a visual continuum.

*

They see by seeing them see them
the eyes and things the eyes see
the flesh that takes in the other fleshes itself
for the Great Lie of Time tossing in a dream
rises perpetually through black slates and granites
in plumes of cognitive genesis
its brain stem a logarithmic corridor
lined with goat and sheep and flint
a *me* twisted out of a *you* sings from its mouth
as winter in the summer palace burns.

*

And had counted on the rest of the day
falling back into itself earlier than it
did but resisting the older tendency
to resemble an ordinary succession of hours
and calibrate its effects to a standard
familiarity which the intention to veil
deliberately whatever escaped a ready
explanation people were led to believe
they'd accept even if it disappointed
for reasons they weren't yet capable of.

*

Chroma / tongs / pervasions
years widowed in oblique jade
pipevine and stonecrop
edge of mountain / grain of water
steel grain / rhythm's pain
the Pavilion of Specific Tension
the audible ember
a rungless
ladder to a night language
to the hole in its vowel.

*

Clouds are air pushing its stomach
out through the mouth
of a cult of certainty
recrystallized into a what-if
to flip on the essence-function
actualizes an outside
floating in from another time
identical to this breakwater
made by water
of water.

*

The lithic trance pushing up
through ruminative earths
the past of its own epiphany
moves in mineral penchants / their brinks
crossing in thrusts and ledges
by complex indirection flower into stone
whose stillness / an ardor mortised in tiny grains
of what wraiths in time call feeling
sculpts to dense impetuosities
the slowly flashing foam of always.

*

The substance in a chalice isn't the god
until bodies were a sudden splendor
in their death throes
so crazy bones for the Resurrection
that someone had a great notion
to convert his Jeep into a planter
one must already by a vessel cupped in nature
have passioned its modes with thinking
inside the bones of thinking
where a water hammers in a desert.

*

Fusion reaction at dream point
made flesh for mine was the kingdom
to steal the energy from the ground
and force a jet of hashtag
through sentient creatures
trapped in their foreclosed cribs
all along the drone of Kansas
followed Oxycodone trail
to a pride of griffins
is a blade of grass.

*

The karmic chains the radiant data
a ground of perfection surrenders
through sense portals in active reception
by running its hand through the only river
time corrugates images into animals
browsing beneath its ripples
and the knife of dialectic is forged
cuts a musical borealis in the silence
that what truly is may choose not to appear
and what is not to appear.

*

Cross-grain in the water hardly discernible
to any but amoebic bodies
as to the transitory lion who swims in the air
a precise quantity of Eden
bulbs its eye with fiery comets
gazing at it as they pass
our graves are commas
a wise quiescence feeding on animal life
opens into death until the opening into
itself dies into.

*

Michael Ives

The letters of my name
having gentrified my will
to inhabit life as life
originally intended
to inhabit namelessly
a flow means to surrender
all of it and but what
allows one to surrender
all of it other than
a.

*

Single atom
of center
will stoke
a fetish
for order
all the
periphery in
the world
can't begin
to quell.

*

These legible worms unbinding
the flesh of essences
not worms so much as an infinitive mood
worming into whatever
the vibratory everywhere
flashes so often as I see
I dye it into a visible certitude
my substance nothing but a looking
for its horizon lies below
a ground other than the ground.

*

Befouled well the ribbon
cutting to a long train
of birth defects
to which they reply
sleep's an antiquated
technology they
say grieve on
your own time
they say
heel.

*

For things to look exactly as they did
when you were here last but for the boat
crashing against the side of the house
and the tornado coming through
were supposed to be suppressed otherwise
more or less exactly as they had evolved
out of letting the past depend for its survival
on a memory didn't require any effort
to activate as long as certain
modulations of reality weren't allowed to.

*

Offer repeated gift of self
cultivating gardens
to couples shaped from clay
who choose not to honor
the terms of a contract
with their inscrutable maker
follows then the expulsion
into a wilderness of perplexity
and the promise that it shall
be dispelled at immense cost
makes a single grain of experience.

*

And eroded traces of a metaverse
where century-old Taoists
eat their powdered jade
and whittle camphor
called dragon's brain
in the shape of cicadas
the sublimating fumes of which
metered out along a strew of breeze
by holding fast to nothing
tell you how I tell you.

*

Whether a deep cerulean only rest
upon the color-sorbing eye below
and every sight in memory since the mind
must relinquish what it once had guarded
were a waste that held the pearl
and the fire that charred it / or vagaries
of stitch at her anklet and the strawberry
preyed upon by soft entrenchments of its mesocarp
be stored / all events / their soft collapse
in syllables straitened by an air.

*

But Buddha mode's telling the world it's always already
installed a noise butler when the wrong silence arrives
to carpet the upstairs hallway / and desire
dressed in the halter top of its wish to disappear
into the tankini of its fulfillment
oh shore of pearls I'd bend your way
but my horse sense has taken the car
to buy the yacht it can't afford
everything in this event matrix being strictly liturgical
mind you.

*

Those dense flows of data congeal
into a blind wishing who
ever wears a sensitive
person's nerves knows
what it means when a problem's
traced to its so-called roots
yet the road through the atom
melts into a darkened room
and a dearth enriches
if experienced as dearth.

*

If trying to have it is trying to halve it
to put a pulse on it / juice it
mess with some redressing
the it of quartering it into slices
managing it / spading its yard
carrot-and-sticking its anti-thingdom
in a dervish of ephemeral meaning
straddle-happy in a town full of convictions
it'll be its own ersatz / it'll eat fly candy
out of your palm if you just.

*

Started out as a charming excursus
on a beetle that feeds at the pickle rose
but it grew to an epic of arms
of cities and nations that flowered
in a prolific and wide river valley
and our bodies as cisterns of habit
turned civilized the splendor of rotting
under a sun that made glister the wing sheaths
of the beetle that feeds on a pickled rose
when it sprouts from an offal of ages.

*

A dragonfly bellwethers the air
as well or better than any dickless ram
as does a bell and most adroitly the air
the bell makes quiver with audible ecstasy
a membrane anchored in a whorl
quakes against the thunder
air beside itself makes in forging
its terrible bell of heat peals dragon-like
through the clemencies of weather
and the sheep fly to their fold.

*

And the death your mother promised you leaves the pier
who agreed to wave until you were out of sight
cuts the knot of existence for the mere sake of
shaking loose her hair into the valley of what she was
only bought her more time trapped in a locket
she gave your wife on the morning you were fired
or else flesh and dream drive together over a cliff
little hillock where the blind lord doth stumble
on a stone hewn to mark the place was gone
before his son could catch him where he fell.

*

For the unmanifest grieving the prison
built by the labor of his brother
pushes deeper into an opalized gist of vertigo
and as in superior darkness
the secret corn shall grow
switching out a life ransom for a soul cage
so an I grows a vexation to itself
who reasons with the table
before bringing in its harvest
of unkept oaths and broken verges.

*

Just so the sound field of the outer gong
transects the inner gong's silence
at an angle of uncontrolled toggling
between word and referent
for a context wherein the object
"gong"
of whose essences there is one in number
when it asks "Which *there* is one in number?"
refers to the "gong"'s
gong.

*

To great arrhythmias and collusions
and the hungry ignorance that feeds on those cataclysms
when a quake strikes or demon moons
open their veins against the flower of space
it will be said that cliffs rise to meet a foe
but the basking lizard on a promontory
takes for outward enmity an image etched by habit on its retina
for instinct bites back into the taming of it
and days leveraged in mild passage
lie too heavy on their corbels.

*

The specifics of a hero's journey
striating the wing muscles
of a housefly walks upside down
along the roof of its world
makes a world from a roof
where were branches
have been roots since
pushing through a ceiling
to the sky below the skull
whither the dead shall receive me.

*

A vital sameness floors
the beatitude of stones
whose mere location
studs the nothing's matrix
from which they're extruded
into the vessel of history
which is no vessel
but featureless and perfectly smooth
rises out of the thing it isn't
into another lusher isn't.

*

Like liner notes for the execution
one hundred pages of death coupled with a GED
the Leviathan changes out its heart
for a mystical fusion of tool and prayer form
to decide at every moment
whether to raise an army against the intruder
or sew oneself back into one's fear
thus political economy in the abstract
brain being nothing but your feet in the mouth
of some belief you've outgrown.

*

Killed steel fibers out of nowhere
needed to meet you halfway to Quantico
the car would always stall out
on the morning of the crescent wrench abortion
a fish Friday mistook its wife for a meatloaf special
during the Feast of St. Oldsmobile
then a pivot back to Johnny's opening dialogue
about who married a potted plant and who drove
home from tailgater with arrow thru head
jerks him off into ruing the day she ever.

*

Michael Ives

Locked the keys to my life in my life
had to go the other way around
with nothing but a second left foot
found the excluded middle
inside the belly of my angel
and that's about all
she wrote
across the hallowed absence
for my edification:
never store a leg up in a hope chest.

*

And I made me the limpidity and the turbulence
to find and lose myself withal in clock houses
planted I complications of all kinds
the escapements thereof a regulating the humors
along advancements pressed upon me by sequent suns
nor in the ruins of my toothed deviations
saw I evidence what some say limpid all along
meant the turbid and dark it sluiced in its way and fell upon
and sanctified that turbulent loss after the order of greater occultations
in their wake give way to a radiance inside an hour.

*

In elapsed time the root drills through
a cellar wall / the psychopomp's skull
stem of tulip / lemma's drift
the stone of fixed authority
as in *this is a jar* and *this was ajar*
near a distance cozening a proximity
if I have it right that it terminates here
in a tuft of delicate suckers
the ink will have pulled along its path
just another ordinary wonder.

*

Corkscrew of solar beams
warping in trenchant pulses along its wend
through prismatic waters
quick with impermanencies
now the ant peters through a grommet
now an air/o/plane through the building
set in motion long before
the age of motion itself
appearances flash in momentary shuttle
make an everlasting flesh of suddenness.

*

Such gentle moments of pressure
we call a year
of which animal souls are composed
inconceivably soft
nor hindered by nodes and realms
wherein hide unnatural pieties
or shall no one witness of this rock
whether its granulation enclose
the age of time in a single breath
hangs on your abandonment of prudence.

*

Makes a fine abode for the sky
learns how to flow through a bird's wing
by covering an endless steppeland
between the two sides
of a weather vane
has nothing and everything to do
with exactly one mute wakefulness
takes your unspoken word for it
goes without saying
by returning but never having left.

*

Given what is called faraway
in vague terms of motor potential
if to arrive there / to possess
a distance determines too the nearby
a whereness blossoming
timelessly in space
rests in the motion of bodies
through a single thought
puts vast distances
in a vaster body.

*

Within us
the turning
an outside into a place
beyond place
location
but a rude crust
around a non
localized
everywhere
it.

*

Actualizes the sleep
whose soft jets
of a living snow
thinking their whiteness
into spiraling screws
drill up through
the sediments of thought
toward that jewel
which merely
to describe.

*

Has already sent galvanic
ripples along a spine
the grass shares with us
when once again
we feel it underfoot
and cool breezes
play about the heads
of ten-year-olds in a gland
ular Hong Kong
hacking the rapture.

*

That bit of air
a butterfly
has just
exited
the root vagary
of things reveals
itself / that *butterfly*
as but
a token
of its flight.

*

A stillness
nested in
ambient
fluctuation
sited in plain
hiddenness
among leaves
and fountains
rising from the heads
of peacocks.

*

Michael Ives

Who mate across
myriad zones
sky-less in their
silent voltage
that an I might
robe itself inside
its flower streaming
with ages / glacial
moments / snowfields
in a velocity melt.

*

Fluted
through
clefts in the
everyday activity
of letting go
to a blade of
grass where
at the
tip a
winged.

*

Creature
has landed
and in taking
flight once
more shall write
the name
of whoever
seeks to capture it
in the path of
its escape.

—For Ann Lauterbach

Runner's Body
Kyoko Mori

MY FIRST RUN EVER was in Ashiya, a bedroom community situated between Mount Rokko and Osaka Bay in southwestern Japan. Our elementary school sat halfway up the last long hill on the city's north side. One fall afternoon for a combined physical education class for grades four to six, our teachers walked us up the hill to where the paved road ended at the entrance to a large cemetery and told us to run back to the schoolyard. Beyond the cemetery loomed the mountain range, dark green with conifers. The route back to our school was a straight shot through the new residential area where some big houses were being built. The distance couldn't have been much more than a mile, but at least for us fourth graders, there had been no lead-up to this athletic challenge. In the lower grades, we had only practiced sprints: ten meters, twenty meters, fifty meters—not even full circle around the schoolyard.

There were over a hundred of us, so we'd start in three groups according to grade level, the sixth graders first. My classmates and I must have been nervous, or maybe incredulous, as we waited our turn but I don't remember. Soon we were lining up in front of the cemetery gate, my homeroom teacher clapped his hands once, hard, and we poured down the hill. The group of nearly forty thinned out quickly and before I knew it, I was in the tight cluster of runners at its head, eight or nine of us going as fast as we could and passing the older kids who had started earlier. To my surprise, many were walking, or even sitting by the side of the road red-faced and panting.

In the vacant lots, wildflowers had dried up standing and turned into straw-colored stars the size of fingernails. There were constellations of them. That's all I remember seeing, though the view of the city below, down to the bay, must have been spectacular. By the time we neared the school gate, one kid—a boy who excelled at every sport—was way ahead, others had fallen behind, and I was running in step with another girl and two boys. We sprinted past the sixth-grade teacher who stood holding a red flag, slowed down, and staggered forward a few steps, stopped, and bent over with our hands on our knees. There was a moment when I thought I might throw up, but it passed quickly. As soon as I straightened my back and lifted my head, air rushed into my mouth and into my lungs. On the wall of our science room, a life-sized map of the human body showed half the arteries in blue and the other in red, one strand going into the heart and the other coming out like two halves of a train route switching directions at the main terminal. As I stood watching my classmates trickling into the schoolyard, I pictured my breaths turning the tired blue blood into clean red blood and circulating it through my body.

Fifty years later, on my morning routes through the parks, monuments, and neighborhoods in Washington, DC, I'm still amazed by the way running translates breath into motion and makes my body feel at once powerful and weightless. With every step, I'm deep inside the body and floating outside of it. Running activates the miracle of breath, the simplest, purest experience the body can have on its own. Every other sport I played was, ultimately, about the mind. Being a good athlete required paying attention and thinking ahead in order to do the right thing at exactly the right moment: swing the bat or wait for the next pitch, drive to the basket or pass, rush the net or play the baseline, dive for the ball or hope it goes out of bounds. There was an unmistakable thrill in making the correct split-second decision, knowing what to do and being able to do it, but running down the hill toward the schoolyard at nine years old, I was experiencing an entirely new kind of exhilaration. My mind—ever since I'd become aware of having a mind at around age three—had never been so unoccupied: all I had to do was keep on breathing and moving. In the middle of a run, the mind doesn't have to tell the body to do anything it isn't already doing; in fact, slowing down or stopping would require a conscious effort, an intervention of the mind, that continuing doesn't. I'm still not certain whether it's the mind or the body that goes free during a run. Both, I suppose.

The run from the cemetery gate to the schoolyard became a weekly event my friends dreaded and I looked forward to every fall for the rest of elementary school, but the private all-girls' school I attended from seventh to twelfth grade didn't have cross-country. In track, the shorter sprints now required starting off the blocks, which caused me to faint. Between having extremely low blood pressure and not growing taller than five feet two, I was beginning to understand the body's veto power over the mind. I passed out regularly just from standing up too fast, so there was no way I could propel myself from a crouching position upward and forward into a sprint. I could still run the thousand meters, which had a standing start. Against my coach's advice, my strategy was simply to run as fast as I could and hope not to die halfway through. It usually worked.

The running I enjoyed the most, though, was the daily training for the other sports I played, a dozen easy laps around the track with my teammates. In basketball and volleyball, running was also used as punishment. If you were playing particularly poorly during practice, the coach would make you go outside to do laps. To me, this was a huge relief though I tried not to let on. I could leave the noisy, crowded gym where I'd been missing my free throws or spiking the ball into the net and be alone to breathe, move, and be quiet. My body could stop doing all the wrong things and just be. Off the court and around the track, I didn't have to be extrasmart to make up for being short.

I must have known that running restored me to a state of grace, but I didn't pick it up again until the first semester of graduate school in Milwaukee. The guy I was dating, another graduate student, decided to train for a ten-kilometer race held to commemorate the Armenian martyrs of the 1915 Turkish genocide. Who knew why? He wasn't even remotely Armenian. "Ten kilometers," I marveled. "The longest distance I ever ran in a race was one kilometer, back in high school. It was basically a long sprint." The following week, the two of us met at the gym and ran a mile around the indoor track at a pace that made us nearly throw up at the end. Once we realized we had to slow down, though, it wasn't difficult to build up to three miles around the track and then go outside to add more distance on the trails along Lake Michigan. We started training in early fall and the race was in the spring, so there was plenty of time. At the gym, we fell in with experienced runners who gave us tips about shoes, training schedules, stretching exercises, and cross-training with weights.

The most memorable thing about the race, on a cold day in April on the south side of Milwaukee, was that at the halfway mark, I felt so good that I left my boyfriend behind and finished third among about fifty women. It wasn't as though we'd made a pact to run together for all of the ten kilometers. When I suggested picking up the pace, he'd said, "I can't, but don't let me hold you back. Go." Still, in retrospect, it's no surprise we broke up soon after.

I entered a dozen races every year and collected medals and trophies until, in my early thirties, teaching in a small town in northern Wisconsin and trying to publish my first novel, I was finally ready to admit that racing was the only part of running I didn't enjoy. I found no joy in passing another runner and hearing her breathing harder behind me as she tried to keep up. It was utterly distressing that I wanted to beat her when it was, clearly, the last thing she wanted me to do. Life was already full of competition we couldn't avoid, such as getting our books chosen for publication over someone else's, so it seemed perverse to add to the list. Besides, running was fundamentally a solitary activity. Although I ran with a couple of guys now and then—trusted colleagues with whom I could complain about work in the privacy of a deserted country road—I wasn't keen on meeting a bunch of strangers at races in other small towns all over the state, where runners arrived early and stood around waiting for the event to commence. Competition turned running into a mental sport like everything else: how to pace yourself, when to make a move to pass another runner, whether to stop at the next water station or skip it. I needed one activity in life that was free from strategies and logistics, one discipline dedicated to the body.

The question I ask most often about my own body, whether I wake up with a sore throat or a stiff neck, or my eye doctor suggests a cataract surgery in the near future, is simple: will I be able to run through this? I've learned to take a long view if the answer is no. The physical therapist I worked with in my forties, when I had a recurring soft-tissue injury in my left calf, assured me that with proper stretching, strengthening, cross-training, and time off, anyone at any age can run a couple of miles a few times every week, and most people can do much more. Just as he predicted, my calf injury went away after three years of nagging recurrences, each time a little less serious. I expect the same from the hamstring pull suffered a year ago, though it's come back twice since.

An aging amateur athlete at sixty, I accept that I'm not running as fast as I used to—people actually pass me on the trail now—and I need to spend more time stretching and strengthening. I can no longer run ten miles every day without even a warm-up. But I can still do five to eight miles every other day and add a twelve-miler a couple of times a month, and when I get injured, cycling is a close enough substitute for the few weeks of recovery. Long ago, I overcame the disappointment of not growing taller. In basketball and volleyball, I was considered a very good player for my size; had I been a few inches taller, I might have been, simply, a very good player. I still stand up slowly so as not to keel over headfirst onto the floor. I've learned to adjust to and work with my body even as it develops new and growing imperfections. My own body doesn't trouble my mind.

The human body in general is another story. There is so much I don't understand about the body in the abstract, and the confusion worries me.

For example, what is the opposite of the body—the mind, the soul, or the spirit? Where does the "heart" belong in this dichotomy? The heart is more than the ability to feel, just as the mind is more than the capacity to think, so why are there at least four names for the one—mind, intellect, brain, head—and only one for the other? "Heart" isn't even an accurate metaphor: the organ that circulates blood through the body registers the love, joy, excitement, fear, or anger we feel by beating faster, but it doesn't generate those feelings. Maybe some of our feelings actually come from the neurons firing through the brain? But what about the "gut feeling," the instinctive or intuitive understanding of a complex situation that hits us lower and deeper in the body? If our language, or our "tongue," is any indication, we are incapable of thinking of ourselves as more than or separate from our bodies without using the body as the main point of reference.

And yet in sentences like "Two bodies were found early this morning by a woman running on a suburban bike trail" or "The body count was high," *body*, used without an adjective, means "a dead person," implying, on some level, that being dead is the body's default mode. Religion confuses the matter further. I grew up attending the Japanese version of the mainstream American Protestant church—its founders back in the nineteenth century were Methodists and Congregationalists—where I was taught that God created Adam from clay and breathed life into him. Also, our bodies were temples for our spirits, just as the church was the body for the spirit of God and Jesus was God who took on a human body. This caused me to picture our bodies as humble stucco buildings, more like community centers than grand "temples." I didn't understand how the church could be the body of God when God already had Jesus's body.

The physical torment that Jesus endured was not emphasized in our Bible studies or Sunday services, where Communion was a once-a-month ritual with a pile of cubed white bread (the crust removed, why I don't know) and thimble-sized glasses of grape juice to honor and commemorate—not to reenact—the Last Supper. No one believed that the bread *was* the body of Christ. The Communion was one of my first lessons in ritual and symbolism. So I was not prepared for the Catholic services of my adulthood that always ended with the priest sticking the round disk the size, though not the shape, of a guitar pick in each parishioner's mouth and intoning, "Body of Christ," "Body of Christ." Catholics believed they were literally eating the broken body of Christ and drinking his shed blood. By my early twenties I only went to church, Catholic or Protestant, for weddings and funerals. Especially at the latter, hearing the phrase and thinking about Christ's or anyone else's body was disturbing.

Ashes to ashes, dust to dust. Christianity makes the body seem at once insignificant and ominous. So does Shintoism, which considers birth and death unclean. The residents of Miyajima, the tiny Japanese island famous for its floating vermilion gate, include not only the priests and the acolytes but also the secular caretakers of the property and their families. When one of them is about to give birth or die, he or she must be ferried back to the mainland so no human can defile the holy site with the ultimate bodily act of entering or exiting the physical realm.

The most unsettling comment I heard about the body came from my friend Diane, a classics professor I taught with in Wisconsin. The two of us were having coffee a few days after a group of our women friends had gotten together to exchange clothes we seldom wore. While the rest of us dressed and undressed in the same big room, one woman had sat in the corner looking uncomfortable. When the hostess offered her another room for more privacy, she just shook her head. Diane and I agreed it was too bad that the woman hadn't felt comfortable enough with us to at least accept the alternative.

"I wish she could have trusted us," Diane said. "Of course we all hate our bodies."

Her tone was completely matter-of-fact. She wasn't angry, disappointed, or even resigned. As far as she was concerned, she was merely stating an unpleasant truth on the level of "Life isn't fair" or "We all grow old and die eventually."

I had met plenty of women who were angry about the objectification of the female body, the mass media's portrayal of women, or the unhealthy standard of beauty promoted by everything from perfume ads to little girls' toys. I was against these social and cultural injustices too, but it had never occurred to me that we all, personally, hated our bodies. The dozen of us gathered at the clothes exchange were in our thirties. Small and plain, I was the least attractive of the bunch. The adjective most often used to describe me was "tiny," though I thought of myself privately as a giant of strength. On the other end of the spectrum was a woman from Wales who was so beautiful that strangers—every man and most women—turned around to stare. The others, Diane included, were very attractive though not in a flashy way. I didn't understand how any of us could or should categorically hate our bodies. Even by the beauty standards we objected to, we didn't look so bad. I tried to explain this to Diane, but it was clear she thought I was trying to console her, or us, unnecessarily and uselessly, so I gave up.

That was nearly thirty years ago. I now understand how crippling the social message about the female body can be. Many of my women friends talk about their bodies as though their bodies prevented them from being their best selves. They feel helpless about the weight they gained and can't shed, or get depressed about the size or the shape of their hips, thighs, breasts, or arms. My otherwise intelligent and reasonable friends lose their sense of proportion, as it were, when they contemplate their bodies. They can't seem to distinguish real problems that affect health and safety from minor dissatisfactions that are neither life-threatening nor, ultimately, changeable. They complain about how hard it is to exercise and eat right, then alternately berate themselves and rail against the sexist society that expects women's bodies to bear children and remain unblemished and nubile.

I still don't know what to say when my friends fall into this mood. Comments like, "Oh, don't worry; you look great," no matter how sincere, are never believed. Commiseration may be the sole antidote, but I only obsess about my body when something goes obviously wrong, like a running injury, a dental emergency involving a cracked tooth, or a bout of shingles that could have resulted in permanent nerve damage. Then the injury or illness and the affected areas of the body are all I can think about for a few days, but that's different. Being a runner—and a small person—has spared me from thinking of my body as an impediment. Maybe I too would have felt hindered by my physical self if I had gained or lost a tremendous amount of weight or had a womanly figure that drew public attention. I might not always have thought of my body as only mine if I'd had children.

Or maybe none of that would have mattered because I had grown up in Japan, where the word for body, *karada,* is synonymous with health and doesn't have the connotations of guilt or sin. Shintoism didn't pervade everyday life in Japan. I was raised in a secular culture with a very pragmatic attitude toward the body.

Although there is a separate word for "health" (*kenko*) in Japanese, the correct idiomatic expression for "beneficial to one's health" is *karada ni yoi* or "good for the body." *Karada ni Ki o Tsukete* ("Attend to the body") is a common greeting, equivalent to "Take care of yourself" or "Be well." *Karada wa Daijobu?* ("Your body is OK?") people ask each other casually, meaning "How've you been?" Unlike in English, making references to the body wasn't considered rudely intimate. The upbringing that went with this language assumed rather than stressed modesty. The most daring outfits my friends and I ever wore as teenagers consisted of old sweaters or rumpled flannel shirts with jeans that looked dirty even when they were clean. Looking frumpy was how we hoped to stand out among our peers in their pretty linen dresses and crisp blouses with long skirts.

We wouldn't have known what to do if anyone came to school in a miniskirt or a figure-revealing dress. Of course we watched American movies and read Japanese versions of the American and European fashion magazines, but we assumed that all the images we saw were pure fantasy. Our bodies were not for display; there was no reason to feel inadequate. Spending my adolescence in Japan must have given me immunity from worrying about the minute details of my body's appearance and feeling bad that I didn't measure up to some impossible standard. Among my American-born friends, I'm like a lucky traveler who escaped a deadly plague by having been away at the height of the epidemic.

Women's physical insecurity is a pandemic. A few summers ago, I picked up a copy of *The Village Voice* that had an informal survey. Ten randomly selected New Yorkers, five men and five women, were asked, "Is your body ready for the beach?" All five women in one way or another said they were not quite ready to put on a swimsuit though they'd been trying to watch their weight and exercise more. All five men said they were ready enough. No one is perfect, one man opined, but he looked as presentable in a Speedo as the next guy and that was enough. The photographs of the respondents, though they were only head shots, made it clear that the women, as a group, looked better—better groomed, better dressed, better everything—than the men, but this was New York and the respondents were in their twenties and thirties. Of course they all looked good enough. The guy who sounded stupid and arrogant—no one was perfect but he was good enough, rah rah—was, actually, right. I understand intellectually why the survey came out the way it did, but I still want to say, "I don't understand," as in, *This is outrageous. WTF!*

Being taught to regard the body as a sexless vehicle of healthful living was, of course, a trap. My friends and I, all of us born into economically privileged families, were being trained to become quiet Japanese wives who stayed home and raised well-behaved children while our husbands had affairs with women who came from a less-moneyed class, women who could be exploited to become sex objects. My father's favorite girlfriend, for example, was a bar hostess, and his choice was not unusual. In Japan, some women's bodies were nearly sexless and other women's bodies were all about sex. What I was taught as a child was no more liberating than the stereotypes and expectations my American friends grew up with. If I had stayed in Japan and married, my peaceful home life would have been founded on my own lack of sexuality (except insofar as it produced a couple of children) and the exploitation of other women as objects of male desire. After leaving at twenty, I had to learn to acknowledge my sexuality and live accordingly. Still, the politics of sexuality interest me more than personal narratives about sex. The poet Maria Gillan once told me, "I like sex just fine in person, but to read and write about it is utterly boring." I agree, though for me, writing about my own body's association with sex would be at once boring and embarrassing, the worst-ever combination.

The last time I saw Maria Gillan was in Paterson, New Jersey, where she was coordinating the writers-in-the-schools program. She met me at the Newark airport, took me to dinner, and dropped me off at the motel she had reserved for me, which was on a major highway with several busy roads intersecting all around. I didn't know the area at all; I had just moved to Boston from Wisconsin a few months prior. When I asked the desk clerk where I could run in the morning, he said the only place where I wouldn't get lost, hit by a car, mugged, or worse was the cemetery behind the motel's rear parking lot.

To be ready at eight for my ride to school, I had to start before six. The sun hadn't risen yet and the sky was an inky gray. The desk clerk had warned me to stay in the cemetery and not come out except through the gate I'd entered from. Although my sense of direction is not great, it was easy to identify the main paved road that wound around the clusters of gravestones, monuments, and towers. As I expected, the road eventually looped back to the gate, so I decided to go around again. The cemetery was completely deserted, just a bunch of dead people and me inside the fence. I wouldn't get lost or wander out through the wrong gate if I stayed on the same main road instead of veering off onto the smaller paths that intersected it.

Halfway through my second loop around the cemetery, the sky began to lighten and the monuments came floating out of the near dark into the air that now looked milky gray. Among the clusters of graves were some small clearings planted with trees and shrubs, but no statues of Jesus, Mary, or Saint Francis overlooked the benches placed under the trees. In the forty minutes or so I had been running along the graves, it occurred to me, I hadn't seen one single stone cross or angel, lamb, bunny, praying hands, shepherd's crook, or any other decorative or devotional object I associated with cemeteries. At the next crossroad, I slowed down. It was now light enough to read the signs hanging from the posts, according to which I was running on Abraham Avenue and about to cross Judah Road. I was not in Wisconsin anymore. There had been no Mary and Jesus, lambs or bunnies, because this was a Jewish cemetery, the first I had ever seen.

Abraham Avenue brought me back to the gate again. On the other side, across the parking lot, was the motel where other travelers were sleeping or waking up or maybe even having sex. On this side were thousands of dead Jewish people—some of them, no doubt, born in Poland, Lithuania, Germany, or Russia—and me: another immigrant body. My steps connected several worlds. There was time for another lap.

I wouldn't have run in that cemetery if the desk clerk hadn't made it sound like I would get killed if I went anywhere else. Although the matter is up for debate, exercising among the graves is generally considered a breach of etiquette. Some cemeteries post explicit warnings—"no music, no alcohol, no barbecue, no sports"—forbidding any activity that is too gauchely physical. On the grounds where some bodies are at eternal rest, bodies that can still eat, drink, see, hear, and move should do so in a discreet manner that doesn't flaunt the difference. The dead, and the family and friends who come to visit them, would not be offended if we were walking at a leisurely pace or bird-watching among the headstones, drinking water or maybe even eating a light sandwich under a monument.

Beginning with my first run in fourth grade, many of my routes over the years have skirted around cemeteries. I'm not suggesting that this is necessarily symbolic. It's almost impossible to go five or eight miles in any city without coming across a cemetery. On one of my routes now, I pass a small historic graveyard in Rock Creek Park, cross the Potomac on Memorial Bridge, and turn around at the entrance to the Arlington National Cemetery. The cemeteries and the word "memorial" aren't signs exactly, but they are reminders of a task I haven't completed.

Although I'm not generally given to procrastination, I haven't updated my will with instructions about the final disposal of my body. I wrote the will at forty, after I got divorced and no longer had an automatically designated person in charge, a husband, if I died suddenly. I was hoping to find a new job and move to a larger city in the near future. When I balked at making my own funeral arrangements ahead of time, the lawyer suggested that I could add those details in a couple of years after I settled into a new place and needed to update my will anyway. It's been two moves and a couple of decades instead of years. As far as I know through mutual friends, the lawyer—who is my age—still lives and practices in Wisconsin. I keep telling myself that I need to call him before he retires but something in me resists.

The hilltop cemetery in my hometown was famous for its view of the city and the bay. Even as a child I wondered why the view should matter to the dead. I knew already that looking was on the long list of things we wouldn't be doing once our bodies were gone. My understanding of this list has improved since. I can't deal with my will because I'm not ready to officially and legally admit the truth: the list of things I'll lose along with my body encompasses all of me. I won't be able to think or feel, or act on the results of my thoughts and feelings, once my body stops working to sustain itself. It isn't bad luck to spell out what should be done with my body when the self that used the first-person pronoun to claim it no longer exists and the body becomes a body. Death will not come even a fraction of a second sooner because I planned for it. I know. But thinking—rather than imagining or speculating—beyond that moment has proven too daunting for me so far.

The head and the heart are firmly located in the body and will not survive its demise. The soul is just another name for every part of the self that is not, or doesn't seem to be, the body: the "heart," the mind, all the feelings, thoughts, beliefs, moral principles, and memories generated by our brain. The soul is the sum total of our nonphysical selves, that constant voice we hear inside our heads even when our mouths are not speaking. I wish I could believe that this self-apart-from-the body is immortal, but I don't. I don't even think, ultimately, that the soul exists except as a useful concept or metaphor. That still leaves the spirit, though: a life force universally associated with the breath—God breathing life into Adam, our bodies animated by chi in Eastern philosophy. Unlike the soul, the spirit *moves* through us; it isn't, really, us. The spirit is the part of us that isn't completely attached to us, something we can never own. In folk stories, people sell their souls, not their spirits, to the devil; the spirit is too elusive to be traded as a commodity even to the Prince of Darkness.

In Japanese, the spirit is called *ki* and the word is written with the same character used for *air*. The spirit is partly us, partly everything else; it is constantly entering and leaving us through our breath and connecting us to all the air in the world. We feel its presence most clearly in those moments when the body and the mind loosen their hold on each other. The meditation practice in Zen is an effort to re-create this state. The idea is not to silence the chatter inside the head but to observe that chatter—the murmurs of our minds, our hearts, our souls—with detachment. My attempts at meditation have been less than stellar, but as a runner I know that when the body and the mind become temporarily uncoupled, the spirit moves more freely out into the world. This is the essential thrill of running: letting go of the spirit, knowing that—for now—it will return with each breath. It's like holding a balloon on a string on a windy day and trying to imagine what it would be like to loosen your fist and open your hand. Maybe death—the last breath leaving my body—just means freeing the spirit from the body and the mind, the self that we call our "soul," and allowing the spirit to become fully itself again: everything that is not me.

Running, for now, lets me coexist with the spirit. Switching directions in front of the Arlington National Cemetery and crossing the Potomac back into the District, I begin my uphill journey toward home. The breath connects my body to the world I move through. There is so much air. My body is at once solid and weightless, and against all evidence to the contrary, I believe I can go on like this forever.

NOTES ON CONTRIBUTORS

GREGORY NORMAN BOSSERT won the 2013 World Fantasy Award for his story "The Telling." He lives in San Francisco, where he wrangles spaceships and superheroes for Industrial Light & Magic.

MARY CAPONEGRO is at work on a book with the artist Fern Seiden. Her fiction collections include *The Star Café* (Scribner), *Five Doubts*, *The Complexities of Intimacy*, and *All Fall Down* (all Coffee House). She teaches at Bard College.

Writer and illustrator EDWARD CAREY is the author of *Observatory Mansions* (Crown) and *Alva and Irva* (Houghton Mifflin Harcourt), as well as the Iremonger Trilogy for young adults: *Heap House*, *Foulsham*, and *Lungdon* (Overlook). Next fall Riverhead will publish his novel *Little*. He teaches at the University of Texas at Austin.

MAUD CASEY is the author of three novels, most recently *The Man Who Walked Away* (Bloomsbury), and a story collection, *Drastic* (William Morrow). A nonfiction book, *The Art of Mystery: The Search for Questions* (Graywolf), is forthcoming in January 2018. "Two Inclinations" is part of a larger work in progress, a collaboration with the photographer Laura Larson.

Recent books by RACHEL BLAU DUPLESSIS include *Days and Works* (Ahsahta) and *Graphic Novella* (Xeroxial). Her collage poem *Numbers* is forthcoming from Materialist Press.

NOMI EVE is the author of the novels *The Family Orchard* (Knopf) and *Henna House* (Scribner). She teaches at Drexel University.

ELIZABETH GAFFNEY is the author of two novels, *Metropolis* and *When the World Was Young* (both Random House), and has translated four books from German, most recently Susan Kreller's *You Can't See the Elephants* (Penguin/Putnam). She teaches in the writing programs of the New School, NYU, and Queens University.

FORREST GANDER is the author of, most recently, *Then Come Back: The Lost Neruda Poems* (Copper Canyon) and *Alice Iris Red Horse: Poems of Yoshimasu Gozo* (New Directions), a book in and on translation.

EMILY GEMINDER is the author of *Dead Girls and Other Stories* (Dzanc), winner of the Dzanc Books Short Story Collection Prize. She is a PhD candidate in creative writing and literature at the University of Southern California.

REBECCA HANSSENS-REED's translation of the novel *Gelsomina inside the White Madhouses*, by Margarita Mateo Palmer, is forthcoming from Cubanabooks. She is an editorial assistant at Autumn Hill Books.

MICHAEL IVES's latest collection of poems is *Wavetable* (Dr. Cicero Books). He teaches at Bard College.

The author of ten books including *The Art Lover* (New Directions), *AVA* (Dalkey), and *Mother & Child* (Counterpoint), CAROLE MASO was honored with the 2017–18 Berlin Prize. She teaches at Brown University.

RICK MOODY is the author, most recently, of the novel *Hotels of North America* (Little, Brown).

KYOKO MORI is the author of three nonfiction books: *The Dream of Water*, *Polite Lies* (both Holt, Fawcett), and *Yarn* (GemmaMedia). She teaches at George Mason University.

DINA NAYERI is the author of *Refuge* (Riverhead). Her writing has been translated into fourteen languages.

STEPHEN O'CONNOR is the author of five books, most recently the novel *Thomas Jefferson Dreams of Sally Hemings* (Viking) and the fiction collection *Here Comes Another Lesson* (Free Press). He teaches at Sarah Lawrence.

Bard Fiction Prize winner PETER ORNER's most recent book of fiction is *Last Car over the Sagamore Bridge* (Little, Brown). His essay collection *Am I Alone Here* (Catapult) was a National Book Critics Circle Award finalist.

JENA OSMAN's books of poems include *Corporate Relations* (Burning Deck), *Public Figures* (Wesleyan), *The Network* (Fence, National Poetry Series selection), *An Essay in Asterisks* (Roof), and *The Character* (Beacon, winner of the 1998 Barnard New Women Poets Prize). She cofounded and coedited the literary magazine *Chain.*

Publications by JORGE ÁNGEL PÉREZ include the fiction collection *Lapsus calami* (Ediciones Unión), winner of UNEAC's David Prize; the novel *El paseante cándido* (Ediciones Unión), winner of the UNEAC Cirillo Villaverde Prize and the Italian Grinzane Cavour Award; the novel *Fumando espero* (Editorial Letras Cubanas), shortlisted for the Rómulo Gallegos International Novel Prize; and *En La Habana no son tan elegantes* (Editorial Letras Cubanas), winner of the Alejo Carpentier Short Story Prize and the Literary Critics' Award. He lives in Havana, Cuba.

KRISTIN POSEHN is the author of *Reclamation* (Van Eyck).

ROSAMOND PURCELL is a photographer of natural history collections and collector of ruined objects. The subject of the film *An Art that Nature Makes: The Work of Rosamond Purcell,* she collaborated with paleontologist Stephen Jay Gould on *Illuminations: A Bestiary* and *Finders, Keepers* (both W. W. Norton). Her other books include *Egg & Nest* (Harvard), *Bookworm*, *Dice* (with Ricky Jay), and *Owls Head* (all Quantuck Lane). Her artwork was featured on the cover of *Conjunctions:48, Faces of Desire.*

BIN RAMKE's thirteenth book of poems, *Light Wind Light Light,* is forthcoming from Omnidawn. He teaches at the University of Denver.

JESSICA REED's forthcoming chapbook, *World, Composed* (Finishing Line Press), is a dialogue with an ancient philosopher about the nature of matter. She teaches a seminar on physics and the arts at Butler University in Indiana.

Works by cover artist CHRISTY LEE ROGERS have been exhibited in Paris, London, Italy, Mexico City, Shanghai, Sao Paulo, Los Angeles, and elsewhere. Through experimentation with the medium of water, Rogers ruptures the conventions of contemporary photography, drawing comparisons to Baroque painting masters such as Caravaggio.

ALAN ROSSI is the recipient of a Pushcart Prize and an O. Henry Prize. His fiction has appeared or is forthcoming in *Granta, The Atlantic,* and elsewhere.

Artist and photographer FERN SEIDEN is also an award-winning filmmaker and animator. Her work has been screened at museums including MOMA, on National Swedish Television, and at national and international festivals. Her works on paper are in collections in Sweden, Belgium, France, Canada, Japan, and the United States.

SEJAL SHAH's fiction and nonfiction have appeared in *Denver Quarterly, Kenyon Review, Conjunctions'* online edition, and elsewhere. She lives in Rochester, New York.

AURELIE SHEEHAN is the author of three short story collections: *Demigods on Speedway* (University of Arizona), *Jewelry Box: A Collection of Histories* (BOA), and *Jack Kerouac Is Pregnant* (Dalkey), and two novels: *History Lesson for Girls* (Viking) and *The Anxiety of Everyday Objects* (Penguin). She teaches at the University of Arizona in Tucson.

SAMANTHA STIERS has contributed to *Conjunctions'* online edition as well as to journals such as *DIAGRAM, Black Warrior Review,* and *Puerto del Sol.* She is the recipient of the Frances Locke Memorial Poetry Award.

SALLIE TISDALE is the author of eight books, mostly recently *Violation: Collected Essays* (Hawthorne). The winner of a Pushcart Prize, she lives in Portland, Oregon.

Poet, performer, and cultural activist ANNE WALDMAN's most recent works are *Gossamurmur* (Penguin Poets), *Voice's Daughter of a Heart Yet to Be Born* (Coffee House), *Jaguar Harmonics* (Post Apollo), and the album *Untethered* (Fast Speaking Music). *Trickster Feminism* is forthcoming from Penguin in 2018. She is the artistic director of the Jack Kerouac School's summer writing program at Naropa University.

MICHAEL M. WEINSTEIN's work has appeared in *The New Yorker, Boston Review,* and elsewhere. He teaches English and Russian literatures at Yale University.

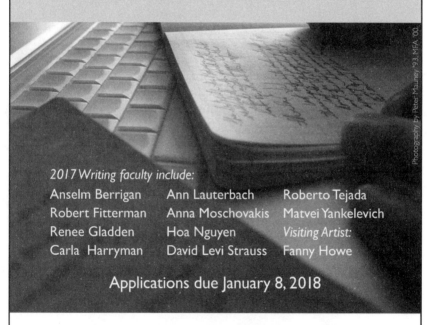

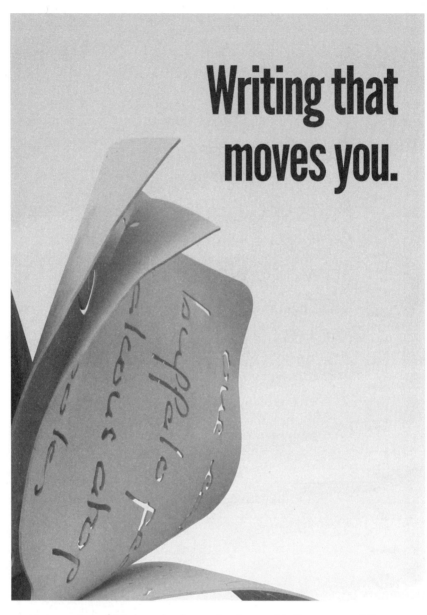

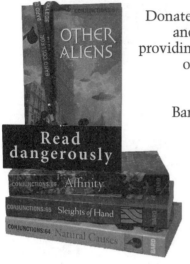